Mail-Order Family

Irina VanPatten

Dear Mimi!
It was a pleasure
meeting you.
     Enjoy your read-
I VanPatten 5/21/23

Classic Day Publishing
Seattle, Washington 98102
206-860-4900
www.classicdaypub.com

Contents

Chapter 1

Toská

All day I had a feeling that some shit was about to happen, and there he was, showing up at my door, unannounced, like he always did.

"Congratulations, Irina Mihailovna, we are officially divorced," Igor said with fake bravado the minute he walked through the door. He dusted snowflakes off of his coat and shook off his hat. The snowflakes melted before reaching the floor.

"I didn't know you were coming," I said, unsure how to feel.

"You don't have a phone. I couldn't call you."

"They wired our house six months ago. Now we have a house phone, thank God. It only took us fifteen years to get it."

"Good to know. Next time, I'll call. I thought I'd bring you the certificate of our divorce. I didn't think you'd like to take a twelve-hour train ride to Crimea just to get a piece of paper." He eyed me, looking for a reaction, but I gave him none. "Sorry it took me three years to deliver it. Better late than never, but I thought you might need it one day, in case you want to remarry."

"Yeah, the men pile up in stacks to marry a woman with two kids."

"Papa!" Lica yelled, and jumped into her father's arms. Her big brown eyes sparkled, her long auburn hair flipping in the air.

"Hello, Lica-Lica-Angelica, my little daughter, angel of my eyes. Daddy missed you."

"I am not little anymore. I'm eight."

"Don't you think I know that? I just like to call you little because I love you. Where is Serghei, the heir of my nonexistent treasures?"

"Pop, you are so funny," Lica said, and put her hands on her hips with the swagger of a teenager. "You didn't see him outside?"

"He's still outside? It's getting dark."

"You know how your son gets when he sees the first snow. He said he'd be right back half an hour ago," I said.

"I'll get him." Lica ran to the balcony, opened the window that insulated our apartment from the cold, and shouted at the top of her lungs from the third floor down to the courtyard. "Sereoja, come home! Papa came to visit!"

"Ira, what's up with all this yelling?" My sister, Mariana, showed up from the other room. "I'm trying to study here." Her annoyance faded when she saw him. "Oh, Igor!" She stopped halfway. "What a nice surprise!" She jumped toward him like a playful goat.

"Mariana Valerievna, look at you. You are taller than your older sister. What the heck, you are taller than me. And you're only sixteen." He shook his head. "Your hair is so much longer since the last time I saw you." He pulled a lock of her hair jokingly. "But when you stand next to each other, you can hardly tell you're sisters. You, the blondie, and Irina, the gypsy."

"We have different fathers. Remember?" Mariana pulled her hair back.

"Of course, I remember. I haven't been out of the picture for that long."

My sister turned to me. "Why is he calling me Mariana Valerievna?"

"That's a Russian thing. Basically, it means that you are Mariana, daughter of your father Valera."

"Oho! A lot has changed since the Soviet Union disappeared," Igor said. "I forgot that Mariana was a baby when the whole country broke into pieces. You don't use patronymics anymore?"

"Not in Moldova, we don't, not since the divorce from the Soviet Union was finalized. We just go by our first names, so I am now simply Irina or Mrs. Iancenco."

"What are they going to call you now, after the divorce? Do you go back to being a miss?" Igor asked.

"I don't think it works in reverse," I told him. "Once a missus, always a missus."

"I messed up your missus thing forever, haven't I?" Igor looked sincerely concerned.

"Don't worry about it. In my English class in college, they told us they have a neutral Ms., so we'll probably all have neutral titles soon."

A scuffling noise of fast-moving feet was coming up the stairs behind our apartment wall. The sound grew closer and closer until the loud *boom* of a door thrown open interrupted our conversation.

"Papa!" Serghei yelled, and jumped into his father's arms, just like Lica minutes earlier. The door smashed into the side wall behind him, and the broken plastic door knob fell to the floor.

"My dear son, what are you doing?" Igor asked, looking over his shoulder to see what had happened.

"Oh, great! Let's break the last thing that has survived in this house!" I yelled, ready to give my son a good smack on his rear.

"Bring me the tools before you get your ass whooped. *Papa* will fix it," he said, and let Serghei down, shielding him with his body. "I see nothing has changed here. The son breaks things, and the father fixes them."

"More like Serghei breaks things and Mariana fixes them, because Ira is working all day at her day care and then goes to college at night." Mariana sighed. "I'm with them after school every day. It's very exhausting."

"Here it is." Serghei brought out the screwdriver and hammer. Igor took off his winter coat, then pushed the bag and the guitar case he'd brought with him to the side and kneeled in front of the door to assess the damage.

"Well, I am impressed, son, that you know where the tools are," Igor said.

"Yeah. It's not a big deal. Are you staying with us for New Year's?" Serghei asked.

"No, I am just here for a few days, if your mama lets me." Igor looked at me.

"Pop, we only have two rooms, but I can put a mattress on the floor for you, and we can sleep together. Isn't that right, Mom?"

I raised my eyebrow, irritated. *Sneaky bastard!* Imagine if I kicked him out now. What drama it would cause with the kids.

"He's definitely not sleeping in my bed," I said, "so you can sleep together wherever you want. I'll go start dinner. You must be hungry from the road."

I set the small table for five. The cramped kitchen could barely fit us all. The old, bulky Soviet refrigerator took up a lot of space in the corner. The tall, yellowish cupboard, which used to be white, looked out of place in the middle. The rest of the space was crammed by the oven and the sink, which had a garbage bucket underneath. Igor and the kids sat down on the bench along the wall. Mariana and I took the two stools on the other side. Igor looked at the wall with amusement.

"How wonderful," he said. "The same wallpaper as the last time I was here."

"We don't have the money to replace it, so it will have to do for a couple more years."

"I'm serious. It's wonderful. It brings me comfort that some things are still the same. It's like going back in time, when things were," he paused, "normal." He shook his head. "But let's not talk about it. I'm really thirsty."

"I don't have any vodka, if that's what you're implying."

"I quit drinking vodka."

"Uh-huh!" I deployed all my skepticism. "You've said that a couple times before."

"This time it's for real, mostly because I don't have enough money to drink." He laughed it off.

"Oh, that I believe."

"Come on, don't bust my balls. You know it's not my fault there are no jobs in that dinky village I'm from. I was digging wells this year for *kopeiks*—that's how bad it is out there."

"How do you dig a well?" Serghei asked seriously.

"With the most superb tools in the world, son, a shovel and human hands." Igor showed him his palms.

"Oho!" Serghei took his father's hand and touched the two large calluses on his palm. "They are hard. Do they hurt?"

"Not really. After a while, you get used to them."

"Isn't it hard to dig a well in the winter when the ground is frozen?" Lica was always asking the practical questions.

"I only dig them in the summer, honey. Winter is the dead season. As soon as the winter starts, there is only *toská*."

"What's toská?" Serghei asked, intrigued by the new word.

"That's a very good question, son." Igor paused for a while to gather his thoughts. "It's like when your mother told me she wanted a divorce, and I drank for six months straight after that. That's toská."

"Is it when you are really, really sad?"

"Yes, son, it's when you are really, really sad. Though I honestly didn't believe you"—Igor looked straight at me—"till the minute we stood in front of the judge. I thought you were bluffing."

"Why would I bluff about something like that?"

"To scare me back to my senses, like a warning shot. I really, really hoped you were bluffing." His eyes softened, but he'd had plenty of chances to call my hand before we stood in front of the judge, but he never did, and he sure wasn't going to now.

"We got some homemade wine from Uncle Vasya from the village," Mariana said, all of a sudden.

"Mariana," I shushed her. "I was saving it for New Year's."

"What? He'll find it in the fridge anyway. It's not like you can hide it from him."

"Irina without the patronymic?" Igor theatrically threw his hands in the air. "For old time's sake, can you pour me some wine? If that's from Uncle Vasya, I have to try it. I'm surprised, though, he still keeps making wine after your grandpa died."

"Well, he inherited Grandpa's vineyard. It's not like he can stop picking the grapes now; they grow every year. Besides, Grandpa always said, 'Wine is the country's liquid gold.' You can buy or exchange a lot of stuff in the country for wine, especially now, when no other industries are working."

"I remember your Grandpa Ivan once took me and your cousin to the vineyard to help him spread the fertilizer—the horse manure—to be precise. We, two young, healthy guys, took one bucket with manure out of the horse carriage and almost dropped it because it was so heavy. Your grandpa looked at us, shook his head and, without saying a word, took the second bucket from the carriage all by himself, lifted it up, and kept on walking like it was nothing. The man was in his eighties! It was pretty embarrassing, son," he said, turning to Serghei. "Let's drink to Grandpa Ivan, the man, one of a kind!" Igor lifted the glass filled with bright-red wine that Mariana had poured for him. He emptied it in a swift gulp, then breathed out like a tired horse, just as he used to do when gulping a shot of vodka. "Is it made from Lidia grapes?" he asked me, wiping his mouth.

"Yes, it is." I nodded, amazed that he still remembered such details.

"God, I missed Moldavian wine. You people know how to make it right." A playful smile brightened Igor's face. There was no way he would ever quit drinking, no matter what he told himself. He enjoyed this ritual too much. Besides, his veins were by in large a stream of vodka. Except today, they were flowing half-wine, half-blood.

Igor's cheeks turned red and his tongue started slowing down a little.

"Pop, eat something. You know you're supposed to eat when

you're drinking, or you'll get drunk fast," Lica scolded her father, concerned for him, as usual.

"My beautiful daughter," Igor answered tenderly. He caressed Lica's long hair, which cascaded to her shoulders. "You are so smart, just like your mama and your Grandma Katya. By the way, how is my favorite mother-in-law, Katya? Still working in Greece?" he asked me.

"Yes, still in Greece."

"Still helping you with your college tuition?"

"Who else? You're not sending me any alimony," I said quickly. It'd been on the tip of my tongue, but now it was out there.

Igor was quiet for a few seconds. "Your mother will be happy that we divorced. She didn't like me much, though I have nothing but respect for her. She is the most hardworking woman I have ever known. I can only imagine what it's like to be there alone and far away, cleaning houses and taking care of other people's families, while leaving your own family behind. How old were you, Mariana, when your mother left?"

"Thirteen," Mariana answered. "But she was gone before then, on and off to Moscow or wherever she could find work. Thank God Ira came back home from Crimea with Lica and Serghei. I was getting tired of being left with neighbors and relatives. You know my father was drinking, so he was no big help."

"What times we live in, when women have to take this burden upon themselves," Igor said philosophically, ignoring the drinking comment. "You women are so much stronger than us. We are the men of a broken country. We aren't breadwinners. We're nobody! Forget Hamlet. Look at what's going on all around us right now. That's the true tragedy of our days."

Lica was right, I could see. Igor needed to eat something. The wine was getting to him already. He put his elbows on the table and dropped his head into his hands.

"Pop, don't cry." Lica stroked his head. Igor turned to give his daughter a hug. His left hand swung wide and overturned the glass of water in front of him, which spilled across the table and all over the floor.

"I'll get towels," I said, and went into the other room. Mariana followed me.

"Why is he crying?" Mariana whispered. "He's a man."

"He is a *broken* man. Broken men are allowed to cry."

"I don't remember Mom or *Babushka* Veta crying like this."

"Your father made our mom cry plenty of times. She just didn't like to show her tears. But I'll never forget how our mother cried when my father died. I was just six, but I remember it to this day."

"That was at a funeral!"

"This is a funeral to him," I told her. "It's one big funeral to every one of us. Do you think it's easy to bury the country we grew up in? When it was all we knew our entire lives? Some of us shook it off and moved on, but others got stuck in the past."

"I don't understand when you speak in metaphors." Mariana looked at me quizzically.

"Then I failed you." I smiled. "I was so good at metaphors. When I was fifteen, I won a regional essay contest among the best schools in the city. It was a beautiful essay about World War II."

"What did you know about war? Did you fight it yourself?"

"It's called research."

"Show off." Mariana smirked, took the towels out of my hands, and marched to the kitchen to clean up the mess.

Igor switched from the bench to the stool to get out of Mariana's way, then picked up his acoustic guitar from the corner, a sign that he was ripe for singing. He touched the strings lightly, moving his left hand up and down the guitar neck. A pleasant, joyful, familiar sound filled the kitchen. I loved hearing him play the guitar until *Babushka* Veta asked me one question I couldn't find the answer to: "Can he feed his kids with his guitar?"

"*Kolotushka!*" Lica yelled excitedly.

"You remember that?" Igor smiled.

"Yes, that's the funny lullaby that you used to sing to us when we were little."

"You remember the words?"

"Of course!"

"Then sing along ... *Kolotushka, tuk-tuk-tuk.*"

Lica stood up beside her father with one hand on his shoulder, straightening her back like a true opera singer. She picked up the next line without forgetting a bit.

"Sereoja, come on, join us," Igor encouraged his son.

Serghei stomped his foot in frustration. "I don't remember the words."

"How come? We used to sing it together so many times. Do you remember the first line?"

"Yes."

"Then let's sing it together: *Ko-lo-tush-ka, tuk-tuk-tuk.*" Igor knocked on the guitar three times, imitating the *tuk-tuk-tuk* sound. I smiled, seeing them swirled up in the music, as if they were on the stage in the stoplight, and the walls behind them disappeared. The raspy sound of the guitar, competing with kids' voices, was bouncing in the air, stirring up long-forgotten emotions.

"You guys all did great," Igor chanted when the song was over. "Except Mariana. You, sister, were not born to sing."

"Oh, come on now!" Mariana swung her hand, trying to hit him on the shoulder.

Igor ducked and burst into laughter. "Truce, truce. Happy New Year's, everybody!" He cheered, and then he lifted another glass of wine, welcoming the year 2000, which was right around the corner.

"It's not New Year's yet," I felt compelled to remind him.

"Does it matter?"

"I guess, today, it doesn't."

Chapter 2

The Snow Queen

Mrs. Lidia, the dark haired, hawk-nosed principal of the day care, gathered us, the teachers, for a pre-Christmas planning meeting. She looked around the room exquisitely, as if searching for her prey.

"Who wants to be the Snow Queen?" she asked. "We need one for the matinee. Mrs. Vera over here agreed to be *Moş Crăciun*. She, I mean, *he* will bring presents for the kids. Irina, can you play the Snow Queen?"

"Sure. Do I get a costume?"

"Unfortunately, the costume went kaput. The moths got into it a couple years back." She shrugged. "We'll have to improvise."

"I can bring my old wedding dress and veil," Nina, the youngest teacher, offered. "It will make a great costume for a Snow Queen."

"Don't you want to sell it?" I asked her, mostly because I didn't like the idea.

"I can't. It has a few stains from spilled wine, but I can sew some snowflakes on them to cover them up."

"Isn't it bad luck to wear a wedding dress for anything but a wedding?" Mrs. Vera asked.

"Please," the principal interrupted her sternly. "That's a folk tale from old times. We are modern, educated teachers, not a bunch of superstitious *babushkas*."

* * *

"Breathe in, breathe in," Nina repeated a few times on the day of the matinee, trying to zip me up in her old wedding dress, which was now a Snow Queen costume, decorated with a bunch of plastic snowflakes. It must have been one fun wedding to deserve so many snowflakes.

"We should have tried it during the rehearsal," I said, disappointed that I couldn't squeeze in. *What the hell?* Nina didn't look much skinnier than me, but she sure was half a mile taller, because her dress was dragging on the floor, and I had to constantly pull up the front to avoid stepping on the hem.

"One more time, we're almost there," Nina said. "Now, don't breathe out too hard."

"How am I supposed to act when I can barely breathe?"

"You'll be fine," Nina said unconvincingly.

I huffed, treasuring each breath. "Let's get that crown on my head before I pass out."

Finally ready, I stepped down the long hallway and peeked through the cracked door into the assembly room to listen in. The room was full of parents gathered for the matinee. Igor was sitting in the corner, too, watching the action, which had already started.

"Mom." Serghei was pulling on my dress. He was wearing a folk costume: black pants, white shirt, a peach embroidered jacket, and a pointy gray lamb hat, just like my grandpa used to wear in the winter. He held a long red sash in his hands.

"You are not supposed to see me," I shushed him. "Why are you wandering around?"

"Mrs. Cristina sent me because my button just came off, and my pants are falling down."

"I don't have anything to sew buttons with." I took the sash from his hands, wrapped it around his waist, and tied it in a double knot. "Here, that will have to do. Don't breathe out hard, or it will get undone."

"How am I supposed to say my lines like this?" he asked, holding in his belly.

"You'll be fine," I answered with a feeling of déjà vu. "Go, go to your class. My part is coming up soon."

* * *

"Who was a naughty kid this year?" I yelled dramatically as I entered the assembly room, flapping my "magic" wand in the air. I stepped to the right, looking for Dina. I was supposed to "freeze" her with my wand. The kids, shocked by my outfit, started screaming hysterically and ran to the left. Little Dina forgot her part and ran away from me too. I stretched out my hand to catch her before she ran too far. *Swish.* I heard the sound of my hemline ripping under my foot. I only realized what was happening when I saw myself in the wall mirror, tumbling down to the floor. The room went silent. Igor, on the other hand, burst into high-pitched laughter.

Thanks for your support, asshole.

Dina tiptoed back to check on me. "Are you all right, Mrs. Irina?"

My elbows were burning, and my left knee throbbed, but my "show must go on" spirit kicked in. I pulled my feet under my butt and quickly, as if we'd planned this all along, grabbed Dina by her foot and said, "You were a naughty kid this year, weren't you?"

Dina screamed.

"Shh! You're supposed to be frozen," I whispered. As if struck by magic, Dina snapped into acting mode, stopped fidgeting, and "froze" into an icy statue.

"Uh-huh! I caught you, evil Snow Queen!" I heard the voice of Mrs. Vera behind me, who looked unrecognizable in a Moş Crăciun costume. "Go away and leave the kids alone!" I got up and backed away to the door, as my role required. "Bring in the *haitori!*" she said out loud then, referring to the kids who were supposed to recite carols. Serghei was one of the boys in folk costumes who lined up in front of the parents.

"*Aho, aho!*" The group started the traditional Christmas recital in unison. Serghei held a little bell in his right hand, ringing it so loudly that I could barely hear his lines. The boy on his left held a stick with a papier-mâché bull's head with colored ribbons, swinging it in the air to make the ribbons float. Another boy held a cardboard roll under his armpit. It looked like a bull's body with a long tail made out of real horse's hair, and a third boy pulled the tail to produce a squeaky sound resembling the voice of a hoarse animal. The only girl in the group had a bag filled with wheat, which she started throwing at the rows of parents, as the last words of the recital wished them all long years ahead: "*La mulți ani!*"

* * *

"Son, I'm speechless," Igor said, wiping his tears when we could finally leave. "I couldn't understand much of what you said, but some things don't need translation." Serghei giggled and wrapped his arms around his father.

"I had no clue he was so good at Romanian," Igor said, this time to me.

"Well, he's learning fast."

"I forgot all the Romanian words I'd learned while we were married," Igor said, disappointed. "Though, I still remember some. Why did they address the crowd as 'brothers'? The folk poems don't have a place for sisters and mothers?"

"I guess that doesn't rhyme, so they threw the words out."

"That's a lame reason to exclude women from a scene in a festivity." He laughed, as if he could fix centuries-long issues with his laugh-

ter. "I'm glad I got to see your production before I leave tomorrow."
Igor turned to Serghei. "That's something your dad will never forget."

∗ ∗ ∗

The next day, Mariana, Lica, Serghei, Igor, and I were standing on the railway platform waiting for Igor's train to Odessa. *Choo-choo* sounds of coming and going trains were floating in the distance. The crisp, cold air penetrated our coats, but the kids didn't seem to mind. Serghei and Lica were blowing steam from their mouths, trying to outdo each other, imitating their father, who was smoking a cigarette next to me.

"So," Igor started the conversation. "You really haven't found anyone since we divorced?"

"I had a fling with someone, but…it's complicated," I answered cautiously.

"I thought 'complicated' was my specialty." Igor laughed. "Speaking of complicated, Tanya and I are back together."

"The Tanya that you were dating and had a kid with someone else?"

"We sorted that old stuff out." He waved it off like it was nothing. "It's not Liza's fault, what happened between us, she's just a kid. I love her like my own daughter. Besides, Tanya is pregnant again, this time with my kid. What can I say? I make gorgeous kids."

"So, you are going to have four children?" It was hard to hold back fiercer words. "How are you going to take care of four, when you can't take care of these two?"

"I might be bad at many things, but being a father is one thing I'm good at. Look at them." He pointed at Lica and Serghei. "Aren't they wonderful?"

"Yes, they are, but not thanks to you. Do you think that showing up once every few years is being a good father?"

"Look, I didn't tell you this to stick it to you." I caught his sneer before his expression softened again. "I'm just telling you so you're aware of my situation. Honesty is all I have left."

"Oh, indeed, letting me know about your situation is one other thing that you are good at. There is always something that stops you from buying them shoes, or school supplies, or paying for the doctors. It's like they don't even have a father."

"You can always bring them for the summer. You know my mom and I would love to have them. In the summer, we have fruit and vegetables in the garden. Feeding them is the least we can do."

"Sure, if I can only find the money for three round-trip tickets to Crimea every year." I shook my head. Though his suggestion was kind on the surface, I knew relying on him would be a mistake. "I'll just keep doing what I always do: take care of the kids on my own," I said, and crossed my arms. I was done talking. I just wanted the train to come, so Igor could finally leave.

A light, anemic layer of snow swirled in the air, covering the platform, but it was too weak to stick. People walking back and forth were wiping it away with their feet.

* * *

I called Gicu one hour after I got home.

"I'm glad you called," he said.

"Nice to hear that you're glad. I finally got my certificate of divorce."

"Yeah?" he answered, uninterested.

"Yeah, my ex-husband brought it from Crimea."

"Your ex-husband was visiting?"

"What's the matter? Are you jealous?"

"No, you're a free woman. You can do whatever you want."

"I was a free woman during the past year when we were dating. Nothing has changed," I said, unsure how to react to his tone.

"I wouldn't call it dating. When was the last time we saw each other? A month ago?"

"That's because I have kids and I'm going to school. I can't just drop everything—"

"Yes, you have kids," Gicu interrupted. "I want to have kids of my own one day, but I don't want to raise someone else's kids."

"What are you trying to say?" I gripped the phone firmly.

"That's the thing I wanted to talk to you about. I found my soul mate. I want to marry her."

"For God's sake, I was at your house a month ago. When did you have time to find a bride? Or were you doing this soul mate search at the same time you were doing me?"

"I thought I'd tell you now, before you get to my house and you bump into each other."

"That's so thoughtful of you!" I said, then dropped the receiver. *What a toská! What a fucking toská!*

Chapter 3

The Test

"I have to go, I have to go," I yelled at Mariana from the doorway. "I have a test today. Don't forget to pick up Serghei from day care no later than six-thirty. The teachers don't like to wait till seven to close. They have families, too, and they would rather go home earlier."

"I don't like bringing him home earlier. He bounces off the walls, and I can't concentrate on my homework," Mariana said. "The day care is one hundred meters away. Worst-case scenario, if he is the last kid there, Cristina will bring him home. She knows where we live, since her apartment is above ours."

"Please don't do this to me. Cristina is his teacher, not his babysitter. They will gossip that I abandon my children. Some of them already think I'm a lady of the night since I go to the city every evening. The joys of living in a place where everybody knows each other. I'm so tired of explaining that I'm taking night classes."

"I thought you didn't care what people think."

"I don't." I paused. "Most of the time."

"For God's sake, just go. You have a test today. Remember?"

"Will you check Lica's homework too?"

"I know, I know. It's not my first time. Goodbye! See you tonight." Mariana waved impatiently.

I ran out the door, though I had an hour and a half before the test. Mom used to nag me: "You should always leave the house earlier. The buses never run on schedule in the winter." I would answer: "I know, I know. It's not my first time." The realization that I had turned into my mother made me cringe. I sped up when I saw a bus right behind me. The orange Icarus, a leftover of the Eastern European bloc alliance, long past its prime, was moving slower than an old lady, trying to get up the icy hill without skidding.

The bus dropped me off in the city thirty minutes later, and I switched to the trolleybus for another twenty-minute ride before my destination. I tried to look through the window, but it was hard to see through the white crochet-like patterns of ice that covered it almost entirely, barely letting in sunlight. It was a useless exercise anyway. More people were coming on board at each stop, as if the trolleybus was made of rubber and could fit an entire city. Everyone was packed so tight, it felt claustrophobic.

"Hey, cutie, what's your name?" said a tall young man in a brown fur hat stuck in front of me.

"Do you want to date a divorcee with two kids?" I asked, looking defiantly into his eyes.

"Shit, no!" he answered honestly.

"Then back off, *krasavchik!*" He took offense that I'd called him "handsome" and pouted for a few seconds. He would have turned away if he could, but the crowd pinned him in tight, so he just stood there breathing above my head.

"Really? You have two kids? You are a cute girl, but you are damaged goods now," he said, genuinely concerned.

"Tell me about it. No Braveheart in my homeland for me."

At the next stop, a wave of passengers poured out of the trolleybus and dispersed like a well-trained pack of wolves, taking my interlocutor with them. A billboard with a picturesque view peeked through the open door, showing neatly organized rows of green vines covered in summer sunshine somewhere in the countryside. The flashy headline: "Moldova—My Beautiful Country" was almost entirely covered in snow. "Moldova—My Beau…ful C…try" was all you could see. *Interesting, when did they hang this billboard? Not the best sign for winter, when everything is dead.*

"State University of Moldova," the trolleybus driver announced suddenly, only then realizing the announcer duties he'd ignored. I stepped out of the trolleybus onto the fresh squeaky white powder of snow, which covered an icy layer. It felt slippery, but I didn't have much time to take it easy. My five p.m. English language test was about to start, and our professor, Mrs. Bondarenco, would accept no excuse for late arrival.

Galina Mihailovna Bondarenco, nicknamed "The Iron Lady" for a few good reasons, liked to repeat: "I teach future diplomats and professors, not losers." I always felt that I was some kind of an impostor in her evening English Translators class, part of Continuous Education for Working Professionals, because I was not planning on being a diplomat or a professor. My dream was to become a writer or a journalist one day, but the collapse of the Soviet Union had turned everything upside down, and I had to lower my expectations. At the moment, I just wanted to get an office job, but that was a challenge too. Even the most casual office jobs listed English as a requirement. My professor had no regard for my lower bar. She was going to beat English into me as if I were on my way to the United Nations.

The classroom was as quiet as a cemetery. I quickly took a seat next to Anya, a physician by day. Galina Mihailovna was ready, holding a thick stack of papers in her hands. I, on the other hand, desperately wanted two things at the same time: one extra day to study and for this test to be over. The professor started walking between our desks, delivering our assignments with her head held so high that her hair bun was making her even taller and more intimidating than usual. I looked at the piece of paper in front of me. *For God's sake, I am thirty-one years old! Why am I shaking like a high school girl? Everything is going to be okay.*

The assignment consisted of two parts. The first part required a written translation of twenty English verbs into Russian or Romanian (the class was a mismatch of bilinguals, so we could choose either). Then we needed to write down two synonyms for twenty English verbs and conjugate the same verbs in past and past perfect tenses. The second part (oh, goody!) was an oral translation of a text chosen by the professor, which we'd have no time to prepare for. The test looked much harder than I'd anticipated.

My heart was beating so hard, it was about to jump out of my chest. All my senses sharpened. I could hear the sound of my neighbor's pen writing on her sheet of paper and the sound of the clock on the wall across the room. Anya, next to me, raised her right hand. The professor waved her in, inviting her to approach the desk.

"You didn't finish here." Galina Mihailovna pointed to the sheet of paper that Anya had handed to her.

"I'm sorry. "Anya took the paper from the professor and wrote in a few more words.

"You guessed this one wrong," Galina Mihailovna said. "This is not how you translate 'to abolish.'"

"I'm sorry. I don't know what I was thinking. I worked a night shift yesterday, so I didn't get much sleep."

"Anya," the professor said in an accusatory tone, "there can't be excuses for a student learning a foreign language. You may never have a second chance to learn what you missed." Without giving Anya any time to recover, Galina Mihailovna handed her the text for the oral translation. Anya started reading the text out loud. She would stop for a moment to gather her thoughts before she translated each sentence, but every time Anya paused for too long, Galina Mihailovna would raise her right eyebrow impatiently.

"You were only eighty percent prepared for this test, Anya," Galina Mihailovna summed it up in the end. "A translator, like a doctor, should always be one hundred percent ready." Then she let her go.

I shrugged uncomfortably but decided it was time to go for it.

There was no point in prolonging my agony, so I took the chair in front of my professor in total calmness, like a person with nothing to lose. Perhaps bravery would impress her. Galina Mihailovna read my sheet of paper in silence, marking it down the lines until she got to the very end.

"Good," she said. "Here is your text." There was no time to celebrate my initial success. I read the first line to myself, waiting for some unknown words to jump out at me. To my surprise, there were none. I took a deep breath and loudly blurted out the first English sentence, stressing the "th" sound as hard as I could. "Zey ah," I said, instead of "they're," swallowing the "r" so fast that I almost choked on it. I quickly covered it up with a fast translation. I repeated the same technique three more times until the text was over. Galina Mihailovna looked at me very seriously.

"Irina, where do you work?"

"In a day care center," I answered cautiously, embarrassed that I did not have a cool profession like others in the class: doctors, bankers, managers.

"Do you have kids?"

"Yes. Two."

"Do you have a husband?"

"I'm divorced," I answered, not really sure where she was going with this.

"Who's helping you with the kids when you are here at night?"

"I have a younger sister. She lives with me."

"So, you are practically raising three kids on your own?"

I paused trying to process her question. "I never thought about it that way. It's more like we are helping each other."

She eyed me closely, still evaluating despite the test being over. "I noticed that you come prepared for the tests every time. I have younger students in the day classes, without families or kids, who can never find any time to study. How do you manage to do it?"

"It's all about organizing your time, I guess. During the week, when the kids nap at day care, I do my homework. On Saturdays, after I'm done cleaning, I hit the books until it's dark. On Sunday, I continue for eight more hours. Then I repeat that every week. I can't wait for summer. I need a break."

Galina Mihailovna nodded and smiled.

"Congratulations," she said. "You passed your test, but you need to work on your pronunciation, so I can only give you a nine out of ten. During this winter break, take a tape recorder and record yourself reading in English and listen back. Then do it again and again, until you get the pronunciation right. See you after New Year's."

"Thank you!" I said, and jumped off the chair. I could barely contain myself. "Guys," I said on my way out, "I just got a nine from Bondarenco! Can you believe this?"

"Good job!" the tall, handsome, and loud classmate Kirill cheered me. He just got a six, but that never stopped him from being happy for others.

"Hey! The last one survived!" he yelled, when he saw Alex leaving the classroom with his thick goofy glasses hanging at the end of his nose, about to fall off. Alex fixed his glasses, smiled, and said to no one in particular, "Are you all up for a little celebration for this year's final send off?"

I hesitated. "I don't know, I have to go home."

"It's only seven o'clock. You have plenty of time to go home," Kirill insisted.

Chapter 4

All Sorts of Drunks

Six of us—Kirill, Alex, Violeta, Anya, Tanya, and I—walked down the street for several blocks until we found a restaurant with a vacant table so small that it could barely fit us all. The waiter brought menus and then forgot about us for fifteen minutes, being busy with a group of four big drunken men with thick gold chains around their necks—the "nouveau riche" of the post-Soviet era—who were loudly demanding more vodka.

"I'm an honest businessman!" the biggest and the loudest of them yelled, flapping his arms.

"I don't know about that," a man opposite of him with blurred eyes answered.

"I had to pay a ten thousand-dollar bribe for permits to this motherfucking mayor of ours. It's getting out of control, I'm telling you. Last year, I only had to pay five thousand dollars. You can't just keep taking and taking from people!"

"You are not people; you are a businessman!" another man next to him yelled passionately, barely staying in his seat. His face was so red, it could put beets to shame. "They are the people!" he continued, one hand sweeping around the room. "We are the elites!"

"With such elites, we are all fucked. No money in the world can buy them brains," Violeta said in English, giving a dirty look to the rowdy group next to us. As she said this, she stood out from our group, almost foreign, with her impeccable bone structure, long brown hair, and big brown eyes, dressed up elegantly and expensively. Even that look she gave our neighbors was classy.

"Hey, this place is expensive," I whispered when I finally read the prices.

"We are here for just a few drinks and appetizers," Violeta said, like it was not a big deal. "Don't worry, I'll help you out," Violeta assured me, seeing my hesitation. She asked the waiter to bring each girl a shot of Amaretto, while the boys ordered some vodka shots. The brown liqueur with a strong taste of almonds dissolved in my mouth and slid easily down my throat. My empty stomach absorbed the liquid so fast that a tingly sensation went down my body to my toes within minutes.

"So, why do you all need your English diplomas?" I asked the group, feeling sassy all of a sudden. "I need it to get out of my dead-end job at the day care," I jumped in before anyone could answer. "You, on the other hand, all have cool jobs. You"—I pointed my finger at Anya—"are a doctor. And you, Tanya, work for your aunt's bank. It's not like she's going to kick you out. And you, Violeta, work for a freaking oil company. Why do *you* need English?"

"Our contracts for the European markets are written in English," Violeta answered. "I need to keep up with the times, or they will toss me out in a heartbeat. It's absolutely brutal out there. There are so many young graduates looking for jobs now that it's scary how quickly you can be replaced with someone who would work for half the price."

"I need English to go to medical seminars abroad," Anya said, adjusting her old-fashioned blue blouse with a pattern of white flowers that she wore often. "I hope to eventually obtain a residency in some European country where it actually pays to be a doctor. Here, I work for twelve hours a day just to get by. Doctors' wages are ridiculous. They stayed the same when everything else went up in price."

Tanya, who was sitting across the table, entered the conversation. "That's because everything is imported nowadays," she said. "Almost all domestic industries have collapsed." Her green almond-shaped eyes, highlighted with dark eyeliner, sparkled as they always did when she got excited or upset about something. She ran her perfectly manicured fingers through her styled, dyed-blond hair and continued. "There are only a few industries left in Moldova hanging on for their dear lives. Our bank loaned money to a sugar factory up north, and we had to restructure their debts several times because they're about to go bankrupt."

She stopped for a few seconds, as if weighing whether to continue. "Then there are bandits like these"—she pointed at the next table—"who come into my aunt's office almost daily, flaunting their guns, demanding bank credits. It's clear as day that we will never see that money again, so she's trying to walk the line." She seemed frustrated, but I could sense her hopelessness too. "I don't know how long she can hold on, though. It's pretty scary what those knuckleheads can do if they don't get their way." She sipped another Amaretto and added, "That's why I need English, to be ready if I need to flee the country on short notice."

"On a lighter note," Kirill interrupted, "I'm learning English so I'm not the dumbest person in the office." He sure knew how to break up a tense moment. "Hey, I'm serious." Kirill raised his voice, trying to talk over the outburst of laughter. "Everybody speaks English there. My mom's protection can only get me so far."

"Lucky you, Kirill. I don't have a mommy who can find me a job like yours," I said after wiping away tears of laughter. "I don't even know if my diploma would help me find a new job. My college degree could be a waste of money and effort for me in the end."

"I don't know about the wasted effort," Alex finally spoke up, his peach cheeks turning red. "If I were a girl like any of you, I'd use my English to get me a rich foreign boyfriend."

"Okay, everybody! We are getting into some deep stuff." Kirill raised his hand. "I think it's time to close the shop."

It was cold and dark outside. The streetlights and bright windows from nearby buildings were trying hard to dissolve the surrounding darkness. We bundled together, holding on to each other, and walked down the street in a long row that took up almost the entire sidewalk.

Three young, slightly drunken men and two ladies were holding hands in a line, just like us, as they walked up the street, loudly singing the Romanian folk song "Sleigh with Bells." In the quiet night, the song floated in the air, triggering pleasant childhood memories.

"Hey, hey!" Tanya cheered and suddenly started singing in unison with the strangers:

Sanie cu zurgălăi (Crazy flying sleigh with bells),

Frumoși sunt căluții tăi (Beautiful horses you have),

Dar mai frumoși sunt ai mei (But my horses are the best).

Violeta and I looked at each other mischievously and, taking a deep breath, joined in:

Că le dau apă cu mei (Magic water they will drink),

Și zboară ca niște zmei (And like dragons they will fly).

When our two groups met in the middle of the sidewalk, the two young men at the end of the other line raised their arms and put them on Kirill's and Alex's shoulders—closing us all in a circle for an improvised Moldavian street *hora*. Stomping our feet on the ground and moving a few steps to the left, then moving back to the right, we kept singing together until we ran out of lyrics we knew.

"That's right, they'll fly like dragons!" One of the singing men from the other group finished the song. "Happy New Year, the Year of Dragon!" they yelled all together to us.

"Happy New Year!" we yelled back at them and parted ways.

At the bus stop, the nimble microbuses picked up my friends one by one and drove them away in the night, until I was left alone with a few strangers who were hoping to catch the next bus going to the outskirts. I felt a gust of cold wind on my face. Then I noticed a wave of white tiny snowflakes coming down. The wind was blowing them sideways, making them swirl and sparkle in the streetlights like little jewels that had lost their way. I raised my hands in the air and caught a few of them with my gloves. *They say there are no two snowflakes alike. How could they know? Whose job was it to catalog snowflake patterns?* It was amazing how a shot of Amaretto could make the harsh winter feel so gorgeous.

Swish! I heard my winter boots sliding on ice. My feet jumped like two catapults in front of me. I flapped my hands as if trying to hold on to air to slow down my fall. *Boom!* My body slammed on a pile of snow gathered on the side of the walkway by the street cleaners.

"Are ... you ... okay?" a stranger standing over me asked, separating each word like a person with a speech impairment or a drunk pretending to be sober. I moved my aching body, trying to figure out if I wanted to answer him or swear first. I'd spent too much time on the ground already.

"I think I'm fine," I answered. My body was sore, but my heavy coat had provided a good cushion.

"You're lucky ... you didn't ... break a leg ... or something." The stranger, towering over me like a giant, leaned forward and pulled me up by my hand, as if I weighed nothing. *His voice sounds so familiar.*

"Oh, look, the bus is here. Are you taking this bus?" he asked.

"Yes."

"Me too." He gave me his elbow to lean on to get in, then dropped onto the seat next to me. The bus light cleared the shadow on his face, and I recognized him.

"Hey, I know you," I said. "Not really *know* you, but I saw you at the restaurant today."

"Oh, you are that girl who was sitting next to us. Grisha," he introduced himself and extended his hand, ready for a handshake.

"Irina," I answered and shook his hand. "Why is a businessman like you taking the bus?"

"I wrecked my car about a week ago," he said, like it wasn't a big deal. "I ordered a new Mercedes from Germany." He trilled his lips, making a funny noise, like a child playing with his toy car. "But it hasn't arrived yet."

"Why don't you take a taxi then?"

"Those taxi speculators will charge me an arm and a leg at this time of night for getting to our neck of the woods."

"Isn't that what you do as a businessman? Charge more if there's high demand but a low supply in the market?"

"That's beside the point." He seemed surprised by my forwardness. Again, amazing what a shot of Amaretto could do. "Money is too hard to make nowadays to just throw it into the wind." He threw his hand in the air, trying to imitate the floating money.

"I wouldn't know. I've never bought a Mercedes."

"Smarty pants, aren't you? But I get it, I get it," he said philosophically. "Unscrupulous men like me take advantage of the new order, but I didn't invent that system. The system was there before me. If you want to be part of the game, you need to play by new rules."

"What rules are those?"

"There is no tomorrow. Take what you can today."

"And break a few laws and bones along the way?"

Grisha laughed, as if I had said something incredibly funny. "Not without that," he said. "Honestly, somebody could shoot me tomorrow, for all I know, and it's *finita la commedia*. So, live fully while you are still young, Irina. Live fully!"

"I don't know if I can do that; it seems immoral and plain dangerous. Besides, I never thought I would get life advice from a ..." I was trying to choose the right word. Was he a racketeer, a thief, an outlaw, or a lost soul? I couldn't decide. "My stop!" I jumped up when the bus stopped on the hill two blocks from my apartment.

"What a surprise! I live down the road from here. I'll walk you home. It's dark out there."

"You really don't have to do this. I walk at night from the bus all the time from my night classes." I rushed to get off the bus as quickly as I could, hoping he would stay behind, but he followed me. The light frivolity was fading, and nerves rose in its place.

"A pretty lady like you shouldn't walk alone at night. Don't worry. I'm not stalking you. I'm happily married. You never know what bandits are out there, so it's better if I walk you home," he insisted, as if he weren't a bandit himself.

"So, what do you study?" Grisha asked me as he walked alongside.

"English," I answered, still not fully understanding how to react to his chivalry.

"Good for you! Everybody learns English nowadays. I, unfortunately, have no talent for languages."

"Here is my apartment. Thank you for walking with me." I rushed up the stairs.

"Happy New Year!" he said, instead of goodbye, and waved from the bottom of the stairs. "May the Year of the Fire Dragon bring you a new beginning, as the goddamn calendar promised, or I will be really pissed at this motherfucker!"

"Me too." I laughed. "I'll be really pissed too." My nervousness faded, and I thought this night would end on a high note.

When I entered the house, Mariana yelled, "Thank God, you're home!" She was shaking, and her voice was trembling.

"What? What happened? Did Sereoja break an arm or something?"

"No! It's worse. Our brother Vitalic showed up drunk and said that he and his wife had a fight, and he's going to stay with us for a while."

"Mom, Vitalic peed his pants." Lica jumped out of bed in her pajamas to tell me.

"What?" This was too much to process right now.

"Yeah!" Mariana yelled. "That too. His pants are wet and smell like pee and shit."

"Mom, he's very, very stinky." Serghei jumped out of bed too.

"Are you telling me that he pooped his pants? How drunk is he?"

"Scary drunk." Mariana was about to cry. "Drunks always scare me." She continued to shake. "Dad used to get into these drunken rages and—"

"There are different sorts of drunks." I tried to calm her down. "Your father is an angry drunk. Our brother is just a stupid drunk."

"Papa is a sad drunk." Lica provided her expertise about her father. "When he's drunk, he just says, `Nobody loves me, and he cries."

"Yeah," I said sarcastically, "and the next day he would laugh it off, because he couldn't remember anything he'd said the night before."

"Vitalic isn't scary, he's just very, very drunk." Lica waved her hand like a professional who had dealt with drunks before.

"And very, very stinky," Serghei said one more time.

"Did he bring any spare clothes with him?" I asked Mariana.

"I didn't see any bags," she answered.

"How's he going to go to work tomorrow in shitty pants?"

Lica giggled, but Mariana snapped, "How the hell should I know? I'm not his wife."

"Where is he?"

"I sent him to the bathroom. There was a half tub of cold water in there that I poured in earlier, just in case they shut off the water again."

I walked down the corridor and put my ear to the bathroom door. "How long has he been in there?"

"I don't know, thirty minutes."

"Thirty minutes? Did you hear him move at all?"

"I heard something breaking, but he's locked in, so I don't know what's going on in there."

"Did you hear any water running?"

"I wasn't listening. I was so freaked out I didn't know what to do."

I put my ear to the door again, trying to catch any sounds. It was dead silent. Not a breath nor a move could be detected. I knocked lightly, hoping to get a reaction, and heard a sudden sound—a huge splash, like somebody falling into the tub.

"Oh, good, he's alive," I said, relieved, but then I paused. "I don't hear him moving. He could drown in the tub if he fell in face first. Vitalic!" I yelled, and knocked on the door in panic. "Vitalic! Open the door!" I knocked again, harder.

"M-m-m…" I heard a mooing in the bathroom.

"Vitalic, are you all right?"

"M-m-m…" I heard again in response.

Lica grimaced. "Is he lying in that cold water?"

"Cold water is good for him." Now I was angry. He'd scared me, my sister, and my children. "Let's roll out the roller bed. He isn't sleeping in any of our beds tonight!"

Mariana and the kids followed me into the bedroom.

"Why aren't you sleeping?" I asked the kids. "It's eleven o'clock."

"Because I told them not to leave me alone with Vitalic," Mariana answered for them.

"I'll protect you, Mariana," Serghei said, puffing his chest.

"Yeah, a six-year-old is a big help." I shook my head.

"I can bite and scratch," Serghei said confidently, as if he'd been thinking about a strategy all this time.

"Well, if that's the case, then we're all safe." I sat down on the bed, then looked at Mariana's scared face, but instead of comforting her, I started laughing. "Tell me, just tell me, how an adult man can poop his pants?"

Lica started giggling. Serghei dropped on the floor holding his belly, laughing hysterically. Mariana finally burst out laughing too.

"Out of all the shit that we've had to deal with, this one by far is the shittiest," I said when I finally caught my breath.

Chapter 5

The Aid

"Irina," my day care co-teacher, Cristina, a middle-aged stocky woman with short hair, whispered through the open door of the preschoolers' bedroom. The six-year-olds were taking their afternoon nap on the old Soviet-style rollaway beds. "There is a lady with some secondhand clothes from humanitarian aid in the assembly room. Do you need any? She sells clothes for kids and adults very cheap."

"Isn't humanitarian aid supposed to be free?" I asked.

"I wish. The Americans ship the containers as free aid, but somehow there is always a businessman who sells their contents for profit. It's still ten times cheaper than at the market."

"I'll be right there." It was perfect timing. I'd just finished my homework. *Where did my winter break go?* I asked myself, getting my last twenty leis out of my purse, the equivalent of two dollars in America. *So how much could I buy from this woman selling clothes?*

A tall saleswoman with wide shoulders and dark hair rolled in a bun dumped a pile of colorful used clothes out of large see-through plastic bags, right in the middle of the assembly room. The rows of mirrors on the right side of the room, designed for a dance class, were reflecting the group of teachers already going through the pile, making the crowd seem bigger than it actually was. They were busy as a swarm of bees, digging through the clothes and putting aside the items they liked. A teacher on the right kept asking how much each item cost. There were no price tags, and it seemed that the saleswoman was just making up prices as she went along.

There was a lot of room for negotiation, I noticed. All you had to do was hold on to a piece of clothing long enough, then frown for a few seconds when you heard the price, and the lady would take a few leis off to appease the customers.

I picked up four knitted sweaters for the kids for one lei each, hoping they would fit. The American sizes displayed on the clothing labels didn't make much sense to me, with the metric system swimming in my head. Then I saw a long-sleeved dress, dark green with a pattern of black flowers and leaves. I asked the saleswoman, "How much?"

"Five leis."

"Five leis?" I frowned. I held on to it, hoping she would budge on the price, but she kept silent. I twisted it back and forth a couple of times. It was unlike anything I had ever worn before. I tried it on, hoping it would not fit so I could let go of it. But then I saw myself in the mirror. The dress enveloped me like it belonged. It hugged me with its soft fabric, covering my neck with a cute short collar and two big black buttons on the left side. It went to my knees, not too short, but not too long either. I turned around to see my back. Around my hips, the dress showed my curvy butt. My long black hair lay on my shoulders, adding to my mystique.

Cristina, on my left, stopped what she was doing and said, "Wow! That looks good on you." I turned around to see myself one more time, head to toe. She was right. It was THE DRESS. I looked like that actress from *Zorro. What's her name? Catherine Zeta-Jones! That's right, Catherine Zeta!* With this dress, I might get an Antonio Banderas myself.

I looked at the saleswoman, who was measuring me with her eyes like a clothing designer examining a model. "You know what?" she said finally. "I'll sell it to you for four leis. A couple of women tried it before, but I think this one has to go home with you." I paid the saleswoman eight leis total, glad that I got a bargain. Treating myself was a rarity, but there was no way I could turn down this dress. I stole one more glance in the mirror, and smiled.

* * *

"Mom, Mom," Serghei yelled as I entered my apartment with my new secondhand possessions. His head, with its short light brown hair and a cowlick on the right, emerged in front of me in the hallway. He bulged his big dark brown eyes as if he'd just discovered something very important and couldn't wait to tell me.

"Did you know that if you whistle in an empty refrigerator, it echoes? I just tried it in our fridge, it works."

"Don't you know that whistling in the house is bad luck? You are whistling our money away!" I teased. "Not that we have anything to whistle away, and it's probably a stupid superstition, but nevertheless. Don't you have anything else to do?"

Lica, who was eighteen months older than her brother but ten years more mature, showed up at the corner, then put her left hand on her hip, the way she always did when she was about to say something with aplomb. She flipped her long auburn hair back, looked at her brother with wide-open brown eyes, and said in an accusatory voice, "I told him not to whistle in the house."

"That's enough," I said, stopping them before it went too far. I had come bearing gifts. "Try on these new sweaters I bought you." They simultaneously took the bag out of my hand and rushed into the bedroom, arguing on the way about who should open it first. I took my shoes off and went to the pantry to look for something for dinner.

The wooden shelves in the pantry were half bare. On the left side, there were empty three-liter jars from the produce that we'd already used. On the right side, a few jars with canned sour cherries, apples, and pickled tomatoes we'd brought from Babushka's last summer were waiting their turn. I looked down at a twenty-kilo bag, once filled with noodles that my mother had prudently left us before her departure. Now, it was lying down on the floor like a sad, wrinkly rag. I scooped the last noodles from the bottom of the bag and put them on the kitchen table.

"Noodles again?" I heard Serghei's voice coming from the other room.

"Well, your choices are noodles or water. You just wait, you'll miss those noodles when they're gone, because we have nothing else to replace them with." I turned around and saw him in his new secondhand blue sweater. Oh, dear, he looked like an awkward kid who'd outgrown his clothes at least a year ago.

"Seems a little tight, and the sleeves are too short." I was disappointed.

"No, that's fine," he answered, like nothing bothered him. He was never into fashion, thank God.

"Mom, look!" Lica yelled from afar. She walked toward me in my green dress, like a model on the catwalk with her hand on her right hip. The dress was baggy and long, and it was dragging on the floor. She stopped, turned to show me her back, then turned around again and struck another model pose.

"This dress is not for you," I said.

"But it will be when I grow up."

"That will be very sad, if twenty years from now you have to wear your mother's dress."

"Why? You wear Grandma's clothes."

"Because I have to, not because I want to. You know what? Get ready for dinner. Where is Mariana?"

"She's spending the night at her father's. She didn't want to go, but he guilted her into it. He said if she stays overnight at his house, he'll buy a bottle of oil and a bag of rice for her."

"Blackmail? How typical."

I placed a pot of water on the stove and waited for the water to boil. Lica's hand was still on her hip as she drowned in the dress that had made me feel glamorous.

* * *

In the morning, we heard a loud slamming noise. That was Mariana, kicking the outside door with her left knee, while the door stubbornly tried to shut in front of her. She stood in the doorway, bathed in sunlight coming from the stairwell window: tall, thin, with her long legs sticking out below her coat, holding four bags of groceries in her hands. Her long blond hair was sticking to her sweaty face. She looked at me with her angry green eyes, resembling her father so much. We definitely didn't look anything alike, me being a brunette and brown-eyed.

"Is anybody going to help me?" she asked impatiently. "It's quite a ways from the bus stop, and these bags are heavy."

Her appearance started a frenzy in the house. Lica took the oil and rice out of the first bag, as excited as if they were New Year's presents, while Serghei went for the juicy stuff.

"Mandarins! Wait, there's more: *kolbasa!*" he yelled joyfully, taking a bite of the sausage without even peeling the skin off.

"Idiot!" Mariana smacked him on the back of his head. "You're going to give yourself diarrhea. Slow down and share." I took the sausage stick out of Serghei's hands and cut a quarter of it into round, thin pieces, saving the rest for later.

"That's much more than I expected." I looked at the table, full of feta, cucumbers, tomatoes, and smoked fish.

"Well, that's because I'm smart. When Dad took me to the market, I kept pointing. 'I want that, and I need that.' Until he finally cut me off."

"I never thought that my alcoholic stepfather would be our savior, but here we are."

"He stopped drinking, you know."

"Wow, that's very nice to hear."

"He's a businessman now." It seemed like everyone was a businessman these days. "He bought a bus and drives a route to Ukraine. It goes near Babushka Veta's village, so he said if we need to go to Babushka's for food supplies, he'll take us for free."

"That's the best present ever!" I almost jumped in excitement. "That will be a great help. Those bus fares are so expensive."

"Well, he isn't doing it for you. He still doesn't like you." Mariana looked at me.

"I'm not surprised." I brushed it off. I didn't care who it was from, as long as it was free. "He probably still has a grudge against me. Once, at sixteen, I dumped his three-liter jug of wine in the toilet and called him a 'drunken asshole.' He was so livid that he threatened to send his buddies to gang rape me, so for a while, I avoided dark alleys."

"Stop saying that!" Did she think I was joking? "He's a different person now. He says he'll do it for the kids, so they don't go hungry."

"Beggars can't bite the hand that's feeding them." I made my peace.

"So, can we go to Babushka Veta's next weekend?" Lica asked.

"Dad said he can't take four of us, only two," Mariana said.

"Then you kids will have to stay home by yourselves. Just don't burn the house down." I looked at Serghei, then at Lica.

"Mom, we know how to use the gas stove. We are not babies," Lica responded for both herself and her brother.

* * *

Valera, limping heavily on his left side (the result of a car accident a few years back), walked toward Mariana and me. His tall figure towered over the people in the busy bus station. But his limp was causing his head, with its dirty-blond hair, to disappear, then reappear above the crowd like a soccer ball bouncing off the players' heads. I recognized his pale, almost yellow face, covered with childhood chickenpox scars. He smiled with his thin lips, which looked more like a grin, and greeted me with a simple "*Zdorova!*"—a casual expression for "good morning." I nodded back and answered with the same. Then he turned to Mariana and hit her playfully on her shoulder with his right hand, a sign of his fatherly affection, and yelled louder, "Zdorova! No sleeping!"

"Dad, it hurts!" Mariana hit him back on the shoulder, trying to outdo her father, but he just laughed it off. Looking over my head, he asked, "So you are going to Babushka's, huh?"

"Yes," Mariana answered for both of us.

"I'll put you in the back. I don't have vacant seats, but I have some wooden boards that I can put between the rows. You can sit on them until you get there."

"You want us to sit on wooden boards for two hours?" Mariana snapped at him.

"Hey, this is a business. I'm not going to turn down a person who paid for the seat so you can ride on the bus in comfort for free."

"That's fine." I poked Mariana's side. "You don't need to accommodate us. It's already a huge favor as it is. Thank you."

"All right, then," he said, looking skeptical of my gratitude. "I'll pick you up tomorrow on my way back from Ukraine. I should be at the bus stop at around two o'clock. Make sure you're there, because I am not waiting."

"We'll be there," I said, following him to the bus.

The interior of his bus screamed "secondhand." The paint was chipped in a few corners. The seat covers were dirty and ripped here and there. Two seats in the front were leaning too far back, a sign that the recline mechanism was broken. Valera sat down in the driver's seat and backed the long and awkward bus away from the platform. He turned the steering wheel sharply to the left, provoking a terrifying screeching sound that made everyone gasp for air. We were expecting something to break at any minute, but Valera straightened out the steering wheel as if nothing had happened and pulled out of the bus station and onto the road heading to the highway. On the highway, the behemoth of a bus suddenly turned into a gazelle and moved quickly and smoothly, occasionally jumping up when running into a pothole.

Sitting down low on the wooden boards, Mariana and I couldn't see anything outside the windows, but gauging by our sore butts, we could tell we were getting closer. I got up to make sure we wouldn't miss the bus stop. We drove by the rusted road sign with the Olympic Mishka, a brown bear with a belt with five rings on his waist, the symbol of the 1980 Olympic Games in the USSR. This was the road that the Olympic Torch was carried over on its way to Moscow, thousands of kilometers away. At that time, the government allocated the money to pave this highway in a hurry for the games. They were supposed to pave the side roads leading to the nearby villages, including my babushka's village. But after the main highway was finished, they ran out of money and paved only a stretch of five hundred meters from the highway. The rest of the road leading to the village was covered in crushed stone, even now, twenty years later. However, an encouraging board, just a few yards away from the Olympic sign, announced that new road construction would start soon with the help of people of the United States of America. *It must be that American grant they talked about on TV, allocated to the roads of Moldova.*

As we approached Babushka's village, Mariana and I asked Valera to stop the bus. Valera looked at us in doubt. "Are you sure?"

It was indeed hard to tell. The bus stop's structure, which was more like a shack with three walls and one roof, used to have a sign with the name of the village, New Bilicheny, on top. But now it was ripped off, and only the rusty metal rods were sticking out. Even the traffic sign that used to hang from the pole on the other side of the road was missing. Actually, the entire pole had disappeared without a trace. The village was about two kilometers away, hiding behind bare hills covered in snow, which looked exactly the same as any other country fields along the road. One could get lost so easily around here. But we knew this road by heart, so we both confidently answered, "Yes."

"I really need to pee," I told Mariana when we were out of the bus, and cold air swirled under my coat. "There used to be a bathroom behind that bus stop."

"It's not a bathroom, it's an outhouse. You'll freeze your pee-pee in there."

I was less concerned about the cold. "Am I supposed to go behind that wall and do my business, hoping that nobody will walk in on me?" I noticed that the outhouse didn't have a door. Strangely, that appeared to be the original design; I couldn't see any door hinges, either.

"Don't ask me." Mariana shrugged and peeked behind the wall. "Foo-oo-oo!" she yelled almost immediately, as if she'd gotten something unbearably disgusting in her mouth, and backed up, stepping on my feet. "Don't go in there." The strong nauseating smell coming from inside the outhouse reached me too.

"I can't hold it until we get to Babushka's." I pushed her aside and looked behind the wall, expecting that she was exaggerating, like all teenagers. But my GOD, she wasn't! The stone floor with a shithole in the middle was surrounded by human feces. There was poop mixed up with dirt and ice everywhere. I paused for a moment, gathering my courage, then I found one clear spot on the floor to step on, then another one a little farther away, and made my move, trying not to breath in. Unlike my brother, I didn't shit my pants.

"You should see your face right now." Mariana laughed when she finally saw me coming out of the outhouse.

"How in the hell did we get our country into this literally shitty situation?" I asked Mariana, as if she had the answers. "I don't remember the outhouses being dirty like this when I was a child. I feel sorry that you have to grow up in this time, when everything went to shit."

"I have nothing to compare it with. I was what, six years old, when the Soviet Union collapsed? That's our life, I guess."

Her nonchalance put me on edge. "This is not normal! Don't you *ever* get used to it. This is not normal!" I yelled at her, trying to get my point across. "Where do our taxes go? Who's governing this country? Why do Americans build our roads instead of us?"

"I don't know. I'm just a child."

Her simple statement made me angrier. "I want you to start thinking about this."

"I'm not stupid. I can see what's going on. Did you know that the students in my class pay bribes to get better grades? The professors already know the rich kids they can milk for money. I'm not paying them anything, so they kinda leave me alone. Do you know how unfair it is, when I study so hard to get a nine, and the daughter of the big pockets rolls in, pays the bribe, and gets the same grade as I do?"

"That's why we end up with a bunch of incompetent professionals, because they buy their diplomas. You should be proud that at least you will graduate with some knowledge in your head."

"Oh, goody! That girl that I told you about, she doesn't need to worry about finding a job after college. Her parents own a grocery store in town, so she is set. Where will I go with my diploma? Work as a driver on my dad's bus?"

"What are we both going to do with our diplomas? We are in the land of unequal opportunities now."

A cold wind blew from the west, bringing in fresh, crisp country air, free of city pollution. The afternoon sun started melting the ice on the road. The dirt between the crushed rocks was turning to slush. As we started going down the hill, in silence, we saw the first houses at the village entrance with Soviet-style slate roofs and blue and green stucco walls. After that point, there was one long muddy road. Walking downhill felt like kneading black dough with our feet.

"Good afternoon!" a village woman greeted us. "Here they are, Baba Veta's granddaughters!"

"Hello," I answered, amazed by the woman with the memory of an elephant. She must have recognized us from all the summers Mariana and I had spent at Babushka's, but for the life of me, I could not remember her name.

"I'm glad to see that you are coming to visit your babushka and not forgetting about her. Many babushkas around here are left behind because their kids and grandkids went abroad for work." She waved her hands to hurry us along. "You go, girls. Baba Veta is at home. I saw her outside cleaning the chicken coop," the woman said with the air of a know-it-all village gossiper.

"Have a nice day," Mariana and I answered in one voice, as village politeness required.

We recognized Babushka Veta's house with gray stucco and white corners from afar. Its gray slated roof had patches of melting snow that were leaking on the cement sidewalk surrounding the house. The land in her garden, Babushka's pride and joy, was perfectly clean and plowed, ready for spring planting. She was indeed outside. Her tall, slim figure, humpbacked from hard labor in her garden, was still showing a strength that you wouldn't expect from a seventy-nine-year-old woman. She was masterfully scooping the chicken droppings from the ground with a large shovel, dumping it in a wide bucket with water, then mixing it up.

Babushka heard the gate squeaking when we entered her front yard and turned around, still leaning on the handle of her shovel, stuck in the ground. Her deeply wrinkled face, browned by years spent in the sunlight of her garden, brightened. Her brown eyes sparkled in excitement. She fixed the shawl tied at the back of her neck, rather than around it, the way she usually tied it in winter to protect herself from the cold. *She must be feeling steaming hot from working with that shovel.*

"Perfect timing!" Babushka Veta smiled at us. "Leave your fancy city coats in the house, put those rubber boots on, and come help me. I need someone to take this bucket of chicken droppings and pour it right there in the compost pile that has cow manure mixed with straw. Let it sink in, then take a shovel and mix it up very good. I'm getting ready for spring. That's free country fertilizer for you."

I looked at Mariana. "Here we go. Another pile of shit, but at least this one helps the human kind." We both followed Babushka's instructions. We knew exactly what she was going to say: "You love the ride? Then love to carry your sleigh up the hill, too."

Two hours later, exhausted, cold, and hungry, we all finally shuffled into the one small room in Babushka's house, which, in winter, was her bedroom, slash kitchen, slash everything else.

"Why is it so cold in your house?" I shivered.

"I hold on, waiting until the last hour of the day, to start the fire. Trying to save on coal so it lasts until spring. But today is a special day, so we can start the fire earlier."

"Where is the firewood?"

"It's too expensive nowadays. Last year I used the leftover wood from my old cherry tree that I cut down two years ago, but that's gone. Now I've switched to dry grapevine branches that I saved from spring pruning, and dry corn stalks and cobs left after I cleared them of corn seeds in the autumn. These are perfect for starting fires. I already set the stalks in the stove this morning. All you have to do is light them up."

I opened the door of the iron stove, remembering Babushka's

particular nature, and sprayed the yellow corn stalks with a dab of diesel fuel from a bottle, the same way Babushka used to. Then I lit a match and threw it on top. The fire consumed the stalks so rapidly that they started spitting out tiny red stars in every direction, making a cracking noise like a firecracker. Tongues of fire were jumping up and down, playing with each other, licking the inside of the iron stove. It felt homey, like a long time ago, when we were kids and watched the fire in Babushka's stove with fascination.

Thirty minutes later, the pot of pork meat, potatoes, carrots, and tomatoes that Babushka had put on top of the scorching stove turned into a boiling goulash, bubbling like hot, red lava and spreading the aroma around the house. Another cast-iron pot with a round bottom was filled with boiling yellow corn flour. Babushka wrapped the pot with a towel, lifted it off the stove, and shook it to see if the corn flour was moving.

"Looks solid," she said. "Put that wooden cutting board in the middle of the table. I think we're ready to flip over the *mamaliga*." Babushka turned the cast-iron pot upside down fast, like an experienced iron worker dumping the melted iron into forms. She let it sit on the cutting board for a few seconds, then lifted it up. Mamaliga emerged from under the pot like a steaming golden church dome. "Look at that! Country bread for you."

"Every time, Babushka, every time, you make it perfectly!" Mariana clapped.

"If you'd made as many of them as I have in my life, yours would come out perfectly too." Babushka smiled. She was not immune to compliments, obviously. She took a long, black thread and pulled on it to make it taut, pushed the string under the corn bread, then lifted her hands up until the thread cut a piece out of it.

"I've always wondered," I said, looking at her. "Why do you cut the mamaliga with a thread and not with a knife?"

"I don't know who came up with this, but my mother did it,

and I do it, and everyone in the village does it. It's much easier to do it with a thread because the hot mamaliga sticks to the knife, so it doesn't cut it, it rips it. You ready?" Babushka put the hot frying pan with bacon chunks in front of us.

"*Shkvarki*, I've missed you." Mariana giggled, took her piece of mamaliga, and dropped it on top of the chunks of bacon, letting it soak up the juice. She massaged the top of it with her fingers, like we used to do with playdough, then lifted it up and put the entire piece into her mouth, fast, as if she hadn't eaten for three days. "I can't believe you still have the canned pork meat, Babushka. We canned this two years ago, when Uncle Nicolai butchered your pig, didn't we?"

Babushka smiled slyly. "I know how to save my best food for special occasions. Did hunger torment you in the city again?" Babushka asked, looking at us slurping up the red aromatic goulash broth from her old, beat-up aluminum bowls. "No worries. I'll fix you up. Eat, eat. You look so skinny."

"Have you seen our hips?" We laughed. "They're from the city macaroni diet."

"You know what keeps you in shape?" Babushka laughed too. "Working on a country farm. Besides, the land can always feed you. I've worked in other people's fields for a slice of bread since I was eight, because my father kept hitting the bottle, so there was never enough food for six of us in the house. When your *Dedushka* Vanya brought me here, and I saw this land, I told myself: 'I will work as hard as I possibly can, but I will never let myself go hungry again.'" There was some sadness in her tone, but quite a bit of pride too. "And that's what I did. I worked very hard all my life, but I never starved after I married your *dedushka*."

"You see, Babushka," I told her, "this house and this little farm of yours with the yard and chickens, that's your dream. You love it here. You giggle like a little child when you see the potato sprouts coming out of the soil in summer." I had to make sure my next point was clear, for I needed to hear myself say this out loud, too, not just Babushka. "But this is not my dream. I want something bigger."

"What do you want?"

"For starters, I want to use the English I'm learning in college to start a career in the city. Who would I speak English with here in the village, your chickens? But right now, even in the city, I feel like I'm stuck and nothing is going the way it's supposed to. I need to find a way out, perhaps go abroad one day for work."

"Aha!" Babushka answered. She always used that little "aha" when she was trying to make a point. "Then may God give you all the strength you need."

The next morning, I woke to the sound of Babushka's feet scraping the floor. *Six o'clock, really?* The coal in the iron stove had already burned out, and the warmth in the room had faded. Mariana and I rolled back and forth on our uncomfortable mattress on top of the clay bed built by Grandpa Vanya behind the iron stove. I hid my face in the heavy blanket that Babushka gave us last night. The thought of getting out of our warm bed into the cold again made me shiver, but Babushka didn't seem bothered by it. She'd put on her outside shoes, ready to go out, and said to me, "I'll go warm up food for the chickens. You can sleep in until seven o'clock."

"What kind of sleep-in is that?" I groaned.

"You'll have plenty of time to sleep in your graves," she said, armed with village dark humor. "But while you are still alive, we have work to do."

"I know, I know. 'Work is never done when you live in the country,'" I cited Babushka's words back to her.

"Take the sieve and sift that flour," Babushka told me after breakfast, pointing at the forty-kilo sack of white flour in the corner. "Put the last five kilos aside. You can take that with you so you can bake some bread at home." As soon as we finished that task, she gave us a new command. "Let's get the two boxes of potatoes out of the cellar and sort them out. Some mice got into them and chewed a few in the middle."

"Gross." Mariana grimaced. "All mice must die!"

"Hold that corner," I told my sister when we got into the dark cellar. I put my hands on top of the box of potatoes, waiting for her to grab the other side. A tickling sensation ran up and down my fingers. I squinted, trying to adjust my eyes to the darkness, and I finally saw it. A little mouse, disturbed by the commotion, had emerged from the potatoes and climbed from the box onto my hand. *Goddamn it!* I shook my hand to get it off, more annoyed than afraid. The creature backflipped like a cartoon Mickey Mouse onto the edge of the box, ran two panicked laps around it, then stretching its little paws, jumped down to the floor.

"Ah-ah-ah-ah!" Mariana yelled at the top of her lungs, hopping from one corner to another and violently shaking her hands. "Don't, don't, don't…" she stuttered, unable to finish her thought.

"Don't let it get away!" Babushka yelled, and stepped on poor little Mickey, spilling its guts all over the cement floor under her shoe. *Rest in peace, Baby Mickey, rest in peace!*

"Is he dead?" Mariana whispered, looking cautiously from the right corner of the cellar.

"Yes, he is," Babushka said. "Why do you look so grossed out? Didn't you just say, 'All mice must die'?"

"Yeah, but I didn't think you'd have to *kill* it."

"That's country living for you. It's either you or the rodents," Babushka said, carrying on as if nothing had happened. "Take a few kilos of potatoes home, but don't touch the last box. These are for planting, so don't forget to come to Babushka's in the spring to plant them."

"We came here last spring," I said defensively.

"Yeah, at the end of April, when I'd already planted most of it."

"That is when planting usually starts, isn't it?"

"Last year it was warm by the end of March, so I started my gardening earlier. Spring never checks the calendar. You need to check the weather so you know when to come to Babushka."

"All right," I answered, even more defensively, and carried the box with potatoes upstairs.

I looked at the duffle bags we'd brought empty from the city, now getting fuller with each completed task. At the end, Babushka was filling them with random stuff for us to take home: onions, garlic, beets, carrots, apples, corn flour for mamaliga.

"Here," Babushka said, returning from the house with a carton of eggs. "That's for cleaning the chicken coop yesterday. I normally sell them at the farmers' market, but your kids need to eat some real, natural eggs, not the anemic ones you buy in the city. Put them in the bag with flour so they don't crack on your way home."

"Thank you. I think that's more than enough," I said. "We need to carry all these to the highway, and I can barely lift these bags up."

"One more thing," Babushka said, ignoring my comment. "See these brown beans? The American Baptists sent them to our congregation as humanitarian aid. I'll give you half, and the other half I'll plant in the spring in my garden. Isn't it amazing? I got beans from America!" It was amazing indeed, that she could be so happy about a bag of beans. "I wish I could send those American Baptists something from my garden as a thank you for their generosity."

"I am sure, Babushka, they have plenty of food in America."

"I bet they don't have cherries like mine."

"Well, if I ever go to America, I'll take a jar of your sour cherry jam for the American Baptists."

"Yeah, like that will ever happen." Mariana laughed. I also knew this would never happen, but it was fun mocking Babushka.

"Let's wrap it up"—Babushka looked at the clock—"or you'll miss the bus."

We thought that getting to Babushka's village was quite a trek, but walking two kilometers back from her village to the highway, loaded with our food cargo, felt ten times the distance.

"Let's stop." Mariana dropped her bag on the slushy road. "My shoulder is about to pop out of my socket."

"Let's carry one bag at a time then," I told her. Mariana sighed but grabbed the right handle of her bag, and I took the left one. We walked ahead, leaving another bag behind. Then we came back and picked up the second bag. We repeated it a few times.

The process was painfully time consuming, but at least we were getting a break from the heavy lifting by walking back empty handed, until Mariana said again, "My fingers are numb. The damn handles are cutting off my circulation."

"We're halfway there."

"We have another half to go?" Mariana whined.

I took a handkerchief out of my pocket. "Here, wrap it around the handle, it will give you some cushion." Then I took the hem of my long winter coat and wrapped a corner of it around the other handle. "We can make it a quarter of the way at once this way." Mariana sighed again and reluctantly followed.

Valera's bus picked us up at two in the afternoon, as he promised. "There are no empty seats, and the wooden boards in between the rows are taken too," he said. "You'll have to stand until the next village. A few people are getting off soon."

I looked at Mariana's tired face. She was about to burst into tears. "Look at the bright side," I said. "At least for two hours, we won't have to carry anything."

* * *

"Look, it's like a treasure chest in here!" Lica clapped when Mariana and I dragged our bags of goodies into the kitchen.

"Eggs!" Serghei yelled. "Can I have one?" Without waiting for a response, he cracked the egg, put some salt on it, and drank it raw.

"Apples!" Lica yelled, and took a bite of one. With the other hand, she was pulling out plastic bags of produce, one by one, and putting them on the table. "I don't know what we would do without Babushka Veta," Lica said very seriously.

"I don't know either," I answered sincerely, but I was too exhausted to carry on the conversation. I dropped on the kitchen bench, unable to move, but just a few minutes later, an annoying ring of the doorbell made me flinch. "Who the hell could it be at this hour? Sereoja, go check it out," I said. "That's probably one of your friends."

"Mom!" Serghei yelled from the hallway. "It's Cristina from the fourth floor."

Shit! I walked out of the kitchen. *This can't be good.*

"I saw you come home," Cristina said, standing in front of the door. "I thought I'd take you with me to the day care center."

"Why? What happened? Did Serghei climb on the roof again?" I asked, worried.

"No, not this time." She smiled. "It's actually good news. US AID sent a food aid container for kindergarten teachers: olive oil, brown beans, rice, wheat grits, stuff like that. Mrs. Lidia sent me to bring all the teachers to the assembly room so she can distribute our rations."

"Mariana," I yelled from the hallway, not believing my ears. "I guess it's our lucky day. Come with me, we are getting more aid from the Americans today."

"I'm too tired. Take those goat kids of yours. They can carry their own food for once."

"I'll go!" Serghei jumped.

"Me too," Lica said, racing to put her shoes on. "America is so nice to send us food." She bolted out the door.

Chapter 6

The Graduation Ball

Spring was a blur. I didn't even have time to enjoy it. It was all work, school, homework, work again, and one exam after another. So when the last test, on the last day of May, was behind me, I decided to take a long walk from the university all the way down to the lake located in the park. It was called *Valea Morilor,* or the Valley of the Mills. This name was a puzzle to me, as there were no mills on that lake, but it was better than the old Soviet name—the *Lake of the Komsomol Members.* The new Republic of Moldova was on a binge of eliminating old Soviet symbols, like removing the statues of Lenin and renaming all the streets in the city, so the lake, thank God, was renamed too.

I approached the two hundred-odd steps leading down to the lake. On my way down, I passed a tall white rotunda with six columns built in the old Stalinist style, a leftover of a not-so-long-gone era. Nearby there was a stretch of tall blue Siberian fir trees, flown in at a capricious request from the local communist leader, at that time Brezhnev, because they reminded him of Siberia. I could only imagine how lonely these gorgeous evergreen trees felt when they were yanked from the Siberian wild *taiga,* away from their brothers, but they somehow managed not only to survive but flourish in this warm climate.

They have outlived the leader and the old country and blended in with the local flora so naturally it's as if they were never strangers to this region. Moreover, they found a few new friends: the ever present red-furred squirrels that were so urbanized that they'd lost their fear of humans several generations ago. When I saw one squirrel swinging from the branch right in front of me, I stopped and squeezed a few seeds out of a fir cone that was lying on the ground. I put them on my palm and stretched out my hand, hoping that the red furball would be brave enough to go for it. It didn't take long. The small baby squirrel swung her red bushy tail and, stretching her four paws like a little parachute, landed on my palm, grabbed the seeds, and jumped back on the branch, all in a matter of seconds.

"I wish I had your problems," I told the squirrel, who was looking straight at me with her small inquisitive black eyes and bouncing on the branch. I walked away, leaving her to enjoy the little stolen treasure. By the time I got to the bottom of the stairs, I felt tired, so I sat down on the first bench near the lake, taking a break and enjoying the view.

The day was a delight: sunny, bright, hot but not uncomfortable. A light breeze was floating above the water, making small waves. One lonely wooden boat from a lake rental was cruising the waters. A young man at the oars took his girlfriend for a ride. The boat renter, an old rough-looking man in dirty clothes, was standing on the half-rotten wooden pier, waving his arm at the couple and shouting, "Your time's up!"

The young man rowed to the shore, got his girlfriend out of the boat, and, holding hands with her, walked by me, chirping something into her ear. *Aren't they the love birds?* I thought, somehow irritated. They seemed to have no worry in the world, unlike me, whose mind could not shut off.

Today was supposed to be a happy day, considering the hardest part was over, but I had another dilemma to solve: to go or not to go to the graduation ball? The official graduation party would take place in a few weeks, at the restaurant near the lake, but I didn't have a gown or money to pay for the party. I could get my English diploma, for which I'd worked so hard, at the office and forget about the party, but it seemed so unfair not to celebrate the culmination of graduation, that I was driving myself insane trying to figure out a solution. Today I was going to concentrate on the first task. I had finally decided to take Tanya up on her offer to lend me a dress. It was time to leave the park anyway.

"Try this one," Tanya said, opening her closet for me and handing me a light summer dress with flowery patterns. I squeezed my lips together, ready to whistle in excitement, but the thought that I might bring her bad luck if I whistled in her house made me stop and think. I was doing that a lot lately, becoming more superstitious, the more uncertainty I faced. I needed to stop, or I'd turn into one of those country babushkas who spit three times over their left shoulder when they see a black cat crossing the road.

I tried on the "summer delight" that Tanya handed me, but when the dress got stuck halfway on my chest, my heart dropped to my feet. The bottom of the dress reached the end of my butt, barely covering my underwear, and it was not moving any lower.

"Tanya," I called to her. "Is that the biggest size you have?"

"Damn, girl. You've got boobs!" she said, looking through her closet for something looser. Her outfits, resembling a French fashion collection, were exquisite but useless to me. I was too fat for Tanya's clothes, or she was too skinny for my size.

"Well, it was a nice thought," I said, and pulled her dress violently off me. "Back to my closet then."

At home, I pulled all my dresses out of the dresser and arranged them in a row on the couch. Mariana commented from the sidelines as I tried them one by one: "Where did you get this one? From Mom's collection? No, not this one. This one is too tight. This one is too short. Where is the green dress from the humanitarian aid, the Catherine Zeta-Jones one?"

I squeezed myself into it, sucking in my belly, bloated by home-baked bread, but the dress was not amused and responded with a loud ripping sound, leaving the left sleeve hanging by a few threads.

"Hello, Cinderella! The one before the ball, you know, in the maiden gown." Mariana laughed.

"That's not funny!"

"Let's call it an emergency and ask our fairy godmother, slash our mother, for help," Mariana suggested. "You graduate from university only once in your life."

"I don't think Mom will go for it. She's cleaning houses in Greece so that we can get an education, not so I can get a gown." I buried the idea, but when Mom called later that night, she brought it up herself.

"So when is your graduation?" she asked.

"On the twenty-sixth of June."

"It's kinda tight, but if I send you some money, do you think Tamara, the neighborhood seamstress, can sew you a decent dress in time?"

"I don't know. I haven't ordered anything from Tamara in years. I don't even remember her phone number, but I can stop by her house and ask."

"You do that, and I'll send you money for the graduation. I don't want you to look like a peasant at that ball," my mom said with classic Moldavian vanity in her voice. "I'll call you tomorrow with the Western Union wire transfer information," she said with a final *fait accompli* tone and hung up the phone. I put the receiver down and looked at Mariana in disbelief.

"What? What?" Mariana was dancing right in front of me.

"I guess I am going to the ball!" I yelled.

Mariana hit my right shoulder hard. "*Kruto!*" she shouted, a word that her father often used when he wanted to say that something was amazing.

I couldn't hold back a smile, thinking about the possibilities. I'd finished the work, so maybe now I could have a little fun.

* * *

The next day, with a fresh, crisp fifty-dollar bill in my wallet, I went to the market, a street bazar to be more precise, with rows and rows of open tents where merchants had their goods on display under the scorching sun. I walked by a stand with kids' T-shirts, dresses, and other Disney-themed clothes, counterfeits from China. I've seen kids in my day care in similar shirts with Tinkerbell and Snow White. The quality of the products was so poor that they lost their bright colors after a few washings.

On the market's right side, there was a stand with a string of posh purses with brand names printed in bold golden letters: Gucci, Prada, Dolce & Gabbana. The leather seams were so uneven that I didn't need to wonder whether they were real or counterfeits from Turkey. The stands in between were cluttered with a mishmash of merchandise: one booth with a string of lingerie, the next full of shoes, the third with hardware, of all things. Organizing the vendors was not a priority of this market. I passed all this knick-knackery without stopping to take a look. I was there on a different mission. "It will take about two weeks to finish your dress," Tamara had said. Therefore, I was in a hurry to buy cloth for the dress today, if I wanted to make it to the ball in an actual ball gown.

A colorful row with cloth from Italy or Turkey or China, or God knows where—the labels didn't mean anything half the time—popped up right in front of me. I stopped, disoriented by the diversity. Then I let my imagination play a little, trying to envision how a finished dress from any of these pieces of cloth would look on me. I wasn't alone to consider for too long, as a short, chirpy young saleswoman with bleached hair emerged from the shade.

"What material are you looking for? It's graduation season, so we've got quite a selection."

"I can see," I answered, annoyed by her intrusion. I tried to keep calm and look disinterested—that always helped with street vendors when it came to pricing. I touched a few rolls of chiffon to get the feel. I was going for spring colors, the blue or green, but the material seemed so flimsy that I hesitated.

"If you're looking to sew a graduation gown, I would recommend silk." She pulled a roll out of the mix and unfolded a stretch of cloth.

"But it's pink. I'm not a pink kind of girl," I said, surprised that she would even suggest something like that to me, but I still put my hand on it. It was smooth and shiny and pleasant to the touch.

"You are a brunette. Pink complements brunettes wonderfully," she said, and let the shiny material roll off my shoulder down to my knees. She put a tall mirror in the corner in front of me. I tilted my head to the left, turned my body back and forth a few times, playing with the material in the wind, the way I did as a child with curtains, pretending to be a bride.

"I'll take two and a half meters of this," I said decisively, seeing, all of the sudden, the potential of the pink silk.

"Great choice," the saleswoman said with a smile. "You will need a better bra, though. This bra of yours is no good," she whispered confidentially, as if trying not to embarrass me in front of everybody.

I turned around to the lingerie stand that I'd passed a few minutes ago and set my eyes on a black lacy bra. An older lady with gray hair, who seemed more like a grandma than a merchant, was selling the underwear and didn't wait to be invited. She took several black bras off the string hanging above her head and brought them to me. She touched my left breast with her wrinkly hand, trying to assess my breast size. I flinched, but she continued calmly.

"Try this one first. It's hard to tell what size will fit you, and the

Europeans use different metrics, so it's best to just put it on." I felt the texture of the lace with my fingers and squeezed the bra, testing the strength of the metal skeleton. I turned it over. It had a neatly sewn back, and the rubbery straps were easy to expand. The bra was sexy and expensive—and very hard to resist.

* * *

"Twenty-five leis? That's a quarter of your wages!" Mariana yelled at me when I brought home my new black lacy bra.

"I bought my last bra five years ago," I said, and though I didn't need to justify anything to her, I harbored some guilt, as I often did when I bought something for myself. "They are all old and ripped up. You've seen them."

"Twenty-five leis?" she asked me one more time, as if the price might go down if she kept asking me over and over. "This better be a golden bra, then."

"I'll make sure I squeeze the gold out of it!" I responded defiantly, feeling guilty nevertheless, as if I'd splurged myself on a feast in the middle of a famine.

Two weeks later, the day had finally arrived. I put on my new pink dress with a playful shiny silky hem, showing off my back, which Tamara had cut into the shape of a heart. The low-cut front, made from a matching pink spandex material, revealed my goods in my new bra in the most favorable way.

"You look so young in this dress," Mariana said, somewhat surprised.

"I'm not old, you know," I said, standing up straight.

"Yeah, but you look younger."

"Now tell me that this bra wasn't worth it." I smiled.

"But twenty-five leis? Seriously?" Mariana pressed back, unwilling to let it go.

I marched on directly to my classmate Elena's hair salon. I'd gotten her phone number by chance, not even knowing she'd become a hairdresser. It made perfect sense. She was always very artsy. I hadn't seen her since high school, and she'd changed quite a bit. She was as tall and thick as I remembered her, but her hair was now dyed bright-red and styled in spikes, the casualty of her profession, I assumed. She wore bright cherry-red lipstick that made her lips look plump and daring, as if she was up to no good. Perhaps she was.

I reluctantly sat down in Elena's chair. I feared she might be a little too creative for my taste. I reminded her that my dress was pink, in case she was considering pulling out the red dye. Elena played a little with my long hair, which was lying on my shoulders. Then she brushed it with her brush, fluffed it once again, and, looking at me in the mirror, asked, "Who styled your hair last?"

"Nobody. My sister just cuts the ends when it grows too long, and I cut my own bangs." She wrinkled the corner of her lips, as if she'd heard the most disgusting thing in a decade.

"What product do you use? Your hair is so thick and shiny."

"Just a regular cheap shampoo."

"Unbelievable. People pay big money to get hair like yours. But you're just getting it for free?"

Interesting, I'd never realized I had a treasure on my head, but now that she pointed it out, it made me wonder what other goods I possessed that I'd never noticed?

Elena tilted her head to the right, examining my hair in the mirror, then her eyes sparkled. I recognized that "eureka" spark in her eyes from when we were in school.

"Do you know what hairdo you want?" she asked me, most likely *pro forma*.

"I'm not an expert in these things."

"Good, because I am, and I know exactly what you need." She pulled my hair back. "Keep your head down and don't worry, you'll look gorgeous." Her voice was full of excitement, like a girl ready to play with her favorite toys.

She curled my hair one lock at a time, spraying it with hairspray, then kept arranging the curls in the back. When she was finally done, she lifted my head and turned my chair with my back to the big mirror. She gave me a smaller mirror, allowing me to see the results of her creation for the first time. My hairdo looked classy and joyful, different than I expected, but so perfect.

"My God, you truly have golden hands!" I said. *Shame on me for judging her!* But Elena wasn't done yet. She decorated the composition with pink roses that she made out of leftover material from my dress, and only then let me go.

I left Elena's hair salon flying and hopped on the orange city bus to get to the restaurant where the graduation dinner was scheduled. A man in a pair of ragged tennis shoes gave me a stare, as if I had just dropped down from Mars. I stared right back at him: *I know, I know, in this pink dress and with this hairdo, I belong in a taxi, but I don't care!*

"My God, you look great!" Violeta yelled when she saw me walking up the stairs of the restaurant.

"I know," I answered proudly. She laughed and kissed me twice on my cheeks.

"At least you're on time. We are waiting for the rest of the beauty queens. They should be here any minute. But our professors are already inside. Galina Mihailovna, Ms. Alina, and Professor V., who has a soft spot for you, is also here."

"You think he has a soft spot for me?"

"Oh, please, we all noticed how he was looking at you this year."

"Really?" I held back my surprise, and how flattered I felt. "He didn't cut me any slack on the finals, if that's what you're implying."

"I'm not implying anything. I'm just saying that, before, he had to follow protocol and all, but now it's different."

"How old is he? Thirty-five? He's not hard to look at, but isn't he married?" I reproached.

"Rumor has it, he's been separated from this wife for months. Maybe tonight is the night. You are two consenting adults…" Violeta whispered into my ear.

"I don't know, it seems complicated." I smiled, but I didn't dismiss the idea. After all, I was all dolled up and feeling adventurous. I turned my head to the lake to gather my thoughts.

The small waves looked like ribs on top of the water. The sun was going down but hadn't touched the water yet. It was hanging in the sky, ready to drop at any minute. The day's heat was cooling off, but the breeze was still warm and soft. I imagined myself and the professor in a little wooden boat on the lake. *Wouldn't that be something?*

The sound of music coming from inside the restaurant brought me back to reality. I took Violeta by her elbow and dragged her inside with me, where the restaurant was festively dressed in white artificial flowers hanging above the windows, and a few vases were standing in the corners. Against the wall, a string of four tables had been connected into one and covered with a white tablecloth. Small bouquets of live flowers were in the middle of each table. Twenty chairs, arranged in two rows of ten, were standing in the front of the room, ready for the graduation ceremony to start.

Professor V. was on the podium arranging our diplomas. His tall, slim figure was hunched over the table as he concentrated on his task. I took a seat and waved to him from my chair, demanding his attention. At last, he noticed me waving but dropped his head down to the list in front of him and coughed, trying to clear his throat, as if something was bothering him. *Do I make him uncomfortable?* I smiled.

"Finally!" Both Violeta and I said in one voice when we saw Tanya, Anya, Kirill, Alex, and a few others entering the room all at once. I scooted a few seats over to make room for all of them.

It created a commotion, as if we were playing musical chairs, until everyone found the seats they liked best.

"I think we're all here now," Professor V. said rather rapidly, giving the room one last overview. He started calling us to the podium one by one. When I heard my name, I jumped and ran like a giddy little girl anticipating candy. I took my diploma from Professor V. and shook his right hand with all my power. When I tried to pull my hand away, he hung on to it for a few extra seconds and kept smiling, saying, "Congratulations! Congratulations!" My palm was getting sweaty, heavy even, overjoyed so much that I was about to faint.

Soft music filled the room, a signal that the official part was over, and the party was about to start. Two waiters moved chairs to the tables, and two others brought plates with cold snacks: salami, pastrami, cheese, small slices of bread with butter topped with sprats and a slice of lemon.

I followed the platter with my hungry eyes. "My God, pastrami!" I said out loud and followed the waiter to the first empty seat at the table. Professor V. sat next to me. Was it a lucky coincidence, or did the professor take the initiative? It was hard to tell, but the evening promised to be interesting. The waiter at the other end of the table was holding a bottle of red wine ready to pour in our glasses.

"*Noroc!*" Kirill yelled across the table, raising his glass. That was his favorite, and most likely the only word he, as the native Russian speaker, knew in Romanian. "Chccrs!" hc said, this time in English, as if trying to correct himself. After all, we were at an English class graduation.

"Kirill, you make me so proud," Tanya said. "You are graduating with one diploma, but with two words. That's all you need to know, "cheers" and "noroc," and you'll do well in any company."

"Did you hear that, professor?" I started laughing and squeezed Professor V.'s left hand, which rested on the table.

"Yes, I heard that." He smiled back.

"*Hora!*" Violeta yelled, when she heard the first chords of the folk song "Costica, Costica," named after a boy with whom a village girl fell in love.

"Hora!" I yelled, too, and jumped from my chair to join the rest of the group, who were already in the middle of the room, forming the circle required for a traditional Moldavian hora. I joined hands with Violeta, who was at the end. Professor V. followed and joined hands with me. I felt my palm grow sweaty from his touch, and I squeezed his hand harder so it couldn't slip out. We started moving in a circle, flipping our feet in the air in unison. In the middle of the dance, Violeta pulled my hand and whispered into my ear, "Go in the middle."

I hesitated for a few seconds, but *what the heck.* I let go of Violeta's hand and stepped inside, pulling Professor V. into the middle of the circle with me. He stretched out his left hand like a ballroom dancer, inviting me to put my right hand on his palm. Then he wrapped his other hand around my waist. I landed my left hand on his shoulder and tapped my foot to the music. He swayed me several times, making me feel like I was floating in air. His body was pressing against mine so close that I started shaking, feeling electric waves from my head to my toes.

"You look so beautiful tonight," he said, and blushed.

"Thank you," I answered, intentionally stepping on his foot. He tried to pull his foot away, but his move only yanked me toward him so hard that we struggled not to fall. I pulled him back to gain my equilibrium. My breasts were pushing against his chest a little too shamelessly.

"Sorry about that," I said, laughing it off.

"Don't worry," he answered quickly, as if he'd been caught doing something that no one should see. "Your perfume is so …" He tried to find the right word. "Smells nice."

"Thank you," I said again, not sure how else to answer. The song ended, and we hurried to take seats at the table. My heart was racing, and we both needed a break from all *this* dancing.

"What are you doing after graduation?" Professor V. asked me quietly. I squinted, trying to find a good response. He leaned over and whispered into my ear one more time. "What are you doing after graduation?" His hot breath went down my neck. I felt my arteries pumping blood twice as hard. I could feel his lips one millimeter away from me. I turned my head so quickly that my nose touched his. Professor V. pulled his head away, but he kept holding on to my hand.

"Tomorrow, I'll place an ad in the newspaper and start looking for a new job," I answered. "But other than that, I don't know."

Professor V. let go of my hand, took his fork, and started poking intensely at the potatoes on his plate. Suddenly, the professor's phone, which was on the table in front of him, started vibrating. He moved it to his right side, letting it ring, and kept looking at it until it stopped. But when the phone rang for the second time, he picked it up.

"I have to take this," he said, and left the table. Something had changed, but I wasn't sure what. I saw him off and turned around. Alex, at the other end of the table, was standing up with a glass of wine.

"I would like to say a toast for Galina Mihailovna!" Alex proclaimed in English, slurring his words. He raised his hand high, almost spilling the wine, and looked at the Iron Lady, who was sitting across the table from him. "It's not easy to teach adults a foreign language, but you made us, excuse me, forced us ..." He stopped there for a second, making us all gasp for air. "You forced us to speak English again and again, until we got it right. We were lucky to have you as our professor, as you are a teacher with the gift of God." We hurried to drown him in applause, amazed that Alex pulled off an entire speech in English, when he was far from sober, or perhaps his speech was so good because he was *not* sober. Alex turned around and handed a basket of flowers to Galina Mihailovna.

"Please, please, there is no need for this." Galina Mihailovna turned her head away, wiping tears from her right cheek. She took a breath, as if deciding whether she wanted to say anything else, then added, "My students always make it big in the world, so mark my words, you are going places." Then, soon after, she cut it short. "It's getting late. I have to go now." She picked up her old-fashioned black purse with worn handles from her chair and left the room with her bouquet.

"It's getting late indeed," I said aloud, realizing that Professor V. had been missing for a long time. Violeta noticed that too.

"Where is Professor V.?" she asked.

Kirill, who'd just come back from a smoke break, answered nonchalantly, "He was talking with somebody on the phone, then said he had to go home, and he left."

"He left without saying goodbye to anybody?" Violeta raised her hands in the air and turned to me. "Do you know who called him?"

"Maybe his wife or his mistress." I shrugged. "How would I know? It's not like he's my boyfriend," I snapped, tapping my fingers on the table. The graduation party was over, as far as I was concerned. I ran my fingers through my hair, feeling the crunch of the hairspray, and noticing a silk flower was missing.

The ride home seemed endless. I took the corner seat on the last bus, leaning with my wet hairdo against the window. The locks of my hair started coming down in some places, tickling my neck, but I didn't have the strength to fix them.

My pink, shiny silky dress was so wet that it was sticking to my thighs. The light summer breeze was coming through the top open window and was giving me some relief. The darkness outside transformed the window into a perfect mirror. I looked at my reflection. Was I exhausted or confused? I couldn't tell.

I stepped out of the bus, hoping it would be easier to breathe outside, but the air felt heavy, as if it was mixed with water. The night was dark and dull. *Crack!* I heard the sound of my right heel, now solidly stuck in a hole in the asphalt, the same hole that I had avoided a million times before. I yanked it out in anger and stepped into the shoe, but my foot started wobbling, as if it had no support. I looked down and saw my heel hanging on a thread of leather.

"Motherfucker!" I took my broken shoe off, bouncing on my left foot like a heron. It was hopeless, the heel was gone. I took off my other shoe and stepped with bare feet on the cracked asphalt. Thick dust on the road immediately glued to my sweaty feet, getting in between my toes.

"What happened?" Mariana yelled, when she saw me walk into the house with my shoes in my hands.

"Well, the carriage turned into a pumpkin, Cinderella lost her shoe." I showed her the dangling heel. "And the prince abandoned her at the ball."

"What prince?"

"Exactly! What prince?"

"Are you drunk?"

"I wish."

Chapter 7

Taiga in the City

"Hello!" I picked up the phone.

"Are you the person who put the ad in the newspaper? The English translator?" I heard a man with a brash tone of voice on the other end of the call.

"Yes!" I answered excitedly. My second ad had been up for a few days. It was about time somebody called me, since I didn't get any calls from the first ad.

"So, how long have you been out of college?"

"I just graduated."

"Then it's too early," the man said abruptly and hung up.

"I wouldn't want to work for you anyway," I said, as if he could still hear me.

I picked up the phone more cautiously when the phone rang for the second time. "Hello!" Mariana peeked from the corner to listen in. The woman's voice, young, smooth, and cheerful put me at ease.

"I'm calling for the person who posted an ad about the English translator."

"That's me."

"It's a pleasure to meet you. What's your name?"

"Irina," I answered. The woman was engaging, so I immediately felt good about the call. I would try to sell myself better this time. "The pleasure is all mine," I continued with enthusiasm.

"Are you able to travel abroad for work?"

"I normally have my kids at their grandma's in Crimea for the summer, so I can certainly do it then. In the winter—" Mariana shushed me, and I pressed my hand over the receiver.

"You are taking that job!" she said. "I'll watch the kids in the winter."

I simply nodded, removed my hand, and collected my nerves. "I can do it in the winter too."

"You have kids? How old are you?"

"Thirty …" I stretched my answer and stopped halfway. *I should have said twenty-seven, it sounds better.* A panicked thought hit me.

"How much do you weigh? How do you look?"

Now that was a surprise. "I … am … in good shape," I answered, feeling the conversation was going sideways. "Is this a modeling job?"

"We're looking for sophisticated, English-speaking women who can accompany businessmen abroad. They sometimes need translators for a shopping spree, and generally to get them around."

"Sometimes … What do they do full time? Is it an assistant job?" I asked, desperate to hang on to some hope.

"You could say so."

"What countries will I have to travel to?"

"Europe mostly, but it could be Turkey or Cyprus, wherever they decide to vacation."

"What kind of job is this really?"

"Look, if you are not interested, I'm not going to waste my time. The girls are practically begging me to find them a businessman."

I wiped the sweat on my forehead. "A pimp, you mean?" *Click.*

"It's one of those escort jobs, isn't it?" Mariana asked with a grimace of disgust on her face.

"If you want to call it so fancy, sure." I dropped on the bench.

"Next time, let's pretend that you're interested. We can have some real fun."

"You realize this is a home phone? People with such resources can track down our home address, so let's not."

"You're no fun." Mariana stamped her foot.

"Oh, believe me, I would be laughing if I didn't wanna cry right now."

* * *

The third call came in at five p.m. A man with a rusty voice greeted me casually in Russian.

"My name is Vasily Gramovich," he said with a thunderstorm voice matching his last name. That was something new. None of the previous callers had introduced themselves, though there were no guarantees that this was his real name. It sounded like a pseudonym to me.

"I saw your ad in the newspaper about the English translator, and it also said that you speak Romanian."

"Yes, that's correct."

"I'm not a pervert or anything. I'm married, and I'm not looking for girls." *What a great way to start a conversation.* I was ready to drop the phone. But Vasily kept talking, so I didn't cut him off. "I'm just looking for somebody to work in the office when I open my business."

"So you don't have a business yet?"

"Not yet. I'm trying to put together a team right now. I'm not just looking for a secretary. I would prefer somebody who could be part of the team."

"I'd love to be part of a team."

"Wonderful. Let's get acquainted. What's your name?"

"Irina."

"Wonderful, Irina," he said again, as if this word was the only superlative he knew. "Would you care to meet with me today, say at six?" I hesitated for a moment, six o'clock on a Saturday evening seemed late for business. "I promise, there will be no funky stuff. I'll meet you in a public place, wherever you feel comfortable."

"What?" Mariana asked, looking into my eyes. "Another one?"

"I don't know," I whispered to Mariana, covering the receiver with my hand. "This guy is goofy but sincere. He definitely doesn't strike me as a mastermind." I heard Vasily's cough, violent like a chain smoker's, in my ear. "In a worst-case scenario, I can outrun him, so I'm taking my low heels to the meeting."

It was a gamble to consider meeting with this man, but these were desperate times. What was sitting at home afraid of what could happen going to get me? Nothing. Besides, I liked my fifty-fifty odds. That was more than I could dream of in the Not So Lucky Charms Casino of my life.

I recognized Vasily Gramovich from a mile away. He was walking back and forth in the park alley on long, crane-like legs. Skinny, tall, with oversized floppy arms. Thick, dirty-blond hair mixed with gray was combed back in a fifties-era hairdo. He had a bushy mustache. It was a miracle that his cigarette didn't burn this artifact to the skin. He wore an old-fashioned white shirt with two undone buttons at the top and a pair of jeans. *Jeans for the first official meeting? Really?* He seemed to recognize me too, because he walked toward me confidently, like he'd known me for his entire life.

"Irina?" he asked, just to be sure. When I nodded, he spread his arms like he was about to give me a hug, but apparently decided it might be too weird and put his right hand forward for a handshake instead.

"I'm going to be honest with you, Irina," he started right off the bat.

"I hope you didn't call me here to tell me lies, because that would be an enormous waste of my bus fare."

"With me, what you see, it's what you get." Vasily roared with laughter.

"Is that a good thing?" I asked, braving up. Vasily laughed again with the same intensity. He sure liked to laugh a lot. *A person with such a laugh could not be evil.*

"I don't really have much money right now."

"So how are you planning to start a business?"

"You see, I have a partner, Victor, who speaks both Romanian and Russian, and he wants to bring a Romanian oil businessman to start a business here. But I am a Russian dude. I don't speak Romanian. I tried to learn it, but it's just not for me, so I need somebody to translate for me between them. It makes me worried when they speak among themselves, and I don't understand what they're talking about."

"How can you go into business with a partner you don't trust?"

"You have to trust somebody nowadays," he said, "otherwise you'll go insane."

"When are you planning to open the business?"

"I'm thinking, sometime in the fall."

"But it's only June. Are we talking three, four, or five months down the road?"

"Honestly, I don't know. In the meantime, we are building the team. I called another girl today, Tatiana. She doesn't speak English, only Romanian, but Victor wants a secretary. I'll give you her phone number, so you girls can talk to each other, build a relationship. It's important for everyone on the team to get along."

"Isn't it too early for a secretary when you don't even have a business? I'll be honest with you, too, Vasily. I can't wait too long. I have kids to support."

"I understand. But if all goes well, can I call you in the fall?"

"Sure, if I don't have another job by then, I'll consider."

"One more thing. My wife said she wants to work in the office too. You know, she lost her job, but she's at retirement age, so nobody will hire her. Besides, she's worried that I might dump her. Swear to God, she insisted she should come with me to this meeting, but I had to tell her, 'Shura, you'll embarrass me.' Anyway, it will give her peace of mind."

"Sure," I said, tapping my purse with my fingers. "It's your business. You do what you need to do. I have to go now." I said my goodbye and rushed to the bus stop. I didn't know what to make of this meeting. It didn't seem like a total waste of a trip, but a promise of a job sometime in the future was as good as a bird in the sky. *Do I really have it so bad?* I was asking myself.

My day care job may have been at the bottom of the scale, but it was the most secure and sexual harassment-free job, at least for now, with a one hundred percent female staff. But outside that, it was like a wild Siberian *taiga* out there with a bunch of predators, swarming around ready to snatch me, with the exception of goofy Vasily.

It's a fucking wild taiga!

Chapter 8

Virgo Time

"Ira!" Mom yelled on the phone. "Baba Era, our neighbor from the other building."

"I know who Baba Era is," I answered, irritated. Sometimes I wondered if Mom felt that she needed to remind me of stuff that I already knew, as if I were an absent-minded teenager. "What about her?"

"Her daughter is taking her to Belarus, so she's selling her apartment. She said she would sell it to me cheap, for old times' sake." She sounded almost giddy. "I helped her a few times when she was very sick."

"Mom, her apartment is a dump. She hasn't repaired it for twenty years. All her plumbing leaks, and those dogs of hers peed in every corner of that house. It smells like a toilet."

"Lots of people buy apartments like these, then remodel them, and they look like new."

"It will take a lot of money to bring it up to human code."

"That's why she's selling it for only four thousand dollars. Anyway, I didn't call to argue with you. I'm sending you the money. I'm buying it," she said in her usual *comandante* voice. "I'm tired of working for years abroad. I want to come home and have my own place. We can't all live under the same roof in two rooms forever. I'll transfer our current apartment to you and the kids. You with your teacher's salary will never be able to buy yourself your own place."

"Thanks, Mom. I'm not a complete loss." I sighed. Mom was good at guilting while gifting you something. Though, one should not look for defects in a gifted horse's mouth, like my grandpa used to say.

"What? I can't hear you," she said, but I didn't believe her. "Anyway, I have another one thousand dollars saved. That should be enough for a while."

"The prices have increased quite a bit in the last five years since you left, Mom." I tried to caution her.

"What? I can't hear you. I'll call you tomorrow with the Western Union information. Baba Era says she's in a hurry. I'm also sending a care package for you guys with a microbus that's going to Moldova from Greece. My friend Jenea will pick it up at the station. You just need to get it from her house."

"Ahhh!" I yelled when the phone call had ended. Too bad nobody was home to share this extraordinary news with. But my mind was already spinning. The possibility of having my own place, away from Mom, was exciting. I imagined how nice it would be to finally do whatever I wanted in my own house: change the wallpaper to something I actually liked, repaint with some lively colors, and generally stop living in a Babylon-apartment where we were on top of each other for so many years. *Maybe I'll even get some modern, radical art.* I didn't know what radical art would look like. My imagination couldn't conjure that far, but I knew it would be awesome.

What was Mom saying about a care package? I finally recalled it as an afterthought.

* * *

"My God, I haven't seen you in years," Jenea (or as I called her, Aunt Jenea) said when she saw me at her door. She smiled at me with her familiar smile, exposing two golden teeth on the left side of her mouth, courtesy of old-fashioned Soviet dentistry that didn't know how to make crowns that looked like human teeth. She was taller than me, so she had to bend over to give me a kiss on each cheek.

"Mom said she sent us a care package, so here I am! But what's up with this blond hair, what happened to being a brunette?"

"Hardly a brunette anymore. The grays have taken over, so now L'Oréal's my new friend. Come in, have dinner with us." She dragged me into the house. "I just set the table."

I glanced at the dinner table, which held steaming mashed potatoes and a full bowl of fried chicken drumsticks or, as we called them, "the Bush's legs," referring to former president Bush who pushed for American drumsticks, infused with chemicals, to be exported to Eastern Europe. They reminded me of an old Soviet joke: What's death to a German (or American) is good for a Russian.

"I need to get the canned eggplant and bell peppers from the cellar," Jenea said. "They're delicious. I canned them myself this summer."

"You have a cellar in your apartment?"

"Everybody who lives on the first floor of our building dug themselves a cellar under their balconies. Come with me, I'll show you."

I followed her to the balcony, which was wide and long with new windows installed for protection from snow and rain. This apartment building was much newer than ours, so everything looked huge in comparison. Jenea pulled a wooden hatch that was on the balcony floor and opened a narrow entrance into the cellar, then turned around and went down the squeaky wooden ladder slowly and cautiously, until her body was fully swallowed by the open hole.

"This entrance is for a Tinkerbell," I complained, trying to go after Jenea.

"That's my measurement standard. If my ass doesn't fit through, it's time to go on a diet."

"You don't have to worry about that, you've been skinny all your life," I said, and stepped off the last step of the ladder.

A long and deep cellar with gray cement walls opened in front of me. The cold underground air hit my nostrils. A dim light bulb, hanging flimsily on a wire from the ceiling, was lighting up the space. The room was neatly organized with built-in wooden shelves full of canned goods and condiments.

"This is so cool!" I was in awe. "How much did this project cost you?"

"It wasn't cheap."

"I might be in the wrong business. I didn't know that accounting jobs pay so well nowadays."

"If the owner of the firm, the so-called new businessman, wouldn't be so cheap, it would pay well. For God's sake, I run his books, know how much he makes, and how much he hides from taxes. In fairness, if our business paid all the taxes, as our stupid government wants," she said, "it would kill the business, and I wouldn't have a job." Jenea pulled a jar of pickles and a jar of red bell peppers from the shelf and handed them to me.

"Take these home," she said. "Mom told me about your situation."

"Thank you. This cellar is so handy. Did you have to get a permit for it?"

"One of my neighbors tried to get a permit. They kept giving him the runaround, saying: 'You need to pay for this inspection, and for the other inspection. You need to come another day.'" Jenea imitated the bureaucrats' manner of speaking. "Basically, delaying him on purpose until they finally said they wanted a bribe for approving his permit. I'm not feeding these bloodsuckers. I built it without any permits, and so did the other neighbors."

"What if they come one day and ask for the paperwork?"

"Who? Those lazy fucks who only want money but don't know

how to do their jobs? I'm not worried about them. If they really want it, they can tear this shit down themselves."

"Talking like a true outlaw."

"This whole government is made of outlaws," Jenea said, agitated. She picked two jars with canned eggplant, pepper, and tomato ragout. "Let's get upstairs before the food gets cold."

"Taniusha, Cristina!" Jenea yelled at her two daughters to get out of their rooms, while showing me with her right hand to take a seat at the table.

"Just a minute," I heard Cristina, the younger daughter, say.

"I'm not going to call you twice!" Jenea yelled back. "I swear to God, that girl just sits in her room all day and watches Latin soap operas. She's seen so many that she can now understand Spanish without subtitles." Ten-year-old Cristina peeked through the door.

"I'm not hungry," she said.

"Call your sister and come sit with us. Ira, Katya's daughter, came to visit."

"I don't think Taniusha wants to come out either. She's still upset with you about Jenechka."

"Who's Jenechka?" I asked.

"My granddaughter." Jenea smiled. "Can you believe it? I'm a grandma, and they named her after me."

"That's so nice. Why did you quarrel with Taniusha, then?"

"She wasn't watching her daughter, that's why!" she hmphed. "That three-year-old daredevil climbed all the way to the top of the cupboard. What if she fell down?"

I was examining the furniture that got Taniusha in trouble to assess the severity of the danger, when the loud pop of a door smashing distracted me. That was Jenechka, the daredevil incarnate, running into the room.

"Baba!" Jenechka jumped into her grandma's arms, pushing her into the armchair.

"Come to Baba, my love!" She smooched the little girl's face. "Grandma will not let you break an arm," Jenea baby-talked to her namesake.

"She was not going to break an arm, Mom!" I heard Taniusha's frustrated voice as she walked into the room. "She climbs that dwarf cupboard all the time."

Jenea wasn't accepting her daughter's disregard. "But what if she fell? Who would pay her doctor's bill? You are a student, and your husband kicked you out of the apartment I bought you as a wedding gift!" Jenea turned to me. "Can you believe this? That motherfucker now claims half the apartment as his and wants to sue for something that I bought her with my own money!" She held Jenechka closer. "That's after Cristina's father found himself an abandoned widow, and we are left here, the lonely female battalion, to take care of ourselves."

The same kind of story everywhere, I thought. At least I was not alone in my troubles.

"Go ahead, tell our sorrows to every stranger who walks through this door," Taniusha mumbled.

"Ira is not a stranger."

Taniusha flopped down on the chair next to me and whispered into my ear, "I wish I'd had your mom as my mother, because this one is driving me nuts."

"I heard you," Jenea said to her daughter while still holding little Jenechka.

"I wouldn't go for an exchange so fast, Taniusha," I said to lighten the mood. "There is a reason these two are lifelong friends. You might end up with the same model with a different name."

"Does your mother know you talk about her like this?" Jenea looked at me with a frown, then turned to little Jenechka and started tickling her, making the girl laugh hysterically. "These two … are … ungrateful … Virgos! Must be a Virgo full moon or something," she was telling her granddaughter between the tickles.

"I didn't know you were born in September." I turned to Taniusha.

"Oh, my mom wouldn't shut up about it. 'It was God's will that we had our daughters seven years apart but both born in September,'" Taniusha imitated her mother. She dumped a spoon of mashed potatoes on her plate, then added a piece of the drumstick she'd taken out of the bowl. "Sometimes I feel like taking my stuff in the middle of the night and just going away from here."

"Please don't go anywhere in the middle of the night." Jenea's voice was full of sincere worry. "I don't want you to end up like our neighbor's daughter."

"Mom, why would you even say that?" Taniusha was beside herself.

"What? What's happened?" I asked, confused by the increased tension in the room.

"Oh, my God, that's so scary," Cristina jumped in. "Vica was coming home from the bus stop, and somebody in a Mercedes started following her. She didn't want to go with them, but they shoved her in and gang raped her, then dumped her on the bridge." The young girl looked distraught. "She barely survived. Her parents filed a police report. After that the bandits who raped her showed up at her parents' house and told them that, if they don't take their police report back, they'll kill their daughter. The parents are certain that somebody at the police department gave those bandits their address."

"That's so horrible. Why would the police do that?" I was shocked.

"Because they're all bought by the mafia, that's why," Jenea said firmly. "Now, the poor neighbors are trying to sell their apartment for half the price and leave the country. So, please, don't do that to me." She turned to her older daughter again.

"All right. I won't," Taniusha snapped back. Finally, there was one thing this family could agree on.

* * *

"Show me, show me." Mariana ripped the bag from my hand before I was even all the way in the house. "Mom told me she would send me a new Adidas track suit."

"Why do you need an Adidas one? You don't do sports," I replied.

"Their jackets are cool. Why is this bag cut on top?"

"Jenea said that's how it arrived."

"No, no, don't tell me they stole my suit." Mariana kept digging impatiently, getting women's dresses and skirts out of the package, fashion's crème de la crème, if you lived in the sixties. I picked up a long, straight skirt with fall patterns made of brown and yellow leaves.

"Oh, God, I don't think our grandma would even wear something like this. Why is our mother spending money and sending this old crap home?"

"She was sending me the new Adidas, so she only added the old clothes to the parcel because she couldn't throw away what the old lady she's working for was getting rid of."

"That's our mama, always a saver, but none of these things are in my size. That Greek grandma might be a skeleton. Like our grandma says, 'These will make some beautiful rags.'"

"Here is something for Serghei." Mariana showed me a worn sweater with blue-and-white stripes on the upper half.

"It seems small. Is this a Greek flag on it?"

"Your guess is as good as mine. But who cares? It's not like people know what a Greek flag looks like. It's just a sweater with white-and-blue stripes."

"And a blue cross in the corner?"

Serghei heard us talking and ran from the other room to try on Grandma's present. He grabbed the sweater out of Mariana's hands and quickly, before any of us had time to object, pushed his head through the collar, then squeezed his hands through the sleeves. He looked like a goofy doll trapped in an undersized outfit, with his hands sticking out halfway.

"Get it off!" Mariana yanked the sweater up. After a few attempts, Serghei, groaning, freed his hands. Mariana pulled it again, but his big head was solidly stuck in the collar.

"Ay-ay-ay! It hurts, it hurts!" he screamed.

"Why do you always stick your head everywhere?"

"Nuh-uh!" Serghei whined defensively, rotating the sweater on his neck, trying to find a better way to get it off.

"That's enough. We'll have to cut him out," I said.

"No-o-o," they both said at the same time. "It's a perfectly good sweater," Mariana said.

"It doesn't fit him. It's not new, so we can't regift it. This sweater's life is over! *Finita la commedia,* as Grisha once said."

"Who's Grisha?"

"Just a local bandit."

"You know a bandit?"

"Everybody knows one. Half the country are bandits. Did you find your Adidas suit?"

"No. It looks like the driver stole it."

"As I said, half the country are bandits. I'll go tomorrow after work and pick up the money from Western Union. Let's hope, at least, Western Union doesn't rob us."

Chapter 9

The Cold September

I should have left earlier. I was blaming myself, waiting for the late bus to take me home from the city. I was shifting from one foot to the other, trying to get comfortable. My high heels were killing me. *Should have changed into pants before I left, too; it's not summer anymore.*

"I don't think the buses are coming," a man said, which was what I'd been thinking for the last forty-five minutes. "They're probably broken again."

"All four of them?" somebody asked, irritated.

"It's not the first time it's happened, so I wouldn't be surprised." He sighed. "All right then, neighbors," he addressed everybody standing at the bus stop. "Neighbors" was the appropriate term. Most of us knew each other, if not by name, then by face. This stop was five bus stops away from our suburban village, so everyone waiting for the Route 36 bus was going to the same place: Bubuieci. "We have two options," the man continued. "We either walk or hitchhike. The longer we stay, the darker it gets. Who wants to split the fare with me? It will be cheaper this way."

"How much?" I asked, holding tight to my purse. My mom's savings, freshly received from the Western Union, were making me paranoid, as if my bag was see-through and everyone could see its contents. Mom would never forgive me if I lost that money.

"At this time of night, probably five leis each." That was five times more than a bus fare, though it was extremely tempting. I could be home in ten minutes.

"I'll wait," I answered, uncertain of my decision. I was hanging on to a last hope that the bus could come at any minute now, after we'd waited for so long.

The news that the buses were not running must have spread down the line, because private cars, eager to earn a buck, were constantly stopping, drivers asking if anyone needed a ride. The man who first came up with the idea teamed up with two women, and they drove away together. The next four people left shortly afterward with the next car, then the next three and the next two. I looked around. There was only a handful of us left: the diehards or the ones who truly couldn't afford it. A svelte twenty-year-old, good-looking blonde approached me after a few moments of hesitation and asked, "Do you want to share the fare with me?"

I looked at her long bare legs, shaking and covered in goosebumps, extending from under a tiny white skirt.

"You're getting cold?" I asked the obvious question. The girl nodded. "Me too. All right, we'll take the next one."

The girl immediately raised her hand in the air, waiting for the next car. An old red Soviet Lada that looked more like a square metal box than a car drove by, then stopped a few meters away and backed up. The driver, a middle-aged man with dark hair, gray at his temples, leaned over the passenger in the front seat and smiled.

"You pretty ladies need a ride?"

"Yes," the blond girl answered for both of us. "How much?" The driver showed his palm with all five fingers spread like a handheld fan. We looked at each other. I nodded, surrendering to the reality, and we both took the back seat of the car. A nauseating smell of cigarettes and sweat hit my nostrils. Under dim interior light, the inside of the car looked even older than the outside. The material on the doors was coming off in places, and it was sticky, like the fur of a shabby dog.

"Let me off here," the passenger in front said when we reached the fourth stop on the route. "See you later, man." He shook the driver's hand and got out.

"I'll get off here too," my girl-companion said, and tried to open the back door.

"Are you really?" The driver seemed disappointed. "I thought you were going to the village. It's one more stop."

"No, I'll get off here. I need to stop by my aunt's house, but thank you," she said, and handed him money for the fare.

"The door handles are broken in the back," the driver said, taking the money out of her hand. The front-seat passenger, who was already out, heard him and jumped to the back door.

"I'll let you out. *Voila!*" he said, opening the door for the blonde, proud of himself that he got to be a gentleman. The girl got out fast and slammed the car door hard behind herself, sending a metal *zing* to my ears. *Did she really have to do that? It's not like she was running for her life.*

"Too bad your friend had to get off here," the driver said when we took off.

"She's not my friend. We just met at the bus stop … Where are you going?" I asked when I noticed he was turning left. "The village is straight ahead."

"I know. I just need to stop, really quick, at my friend's work to pick up something."

"It's already nine o'clock. What business works so late?" I asked very cautiously.

"He's a night watchman," he said, and looked at my face in the rearview mirror. "Don't worry, I won't harm you." His smiling eyes were supposed to calm me down, but my heart started beating harder.

The car was moving slowly, trying to go around potholes in the broken asphalt. Then it made another left turn through an open chain-link gate, skidding on the gravel, and stopped at an industrial building. One lonely streetlight was hanging on a pole above the entrance, dropping a cone of light over the stairs, but the weak light couldn't penetrate the pitch-dark lifelines around the perimeter.

"You look scared," the driver told me, turning his torso toward me.

"Why are we here?" I asked, still hoping for an innocent explanation. I touched the inside of the car door, hunting for the handle. We weren't far from the bus stop where we left the other two passengers. I could walk there or even make a run for it, if the situation required.

"The handles are broken back there," the man reminded me, as if he could see what I was trying to do in the darkness.

"Stepan, is that you?" I heard somebody yelling from the stairs. A tall, dark silhouette of a man popped up in the doorway. The bright light coming from inside, behind his back, made him look darker and more imposing.

"I'll be right there," Stepan yelled at his friend, then turned to me. "As I said, we won't harm you, if you behave like a good girl." My ears rang when I heard "we." My eyes turned to the silhouette in the bright light. *How many of them are inside?* The image of Jenea's neighbor girl with a bloody face, held down by three men while the fourth was raping her, popped into my head.

"I'll go get a blanket," Stepan said in an unusually measured tone. "Don't try to get out." He pointed his finger at me. "The handles don't work anyway." Stepan left the car and locked the driver's door, then walked to the other side and locked the other door too. He looked at me through the windshield and slowly, as if he had doubts, walked away, turning back a few times to check on me.

The minute the building's door swallowed Stepan, I frantically started tapping up and down the doors to find handles or a crank that could roll the windows down. Holes, holes, and more holes were all I could find. *Did he break all the handles on purpose?* I leaned over the front seat to the driver's door, but the old Lada, which now seemed like a zinc coffin, trapped my body between the top of the seats and the roof. I squeezed myself in between the seats, but they were too close to each other. Lying on my side, I took a deep breath, trying to gather my thoughts and focus. My eyes finally got used to the dark, and I spotted the handle on the front door. *One more minute, one more minute.* I was anxiously keeping an eye on the entrance, and the door suddenly opened. When I saw Stepan walking toward the car, I slid back and dropped down into the back seat, hoping he didn't notice my maneuvers. I looked past him, trying to see if somebody else was coming, but he was alone so far.

"They don't have the blanket," Stepan said when he opened the back door, next to where I was sitting. "They took it home. I don't know why they would do that." Stepan was visibly upset.

I grabbed my purse, suddenly realizing that I had Mom's money in it. A wild idea came to my mind: *What if I offered him the money in exchange for my freedom?* I brushed the idea off immediately; there was nothing that would stop Stepan from taking my money and carrying on with his plan.

Stepan offered his right hand to help me up. I turned around and, without looking at his face, dropped my feet to the ground. He lifted me by my left hand, but my knees started shaking uncontrollably, and my heels sank deep into the gravel, throwing me back. Stepan grabbed me with both of his muscular arms and pulled me toward himself so fast that I landed on his chest with my feet dangling in the air. *What a fucking gentleman.* I smirked, trying not to vomit on his shirt. *Or should I vomit on him to wipe out the scent of his expensive cologne. Let him explain to his wife where he got the stains from.*

Stepan put me down, took me by my hand, and pulled me after him. My palm was getting sweaty from his unnaturally warm palm, but the cold, sharp September breeze was going down my wet shirt, giving me shivers.

"Where are we going?" I asked, barely recognizing my voice. He pointed ahead to a small stand-alone structure in a dark corner of the empty lot. I looked over his shoulder. *If I push him now … * I was gauging the distance between us and the open gate, then the distance from the gate to the road, then from the road all the way to the bus stop, where there were people. The entrance door suddenly squeaked. I could feel somebody else's eyes on me. I sped up, trying to get to the shadow. Was it shame, or fear, or the desire to become invisible? I couldn't tell. The structure was an empty space with cement walls and an open doorway. I stepped into it carefully, but I couldn't see anything. It was pitch black inside. Debris kept cracking under my feet, sounding like dull firecrackers.

"Don't worry, that's just the wood cracking," Stepan said, like a person who'd been here before, perhaps *many* times before. "You're shaking," he said as if he cared.

"I … I … I can't do this," I said, backing away. "I'm … I'm … I'm on my period."

"That's such a pity. Then we'll have to do something different. Get on your knees."

"No, no, I don't do this."

"Listen, you got me all excited."

"I didn't get you anything. I was just trying to get home. I have two kids and my baby sister waiting for me. I really, really need to go home."

"I'll drive you home myself after this, I promise. Come on, be a good girl," he said, and unzipped his pants, then pulled my hand down hard.

I fell on my right knee, hitting sharp cement crumbs. I turned my face away, but a few seconds later, he poked my cheek with this wet, hard penis. I dropped my second knee onto my purse, which had fallen on the floor in front of me and, using both my hands, pushed myself up. But Stepan kept pushing down on my shoulders.

"Shhh, shhh, shhh …" he would say after each of my attempts, moving his hands like he was in a bizarre kabuki theater performed in total darkness, until he finally got his way. He pressed on my head. The feeling of being choked by his penis made me gag.

"You really don't know how to do this?" he asked me, seeming surprised. He pulled back a little but didn't stop. I gagged again, and again, hoping that I would throw up eventually, until I felt the salty, mushy goo of Stepan's sperm in my mouth. I pushed him away to spit the substance out. I was spitting and spitting, until the nauseating smell of it unleashed the bitter bile acid from the depths of my empty stomach. There was nothing to throw up. I hadn't eaten since morning, but my body was convulsing, trying to get anything out. I couldn't stop.

"I'll be back with a towel," Stepan said with disgust and quickly left the scene. The sound of his steps moving farther and farther away were calming me down, so I found the strength to get up and peek out of the shed. I couldn't believe my eyes. He was really gone. I stepped out carefully. In the quiet night, with just the occasional bark of a dog, the sound of the shifting gravel under my feet sounded like whistling shrapnel. I kept moving on my tiptoes to make less noise, until I reached the gate. I looked back once to make sure the door of the building was still closed, then I leaned on the pole to take my shoes off. The soles of my feet almost instantly lost their warmth to the rigid asphalt, but there was no time for hesitation. I sprinted out of the fenced area like a wild gazelle. *God, give me a few minutes, just a few minutes.* I kept praying, looking at the distant lights at the bus stop down the hill, the place I was struggling to reach at any cost.

More than halfway through, the noise of a moving car made me freeze in horror. I could clearly see the car was down the road in front of me, but my fear was playing mind games with me, shifting the sounds in the air, strumming them like the strings of a guitar in my ears. I was convinced the sound was behind me, so I had to turn back, but to my relief, there was nothing there.

I used this unexpected pause to fix my hair that stuck on my sweaty face while I was running. I tucked in my shirt, which had gotten loose and was now flopping in the wind. I put my shoes back on. I didn't want people at the bus stop to see me like this, looking like a lunatic who'd just escaped from a crazy house. *Where did I just escape from?* My mind was jogging bits of memories, trying to process what I just went through. I slowed down and moved toward the people as calmly as I could, trying not to breathe so hard, and keep my shaking hands in check. But when I saw the yellow silhouette of a bus in the distance, my heart started racing again. I had to make it to that bus, it was the last one for the day, so I ran again.

* * *

"Where have you been?" Mariana yelled at me when I rang the doorbell. "Do you know what time it is?"

I told her the first lie that came to my head. "The buses weren't running." I leaned on the wall, trying not to burst into tears, now that I finally felt safe.

"Did you *walk* home?" Mariana asked me suspiciously, as if smelling my fear.

"I wish I had walked. I just waited for too long," I diverted her question as vaguely as I could.

"What's wrong with you?" she asked, pointing at the black patches of dust on my feet.

"Somebody stepped on me on the bus. What's up with this interrogation?" I pushed back hard, hoping to dissuade her from the next round. A few more questions and she would break me, and I wouldn't be able to hold back and would just spill it all bare in front of her. *She is too young to deal with this.*

"I was worried about you. The kids were worried, too, you know. You were out there so late with Mom's money."

That's what she was worried about?

"God knows what could have happened," she said. "You did get Mom's money, right?"

"Yes, I got Mom's money!" I shouted. "Go to bed. I don't want to talk to you right now. I'm tired. I'm so incredibly tired…"

Chapter 10

The Tale of Two Zinas

"Congratulations on your purchase!" the notary public said when we signed all the paperwork for our new apartment.

I couldn't wait to get rid of the money. It was supposed to be a happy time, but when I went to work the next day, everything looked different. I was watching the kids from my class playing outside in the courtyard, as usual. I could see that they were yelling, but I couldn't hear them, as if their mouths were moving and their hands were flapping in a soundless vacuum. I couldn't feel my body, even my toes were numb. My brain was still trying to process what the hell happened three weeks ago. I knew that I was not going to report the incident. I felt safer being incognito. At least Stepan didn't know my name or where I lived. Even if I wanted to do something about it, I wouldn't recognize his face in a lineup. It had been too dark in that shed, and I was not exactly looking at his face. Besides, he could say it was consensual.

"I got lucky," I murmured, then covered my mouth with my hand. It was making me sick to think about myself as lucky to get away with just being violated and not beaten or brutalized otherwise, not even a bruise. "I got lucky," I repeated again, taking in a deep breath.

But how do I erase this from my memory? How could I continue to live my life in this country, where rapists roamed free? It wasn't safe here for me, or for my sister, or for my daughter. I needed to get out of here. I had to get out of here. But how? There was no way out. I would grow old working at this place, just a few steps away from my house. That would be my daily routine: get up in the morning, go to work, go home, repeat the next day. All within a two hundred-meter range until I died, just like this overused metal slide called *starushka* (the old hag) that had been stuck in the middle of the kindergarten yard for the last twenty years.

A group of five- and six-year-olds climbing on the top of the slide brought my attention to its worn colors and the brown rust that touched its edges. The middle, on the other hand, was well polished by the kids' butts sliding down all day long. Maybe it survived for so long because the kids didn't give up on it.

"Hooray!" A group of three slid down, giggling with their hands shaking in the air. The new girl, Dana, who had climbed onto the slide for the first time, was sitting at the very top, holding on tightly to the rails, afraid to go down. She created a jam when more kids climbed up the stairs.

"Just slide down," the older boy, Victor, yelled at her. I got up to regulate the traffic.

"Dana, go down. I'll catch you at the bottom."

"I'm scared," she whined.

"Dana, I can't reach you there, and you can't go back because there are already ten kids behind you. You'll have to come down. Come on, don't be scared. I'll catch you."

"Come on!" Victor yelled at Dana again.

The third boy in line, Octavian, was peeking over Victor's shoulder, getting annoyed that the line wasn't moving.

"Stop pushing me!" Victor screamed at Octavian and elbowed him. Octavian hit Victor on the shoulder.

"Hey, hey, everybody. No shoving up there." But Victor was already upset. He turned around and pushed Octavian so hard that Octavian's body flew over the slide's edge and was going down like a rag doll. I imagined how Octavian's head would hit the dry, solid dirt on the bottom, spraying blood everywhere. I sprinted to the edge and caught the little boy in midair, more with my face than with my hands. I tasted blood in my mouth from my split bottom lip. From the corner of my eye, as if in a parallel reality, I saw Dana flying down the slide yelling at the top of her lungs. It was too late to catch her. The girl landed awkwardly, slamming her face on her knees, and started crying.

"Everybody down!" I yelled, when I put Octavian on the ground. My heart was racing, ready to pop out of my chest. *Like I don't have enough drama in my life!* These little monsters were about to finish me off.

"Danachka, come here." I picked up the little girl from the bottom of the slide. I kissed her on the forehead. "Better now?"

"Yes," she said, and wiggled, trying to get away from me, so I let her go.

Victor's teacher, Zina, ran toward the trouble zone, pulled Victor out of the crowd, and with the calm voice of a serial killer said, "You are in time-out, mister."

Victor put his head down and, with a tragic-clown expression, went to take his punishment on the bench under the tree.

Zina approached me. "I'm so sorry you had to deal with this. He's not a bad boy," she said, "he just plays rough." She was talking about him like a protective mother who was not willing to let her kid hang out to dry. "So what's new with you?" Zina changed the subject, trying to cheer me up. "How are your English classes?"

"I graduated this year," I said flatly.

"That's exciting."

"Somewhat," I said, trying to end the conversation. I didn't feel like crying on my coworker's shoulder. This place was already a gossip mill, and in a small town like ours, rumors spread like wildfires, but Zina must have felt sorry for me, so she continued.

"My sister-in-law, also Zina by the way, graduated from the same university as you, and she did very well for herself after graduation." She touched my shoulder. I flinched, but she didn't notice. "As a matter of fact, she found herself an American husband online. She's leaving for Texas soon. You probably know her. She tutored English classes here at the local school a few years back. I thought you took lessons from her too."

"Do you mean Zina Pascal? Of course, I know her. I just never knew she was your sister-in-law." I didn't quite know which news was more shocking, that Zina Pascal, the English guru, the extraverted prima donna, was the sister-in-law of the modest, introverted teacher I'd worked with for the past four years, or that Zina Pascal had found herself a husband online. She was all personality, but by no means was she pretty.

"How old is she?" I asked, unable to hide my curiosity.

"She's thirty-nine. Zina didn't want to leave this year, because she has this astrology business that's going very well for her here, but her son is turning twenty-one next year. If they don't leave now, she would have to leave him behind, and she wouldn't do that. These two have been joined at the hip since her husband dumped her eighteen years ago."

My brain almost short-circuited as I tried to process all this information. A thirty-nine-year-old, unattractive woman and astrology aficionado with an adult son found herself a husband from America—online! Where were those American men from? The moon?

As if reading my mind, Zina added, "If I were as young as you, I would totally go for it. The men of a civilized world, they know how to treat women right. Our men are spoiled pigs who got used to us cooking and cleaning up after them, raising our kids practically on our own, even if we have husbands."

It was bizarre, to say the least, that on this particular day, at this particular time, the subject of online dating came up in conversation with Zina. She and I rarely talked. She was not an over-sharer, and I was very private. I knew that, behind my back, they called me "the nose in the sky" because I never socialized (aka, gossiped) with my coworkers.

Then, all of the sudden, Zina was done talking to me. She turned to Victor. "Your time's up," she said. "No more slides for you today. Go play on the monkey bars for everybody's sake."

Victor ran off the bench, as if it was the last day on earth he could still play. He climbed up the bars quickly, trying to catch up with another boy, Damian, who was seated on the top bar, preparing to swing. Victor sat next to him, squeezing him to the side.

"Stop pushing me." Damian resisted, but Victor pushed him with his shoulder anyway, and Damian fell in between the bars, landing on the ground underneath.

"You are evil!" Damian yelled in frustration and tried to hit Victor's foot, which was hanging above his head. Victor pulled both his feet up, grabbed the front bar, and swung above Damian. The fighting made him hurry, so on his swing back, Victor's palms slid off the bar, and he belly-flopped on the ground with his hands spread in front of him, making the sound of a squished giant frog. A screeching, almost unhuman scream came out of Victor's mouth. Zina and I ran to check on the boy. As soon as Zina turned Victor on this back, he grabbed his right hand, which was bruising before our eyes.

"Mommy!" Victor screamed.

"I think his arm is broken," Zina said, scared.

"Karma," I whispered instinctively.

How could a completely normal, regular day turn into a disaster so quickly? How? There are things beyond our control. But the thought that there was karma in this world gave me peace. I was not going to dwell on what had happened to me, or let it destroy me. I would let karma take care of Stepan. I was going to work on getting us out of here, and now I knew how.

Well, not exactly. I had an idea for the first step, like a general getting a map before the battle. But now I needed to work up a plan, arm my troops, and figure out the rest of the logistics. *Where do I even begin?* Later that night, I took a piece of paper and wrote down my action plan:

1. Find a friend with a computer at home. *I don't know anyone. Question mark.*

2. Find a friend with a computer at work. *Violeta? Tanya? Will their bosses allow me in their offices? Can I use their computers? Will my girls have to receive my e-mails and type my answers for me? Last resort.*

3. Buy a computer ($500). *$500/$50 a month salary = 10 months without food and utilities. Add installation and Internet monthly fee. One to two years. Too long! Scratch that for now. Ask Mom only if I absolutely have to. Second-to-last resort.*

4. Find a dating agency with a computer. *How much?*

Looking for a job costs money, and looking for a man costs even more money! How can a single woman get ahead? I shook my head, feeling like a trapped butterfly that somebody was trying to shove back into its cocoon. No fucking way was I going back in there. This butterfly was going to fly or die trying! And try I did. All fall and all winter, I was on a scavenger hunt, asking around, gathering information that was scarce and scattered. There was no one in particular with all the answers, so I lost weeks calling people who either didn't respond or sent me down endless rabbit holes and dead ends. Until, finally, late in the spring I found an agency in a newspaper ad.

Chapter 11

The Dating Agency

"We can certainly help you here," said Larisa when I walked into her small office downtown. She was a woman in her late thirties with ferocious black hair. Behind her, a white Xerox paper with printed bold letters—**We provide dating services**—was glued to the wall with two uneven Scotch tape strips.

"Do you have an account with us?" she asked, clicking on her keyboard.

"No."

"We will create one for you. Did you bring photos?" Larisa got up to grab a folder from a drawer with shabby corners.

I pulled my two most recent photos from my purse. The first was not my favorite, because it was a group photo showing me with two of my kindergarten coworkers, but I'd taken it with me as a spare, in case the other ones wouldn't work. In the second one, I was alone in a knee-length black skirt and a buttoned up white blouse, next to a Christmas tree. *The only thing missing is Jesus hovering above my head*, I thought, looking at my photo. I put it on the table in front of me and turned my head away. On the left side of the table I saw another client's folder with an upside-down photo of a woman in her late forties. She was standing next to a Christmas tree too.

"You know what, I don't think I brought the best photos today," I said, and got off the chair.

"No, no, stay. Let's finish the paperwork. You can bring the photos later." Larisa sprinted toward me. I stopped in the middle of the room like a girl in front of a jump rope, deciding if I should jump in now or later, but Larisa wasn't giving up on me.

"Here are some profiles of men we have." She handed me about ten printed letters with black-and-white pictures at the bottom. The images were faded and smudged; the men's faces looked gray. I wondered how many hands had touched these papers before me.

"Are those local men?" I asked.

"No!" Larisa reproached me passionately, as this was so obvious that I shouldn't even have asked. "No serious woman nowadays is going to waste her time with our men. They are from around the world." Larisa lifted her chin up, as a proud manager who had a superb product in her store. "You can pick as many e-mails as you'd like for five leis apiece."

"You are selling e-mail addresses?" *That's like giving up one Catherine Zeta-Jones dress for a could-be fiancé!*

"We are maintaining our clients' accounts, so this is how it works."

I tapped my foot under the table and dropped my head down, shuffling through the printouts in my hands, trying to calculate how long my money would last with such a business model in this dating market. I picked the three that I thought were worth my money: a serious, well-dressed Italian university professor, Vittorio; a good-looking Spaniard called Rafael in light summer shorts; and a man named Craig with no clear place of origin, whose picture showed him rowing down a river.

"Only three?" Larisa asked, disappointed. "You didn't pick Jonathan from Australia."

"I would like to stick to Europe. Australia is very far."

"That's a pity. Everyone picks Jonathan."

"And how come he's still on the market?"

"We don't have any control over whom the men respond to. We just provide the contact information and supporting services, like English translation of your letters. It will cost fifteen leis for a quarter of a page." *Three Catherine Zeta-Jones dresses for a quarter of a page?*

"Thank you, but that will not be necessary. I speak English."

"Is your English good enough?" Larisa asked with the voice of an irritated cicada. "I would still suggest we proofread your letters for a reduced fee. The typographic errors would cut your chances in half. The educated men will dismiss you right off the bat." She put her finger on Professor Vittorio's profile.

"I'm not paying for this." I shook my head firmly, looking straight into Larisa's eyes.

"Fine. Then you will have to type your own introduction letters in English. I'm not typing them for you. The second computer is over there in the corner. Help yourself." Larisa turned her head away from me, demonstrating with all her posture that she was done talking.

"How will I know when they respond?"

"We'll call you," she answered, concentrating on her monitor.

* * *

I didn't hear from Larisa for two weeks. When I called her to find out if there was any progress, she told me, "You have no responses. I would suggest you buy more e-mail addresses. You need to cast a wider net. Three correspondents are not enough."

"Thank you," I told her, and hung up. "I'm wasting my summer!" I said to myself out loud, feeling that I had reached another dead end. It was evident that I was doing something wrong, but what exactly was wrong? Did I pick the wrong agency? Was Larisa's database no good? Or was it the lack of money on my part that was not allowing me to spread my net? If money was the reason, then I was out of luck again.

August was approaching, and I had no extra funds to spend. I needed money for train tickets to Crimea to pick up the kids from their grandma's, who'd taken them in for the summer break.

* * *

"*Allyo!*" my ex-mother-in-law Tamara yelled into the phone when I made my long-distance call to her. "Ira? Is that you?"

"Yes, it's me. How are you all doing over there?"

"Life is wonderful, Ira!" she answered in her usual cheerful voice. I smiled. Nothing had changed. "Life is wonderful" was her favorite thing to say, year after year. Even after her father lost his vision and she had to take care of him four years in a row, and after her husband had a heart attack last summer, and she herself suffered from high blood pressure that was giving her severe migraines. How could she be so "glass half full" all the time when the glass dried out a long time ago?

"How are the kids behaving? Did they give you all any trouble?" I asked.

"What are you talking about? You have golden kids. I cannot thank you enough for letting them stay with us every summer, even after you and Igor got divorced." As if I had forgotten that last part. "It is such a joy to see them here. Oh, here is Lica trying to rip the phone out of my hands."

"Mom! Allyo!" Lica yelled into the receiver.

"Now, Lica, tell me the truth. Did you guys listen to Grandma and Grandpa?"

"I did. You know me, I am the perfect child. Sereoja, though, climbed on the monkey bars in the park while they were wet, though Grandpa specifically told him to get down because it was too dangerous, and he fell and broke his right arm!"

"What? When did this happen?" I yelled.

Tamara took the receiver back from Lica.

"Ira, don't worry. It happened like a month and a half ago. Tomorrow we are going to the doctor to take his cast off. He will be like new when you come to pick the kids up."

"Why didn't you call me?" I was perplexed. What possible explanation could she give that would make me feel better?

"After the doctor put his cast on, there was nothing else you could do," she said simply. "We didn't want you to worry from one thousand kilometers away." I swore I heard her shrug, like it was not a big deal. There were so many questions I wanted to ask her: How was my son eating for the last month and a half with his arm in the cast? What if his bones didn't heal yet, and he'd have to go to school for the first time with a broken arm? But she interrupted my rambling thoughts:

"Igor was here all summer helping with the kids. He was taking him to doctor's appointments and physical therapy."

"I thought Igor was in Moscow working." I couldn't believe my ears. "Wasn't he supposed to send you money for the summer?"

"Well, that didn't work out. He lost his job, so he couldn't stay in Moscow anymore. I sent him money for the train ticket for him to come home."

"I bet my father-in-law wasn't happy."

"He never is. He tells me that I am his enabler. You know him, an old grumpy man. Anyway, it was a great opportunity for Igor because he rarely gets to spend the summer with his kids."

"Mom, Mom!" I heard Serghei's voice as if he was yelling from the inside of a barrel. "I learned to eat with my left hand."

"It sounds like you had a summer from hell!" I finally felt pity for Tamara.

"Not at all," Tamara continued. "The kids made our life wonderful. Otherwise, we would have died of boredom or gnawed each other. But what's going on with you? Did you find yourself a man?"

"Ah!" I stretched my answer, trying to find the right words.

"Ira, don't be ashamed," she cooed. "You are a young woman. Don't waste your young years without sex. You'll never get them back. Why do you think we take the kids off your hands every summer? So you can arrange your private life and find yourself a decent man."

"I'm … I'm … working … on it."

"Good for you, and good luck. If I wasn't an atheist, I would pray for you. So, when are you picking up the kids?"

"I'll be there on Thursday."

I went to the other room to prepare my suitcase for the road. A weird sensation—that my ex-mother-in-law was watching me all along—was not going away. *Or maybe she was watching over me? Neh!* I brushed it off. *What is she? My guardian angel or something?* I turned on the TV to drive away my silly thoughts. Besides, I didn't like the silence in the house when I was home alone, since Mariana had gone to her father's. A short fifteen-second written ad with just two lines popped up on the screen:

Dating Services

Call Leonid at 44-33-22

"I'll be damned! You know what, Leonid, it's a sign! I am going to call you right now," I said aloud and went back to the phone, grabbing a notebook on my way there. To my surprise, someone picked up the phone before I was ready to talk.

"Hello, Leonid?" I said.

"Oh, God, I don't remember the last time someone called me by my full name. I just go by Leonya," a man with a deep voice answered.

"Well, that's what the ad said: 'Call Leonid.'"

"What ad?"

"The TV ad about dating services."

"Oh, that one. Jeez, I totally forgot about it. I placed it several weeks ago, and nobody called. I thought it was dead. But you called, that's wonderful. Would you like to stop by and check us out?"

"Before I do that, can I find out your rates? How much do you charge for an e-mail address of the potential candidates?"

"Oh, God, I don't charge for e-mail addresses. Is that what they do out there? Darling, they are ripping you off. I'm just charging one lei for each letter you print, and we can talk about the charge for computer use. Would you like our address? You can come in today, if you wish. Summer is kind of a slow season. Everybody's on their Black Sea vacations, either Ukraine or Turkey, so I'm available."

"Today is not exactly perfect timing. I'm leaving for Crimea tomorrow."

"You're going to the Black Sea too?"

"Not really. I'm picking up my kids from my ex-husband."

"Oh, dear! You've ended up in different countries after a divorce, haven't you? What did this breakup of the country do to all of us? *Bon voyage!* See you in September then, when you come back."

Only then did it hit me. It had been almost a year since the last unfortunate September that I had shoved deep down in my memory, hoping never to recall it again. I had accomplished nothing in an entire year!

I shifted all my hopes to the upcoming September, but that month didn't live up to Leonid's expectations—or mine. The kids outgrew their clothes and shoes, so their apparel and school supplies ate up my monthly budget in one trip to the bazar. It was not until late October that I finally saved enough money to make a trip to Leonid's Dating Services Agency.

His office was located on the last floor of a sixteen-story building. The old and cranky elevator stopped on the fifteenth floor, so I took the last flight of stairs on foot, stepping a few times on my long winter coat. Afraid that I might change my mind, I quickly knocked on the old-fashioned door, which made a shallow sound, then walked into a simple room with bare gray cement walls and two desks with computers on the left. A middle-aged man, slightly overweight, with uncombed hair and a reddish beard, was sitting at an unpretentious desk propped by two layers of cardboard to keep it from wobbling. The man wore a cheap, fluffy sweater, perhaps trying to do both: to stay alive (the room was so cold, I could see his breath), while also saving on the electric bill. He didn't look like a businessman, unlike the very busy Larisa from the other agency, who never delivered any results anyways. He was more like a goofy cartoonish bear who had wandered out of the woods by accident. But when he spread his arms, still sitting in his chair, and yelled in English, "Welcome!" I didn't need to wonder who he was. I recognized that deep velvety voice. Without any doubt, it was Leonid.

I smiled back at him, but I stopped halfway when I noticed my competition: three other women at the table on the right side of the room who appeared to be there on the same business as me. Was I supposed to talk about my situation in front of them? But a good-looking blonde in her late twenties raised her head and smiled at me. "Oh, reinforcements have arrived," she said.

"Reinforcement to what exactly?" I asked her.

"To the Legion of Single Women of Moldova. My name is Alyona. To my right is Sonya, and to my left is Valeria. What's your name?"

"I-ri-na," I answered, stretching my vowels. I was not sure that having an entire regimen of single women was a good thing, considering that I appeared to be the oldest in the group.

"Oh, are you that Irina that called me two days ago?" Leonid interrupted.

"No. I called you two months ago," I answered, somewhat disappointed that he had forgotten me already. I thought I was quite memorable, for some reason.

"Come on, get over here." Leonid waved me in. "Don't worry about them. Those three are already taken care of. They are busy writing letters to their online boyfriends today. Let's see how we can help you."

"Let's talk about pricing first," I said as soon as I sat down in the chair, still trying to catch my breath. Leonid squirmed in his seat as if he'd found a nail under his butt. He checked his numbers a few times, then handed me his price list in both Moldavian currency and American dollars, as most businesses did:

- Setting up an online profile: 50 leis ($5)
- Printouts (depending on the text): 1 to 3 leis (10 to 30 cents)
- Computer usage: 15 leis per hour ($1.50/hr)
- Translator services: 15 leis per letter of 100 words ($1.50/ letter). (Price negotiation with the translator possible.)

"I'm so sorry to charge you for all these, but I have to, at least, to get my money back for paper and ink, and to make something extra to run the business." Leonid's face was changing colors—from white to pink, to red to white again—while I read through the list.

I was adding up numbers in my head, trying to look for ways to save on the final tab. I scratched out the translation fee, overjoyed that I wouldn't, at least, need money for that. I would need to start with Leonid setting up my online profile. *Ka-ching, five dollars!* Judging by my experience with Larisa, the responses from men wouldn't come back for weeks, so the rest of the payments could be stretched out and piecemeal.

"I can work with that," I heard myself voicing my final conclusion. "Most importantly, I can see you deliver results, so I'd like to sign up with you." I gave Leonid his paper back.

"Glad to hear that. Let's see what you've got." Leonid was visibly relieved that this part of the business was over. He took my pictures out of my hands, but just a few seconds later, he returned them to me. "You need to get some new pictures," he said, "preferably done in a studio. These homemade pictures with poor lighting and bad angles don't show you at your best. It's also not a good idea to have group pictures. You should bring pictures with kids later. Right now, we need to focus attention on you," he added apologetically but sternly. "Here's a phone number of a studio photographer just two blocks from here. His name is Stanislav. He runs his business out of his apartment, and I swear to God, I don't get a cut from him. He makes exquisite photos." *Exquisite sounds expensive.* "Believe me, it will be worth every lei," Leonid said, and pointed with his eyes in the direction of the three girls sitting across the room.

All the way home I was wrestling with the question of whether I should bank on the photo studio, trying to weigh the pros and cons:

Pro: Exquisite photos equal good outcome in the far future.

Con: Money spent on photos means less money in the house in the near future.

Pro: If this works, all of us can start a new life.

Con: If this doesn't work, we'll be in the same place but in a worse financial situation.

I still had doubts, even when I reached home, and dropped into the armchair in the living room, rethinking it over and over again. Nevertheless, I gave Stanislav a call to ask how much the photo shoot would cost.

"It all depends on how many photos you order, but I charge ten lei per photo," Stanislav said. *A dollar per photo, I can do that,* I thought, *if I just stick to the minimum.*

"Bring several outfits and different pairs of shoes for the photo shoot, so the photos don't all look alike."

Mariana looked at my distraught face. "What's wrong?" she asked.

"This dating business is going to be the death of me. I don't have money for new clothes, so let's get everything out of the closet and see what I have to work with. I don't want any churchy skirts this time!"

"I'll get mine out then," Mariana said, happy to help.

"You realize that you're seventeen and I'm thirty-two? Not exactly the same age bracket."

"You've got potential," Mariana said sarcastically and threw me her black miniskirt with a slit on the right side. Then she handed me her new blue skirt-and-jacket suit that her father bought her as a reward for starting college in September.

"The jacket doesn't fit," I said after trying a few times to button it up.

"Your boobs are too big! How about the skirts?"

"Tight, but will do. They are well above my knees, though."

"You can rock my miniskirts just fine." She waved me off, as if that would knock my insecurities out the window. "Try this gray blouse that I bought yesterday. It's stretchy, so it should fit."

"You call this a *blouse*? Look at this V-cut that goes right between my boobs. Why does it have only three buttons and part in the middle? My belly is exposed."

"Then suck it in! You said it yourself; you don't want a churchy look. What else you got there?"

"I have this turquoise dress with a green shawl from five years ago, which is so old it's back in fashion, and these two black dresses from the Humanitarian Aid. This velvety one is badly worn out on the sides, and the black dress with white polka dots is washed out, if you look closely, but hopefully they can work in the right light." Something caught my eye. "What's there—in that bag?" I pointed it out to Mariana.

"That's the bag with some merchandise that Mom couldn't sell before she left for Greece." She pulled out a spring raincoat, a few brushes, baby clothes, and a cheap, short polyester summer dress with a flower pattern. "Try this one." I took the dress from her hands with some hesitation, like a sophisticated wine drinker who just realized that all she could afford was cheap booze. *Had I really hit the polyester rock bottom?*

"You know, that's not too bad if you look from far away," Mariana said, backing up a few steps to look at me in the mirror. "I think you've got your collection."

*　*　*

I took the stairs to Stanislav's home photo studio on the first floor of a tall apartment building, bouncing my heavy bag with clothes and shoes on my left shoulder and stopped in front of the door of suite number three. The wood around the lock was chipped, as if someone recently tried to open it with a crowbar. I rang the bell and waited nervously, listening to the sound of a key moving in the lock. Stanislav, a man in his early thirties, short, balding, and unhealthily thin, kept a cigarette propped in his mouth as he opened the door and let me in.

The heavy door, which from inside was made of metal, slammed after me. Stanislav locked it with his key, then moved the two slide bolt locks from left to right, shutting the door even tighter. The locks rubbed on the metal underneath, making a screeching sound like a machine gun being reloaded.

"What's up with all these locks?" I asked, trying not to think of what would happen if I had to leave his apartment in a hurry.

"We got robbed twice last year, so I installed this metal door for safety. The third time, they weren't so successful," Stanislav said casually. "I don't know what those creatures hope to find here. I don't keep cash in the house, and we have sold almost everything we own. My wife is a Jew, so we're moving to Israel as soon as we get our immigration paperwork finalized. It's been six months, so it should be any day now. I can't wait to get out of here. This sitting and waiting is getting on my nerves. In the meantime, I do photography so I don't go crazy. There's a changing room down the hall, so let's get started. I have another girl coming at three o'clock."

"Changing room" was an ambitious name for an empty space with an old couch. The only other decor was a tall skinny mirror on the floor leaning against the wall. I dropped off my winter coat and my scarf, letting my hair down. I regretted taking my boots off, though; the parquet floor was unpleasantly cold. It seemed that everyone in the city was trying to save on heat that winter.

"Do I have time to curl my hair?" I peeked through the door to ask Stanislav.

He looked at me. "Before you do that, let's take a couple of trial shots to test the lighting."

I quickly slid my feet into the blue high-heeled shoes and walked out of the changing room. The studio was spacious with a huge gray cloth hanging from the wall all the way down to the floor. Light was shining from a lamp with an umbrella in the right corner. On the other side, there was a tall mirror, where I saw myself from top to bottom in the bright light for the first time.

The boot-cut black pants that I'd borrowed from Mariana were too long for a shorty like me, but the high heels were giving me a few centimeters' boost. The low-cut black top with long sleeves that I'd taken off my sister just before I left the house finished the look. *Damn, girl!* I stood in front of the mirror with my hands down, waiting for directions.

"What do you want me to do?" I asked Stanislav, when he kept looking into the camera without saying anything.

"I want you to move back and forth very naturally. Don't force it."

"Move how? Do I look into the camera when I'm moving?"

"Don't worry about the camera, just walk." I made a few robotic steps to the left then to the right. "Loosen up!" he yelled at me. "Don't flap your arms. Control them like you're in a ballet class." I took a deep breath and tried to relax. "Great! I like that smile!"

I didn't even realize I was smiling. I thought I was laughing at

Stanislav's commands because they reminded me of the day care matinee rehearsals, but this time I was not the teacher, but the kid. I walked all the way to the end of the room and landed my left foot on the wooden cube in the corner striking a pose: my left hand on my knee and my right hand on my hip. I heard *click, click, click,* and Stanislav yelled out, "Wonderful!"

He looked at the pictures in his camera, then at me. "In my professional opinion, don't curl your hair. You don't want to look like everybody else. Ready for the next outfit?" And so the game of dress up began. I ran to change into my turquoise dress.

"Oh, I can do so much with this green shawl!" I whispered, running back. "How about that?" I asked Stanislav, lifting my right hand with the corner of the shawl over my head, then dropped it on my shoulders, then changed my mind and wrapped it around my hips.

"Don't stop," Stanislav said, working with the camera. "Let's get a few close ups in the summer dress."

"But I have dark circles under my eyes."

"Let me worry about that. Play with your hair a little."

"Like that?" I asked, fluffing my hair, getting more confirmation that hairdresser Elena was so right about the treasure on my head that I was getting to flaunt now.

"Take this purple daisy. It will lighten up the picture," he said when he saw me in my next outfit: the black mini-skirt and gray top. I stuck the plastic flower in my hair, but the stiff stem was not bending, so I kept moving it around: on my chest, on my knee, across my skirt, at my nose.

"Don't cover up your face!"

"What if I do this?" I came up with an idea, as if I'd done this many times before. I laid out on the floor on my right side, holding my head in the air. Then I put the stubborn flower in front of me, so my eyes and the flower petals were looking straight into the camera.

"Beautiful!" Stanislav said, squatting to take a few close shots. Then, I threw the flower into the corner and sat down on the floor. I bent my left leg, crossing it over my right, which was stretched out in front of me. I put my right hand behind me, leaning back, and casually dropped my left hand on my knee. A confident, radiant smile lit up my face.

Oh, Leonid will be so happy to see these! Why only Leonid? Men of the world, beware!

I didn't even take a bus to get to Leonid's office from the photographer. I walked several blocks down the hill, as if I had little, happy wings flopping behind my back.

"Here!" I said to Leonid. "I think these three photos will be excellent for my profile."

Leonid looked at the first photo of me in the black dress with white polka dots leaning far, far forward on the white classic chair with my breasts almost jumping out of my tight corset. My left leg in yellow shoes stretched as far as it could. The hemline of my dress pulled back, exposing my knees. Then he looked at the second photo of me on the floor in the miniskirt barely covering my bottom, my legs showing their best (I thought) in skin-color pantyhose. My lips plump with red-cherry lipstick displayed a smile that looked like I was about to conquer the world.

"That's all you've got?" He set the third one aside without even looking closely.

"I couldn't stop myself at three," I answered and gave him the rest of the package. He picked a close-up picture of me in the summer polyester dress fluffing my hair. *Out of all outfits, this one? Seriously?* Then the second picture in my five-year-old turquoise dress with the green shawl wrapped innocently around my arms, and the "surprise" picture in black pants with the black top.

"This one with the pants is just a trial picture," I explained, confused by his choices.

"This is a lucky trial picture, then. You look very commanding here. Western men are quite different; they like a woman in charge."

"But the rest of the photos are so … modest."

"Irina, we are trying to attract the serious men."

"But I have serious intentions."

Leonid looked at me sullenly.

"Do I … seem … so … desperate?" I asked, barely able to say it.

"A little bit. But that's why I'm here to guide you in the right direction."

It had never occurred to me that I needed direction, or help, or advice in dating matters. Perhaps it was divine intervention that I ended up with Leonid. *Bless you, atheist Tamara, for watching over me!*

Chapter 12

Herpes Man, Casanova, and Silicone Brains

The printer in Leonid's office was puffing like an old man, using its last strength to spit out the e-mails I received after my profile was published online. I was tapping my foot while waiting for the slow-moving gadget to finish its run. The white page was already showing the full text on the top when the paper jammed with a gargling sound. Leonid pulled the paper gently, trying to straighten out the ripples, but the accordion-like bottom gave in and with a loud *whizz* ripped in half.

"Don't bother printing it again," I told Leonid, taking the paper with edges that looked like a map of Africa out of his hands. "I can read that."

"Are you sure?" Leonid asked, but I was already busy reading the first letter.

"Hi, there. My name is Engel. I live in beautiful countryside in Yorkshire, Great Britain. I saw your pictures online and hope to hear from you soon. PS: How is the weather over there where you live?"

"Two lines, and one line about weather? Really?" I murmured and flipped through other letters. I decided to switch to men who took the time to write long letters first, so I picked the longest letter out of the pile.

"Hello! I saw your profile online, and it prompted me to write you a letter. I am Jonathan and I currently live in Australia." *Is that the same Jonathan whose e-mail Larisa tried to sell me?* "I have serious intentions, and I am looking for a long-term relationship with the possibility of marriage." *That's serious indeed!* "I promise to always be honest with you and would appreciate the same in return." *Always, always?* "In the spirit of being honest, I would like to disclose upfront that I suffer from genital herpes." *What the hell ... is ... genital herpes?* "Therefore, I'm looking for a partner who also has genital herpes." *So, am I disqualified since I don't think I have one?* "Though if you do not have herpes, it is still possible to have safe intercourse." *Is that what I think it is?* He finished his letter with a page from a medical encyclopedia about what genital herpes was and how to live with this disease.

I leaned back in my chair, feeling like I'd just been splashed with a bucket of acid, and I needed as much air as I could get. Two things were clear: Jonathan had a penis problem, and my vagina was refusing to be his saving grace!

Who in the world would write an introduction letter like this? I got up to show my letter to Leonid.

"Huh!" Leonid said out loud. "You got a letter from the Herpes Man. I printed a few of those a couple of days ago, I don't remember for whom. Who got the letter from the Herpes Man?" Three women in the room raised their hands.

"My God, how many women did he write his herpes story to?"

"You know what? Throw the damn letter away. I'm not going to charge you for that. I fixed the printer, so here's another one for you. It has a picture with it." I took the letter out of Leonid's hands and sat down for another Wild West dating session.

"*Buongiorno,* Irina!" *Oh, that's an Italian man, and he called me by my name—that's promising.*

"I saw your profile photos, and I'm smitten. You are a beautiful woman with incredible eyes and a gorgeous smile." *Leonid was so right to pick those photos. Now it's all about my eyes, and not about ... other things.*

"But let me introduce myself: My name is Vincent and I live in Milan. I'm a romantic at heart and believe in love at first sight. I'm looking for the woman of my dreams for a serious long-term relationship. I hope that's you. Looking forward to hearing from you. Ciao, Vincent."

I looked at the printed photo of Vincent at the bottom of the letter. It was smudged and blurry, but I could still see a man in his earlier forties with a charming smile, swimming in a pool in a pair of orange shorts. His bare, tanned chest was above the water. A week ago, I would have called him *krasavchik*, but today I caught myself thinking like Leonid: *That's the best he's got, a photo of himself in a pool?*

The last two letters were from the US: Thomas from Texas and Sam from Missouri. Strangely, they were very similar: dry, matter of fact, not much warmth, so I set them aside and returned to Vincent's letter.

"Let's give you a chance, *Italiano.*" I sat down at the computer to write him my response.

"You know what I do?" Sonya said. She was using the computer next to me. "I just copy and paste the same response to all my men to save time and money."

"I don't think that's appropriate. They all write different letters and have different questions. Besides, I think, today, I'm going to write only one response. I've decided to narrow my geography to Europe. America and Australia are too far away."

"If I were you, I would not dismiss the Americans. The most success we've had in this group has been with Americans. They will travel to meet you, and after that, they're not afraid to make a decision. The Europeans—Italians, Spaniards, and even Englishmen—will play with you for several months, then promise a bunch of things, but they never seem to pull the trigger. My French fiancé was absolutely gorgeous. We met several times in

Prague, since, for us Moldavians, it's hard to get a visa anywhere else. We had an amazing time together, but six months later, he was still just my pen pal. No proposal, no serious talks about moving to the next step. I told him I'm done waiting. I'm not getting any younger, and I need to take care of my kids. The more time goes by, the harder it will be for them to learn a foreign language, so I have no life to waste."

"I hope it works better for you next time," I said, and went back to writing my answer to Vincent.

His response came back swiftly. I was reading it slowly, absorbing every word: "Your wonderful letter made my day. I must say, you are not only beautiful, but also intelligent and well spoken. I can't wait to hear more from you." I stopped in the middle, unable to continue. Hot tears were pouring down my cheeks. Nobody had written like that to me before. Nobody had ever told me that I made his day.

I turned around to the room of single women and said, "This man is asking me for my phone number."

"Oh-ho, he's getting serious!" Alyona jumped in first.

"Don't blow it." Leonid was less enthusiastic. "I know you all think that once you get one man to call you, you've got Jesus by his feet, and you stop coming here. Irina," Leonid addressed me this time, "this is just the first man. Don't put all your eggs in one basket."

There is no point in me playing hard to get either, I thought. There was only a one-hour time difference with Milan, so it could all be clear soon.

On Friday night, the sound of a long-distance phone call made me pause. *Is that real, or am I just hearing things?* When the second ring came through, I ran, tripping on my son's shoes in the hallway. *How many times have I told him not to leave those there?* I kicked them to the corner.

"Hello!" a man's voice said in English, but softening the "L" sounds like a true Italian. "Is that Irina?" He even pronounced my name right, stressing the "R," so I knew exactly who was calling.

"Yes. Is that Vincent?"

"Yes, of course. Who else could it be?" Vincent laughed. His voice was deeper than I thought it would be (most likely he was a smoker), but his laugh was so reverberating, it made me giggle, though he hadn't said anything funny.

"You have ... *cuomo se dice?*" He tried to find the English word.

"Go ahead, say it in Italian. I speak Romanian, so I will probably understand half of what you say."

"*Hai una bella voce,*" he said in playful Italian, raising the tone on the first syllable of every word, as his native language required. The switch of language changed his manner of speaking so drastically that it was hard to believe I was talking to the same man. English was robbing him of his personality. I frantically tried to recall all the Italian words I ever knew for a quick response, but English came in faster.

"Oh, I don't think my voice is beautiful. It is just a regular voice. *Grazie,*" I said in the end, stressing the first syllable of the word, just like a native speaker would, without even realizing it. Vincent, pleased that it was going so well, responded in such fast-shooting Italian that I was able to decipher just a few expressions: *grandi occhi, sorriso, abbraccio.* I figured he was complimenting me on my big eyes and my smile with a bunch of other words in between that I could not understand.

"*Abbraccio, abbraccio,*" I repeated a few times, trying to match it to the closest Romanian word. *Ah! He wants to give me a hug! This sounds so much sexier in Italian!*

"Mom." I heard Serghei, who was tugging at my sleeve.

"*Ce?* (What?)" I asked him in Romanian. "I'm on the phone."

"Can I go outside?"

"Did you finish your homework?"

"I'm almost done."

"When you are done, then you can go."

"Who are you talking to?" Serghei grew curious.

"None of your business. Go back and finish your homework." I sent him away. "Sorry about that." I resumed my conversation with Vincent. "That was my son."

"You have a son?"

"Actually, I have a daughter and a son."

"I have a son too. My wife and I divorced many years ago. He's all grown up now. Kids, they are the joy of our lives, aren't they? I will let you go back to your duties then, but we will keep in touch. *Ciao.*"

That "ciao," pronounced with a very distinctive "ch," was giving me the flashes. I sat down to process my conversation with Vincent. He seemed normal: courteous, chatty, perhaps a little too schmoozy, but he was Italian, after all. I was pleased that he was a father; he would understand me better as a parent. Mariana flew in from the other room.

"Serghei told me you were talking to somebody in English. Who was it?" I made a mysterious face but did not say anything. "Was that a job?" I shook my head. "Was it a man?" I nodded. Mariana hit me on my left arm with excitement, the same way her father used to do to her. "Is it serious?"

"I don't know yet. I just talked to him for five minutes."

Vincent didn't disappoint, however. He called me the next day, then for a few more weeks. Then one day, out of the blue, he asked me: "Would you like to meet me in Kiev after the holidays? I'm going to Ukraine for business."

"What kind of business?"

"I work in textiles. You know, Italians are crazy for fashion, so we're looking for some natural fabrics in Ukraine. That will be a great opportunity to finally meet each other. I looked it up. It's not far from Chişinău, about four hundred kilometers, the map says. And I know Eastern Europeans do not need a visa for Ukraine."

"That's correct, but that's very short notice. I don't know if I can take time off work. Besides, I don't have the money for the trip right now. I need to budget for train tickets and hotel."

"Don't worry about the hotel. I'll cover that for both of us."

"I should probably have my own room," I insisted. "Let me get some information about the price and ticket availability, and we'll talk about it later."

That's an interesting twist. I was pacing back and forth in the room. *This Year of the Dragon is full of surprises and new beginnings, as the goddamned poster promised. I have a decision to make, don't I?* The sound of another phone ring disturbed my thoughts.

"Irina?" I heard Leonid's voice. I cringed. I hadn't been at Leonid's office for a few weeks, consumed by conflicting emotions over developments with Vincent. "There are quite a few e-mails waiting for you here."

"All right," I said half-heartedly. "I need to get out to the city for an inquiry at the train station today, so I'll stop by."

* * *

"Long time, no see," Leonid said in English when he saw me at the door. He liked to use English expressions when they fit the situation better than the Russian language would. "Here's your stuff, but watch out for Vincent's e-mails. If you see one, give it back to me, I'll shred it for you and I won't charge you for that."

"Why do you want to shred letters from Vincent? I talked to him on the phone today."

"Vincent from Milan is talking to you?" Leonid asked, and looked at Sonya.

"Vincent, Casanova Vincent?" Sonya asked me.

"I don't know what you mean."

"That Vincent writes letters to everyone here. He doesn't even have the decency to switch it up a little." She pulled a letter from her pile and read it to me: "*Buongiorno*, Sonya! I saw your profile photos, and I am smitten. You are a beautiful woman with incredible eyes and a gorgeous smile." My hands started shaking. I recognized the text of Vincent's first letter almost verbatim, minus the name.

"Did he ask you to meet him in Kiev yet?" My blood pressure jumped to two hundred.

"He asked you too?" I said.

"Don't bother with Kiev," Sonya said conciliatorily. "I met him in October. That photo of him in his shorts is at least twenty years old. He's just an old desperate man looking for another Russian chick to bang. Not like he can bang anyone. He couldn't get it up—even with Viagra."

I had to take a seat. *Casanova-Motherfucker!* All I could come up with to express my anger and the feeling of betrayal. *And I am here fighting with myself to hold on to standards like a Virgin Mary!*

"I don't know who's worse," I said. "The Herpes Man or Casanova? The Herpes Man was creepy, but at least honest."

"Oh, it gets worse." Sonya pulled another letter from her collection. "I call this one Bob, the Silicone Brains."

"Why silicone?"

"Because he's obsessed with silicone boobs. He was very disappointed when I told him that I don't have silicone breasts and kept asking me if I would consider having implants. Oh, I had so much fun with this one, but in the end, I decided he's not worth my money. I told him in my farewell letter that I would have definitely considered this option, if he could transplant some real brains into his head to replace his silicone brains. It's like a jungle with wild monkeys out there, I'm telling you."

I looked at the letters in my hands, unsure what to think. *Is it even worth it to start over?* I laid them all down in front of me, trying to filter them based on the Legion of Single Women of Moldova's accumulated knowledge. I discarded the letters with an emphasis on my appearance. *I don't need another Casanova.* I also set aside the one liners and the long rambling letters.

"Before I get myself into another deep-shit situation"—I held the last letter above my head—"does anyone here have a letter from somebody called David?"

"Not me," the women responded in unison.

"I think David is a new one," Leonid said. "I don't remember printing letters from him for anybody else. But that's doesn't mean he can't write to someone else later, so I'll keep you posted."

Chapter 13

David

I was reading the e-mail, jumping over the lines, back and forth, like a spooked gazelle unable to shut off my mind: *Please don't be a weirdo, please don't be a weirdo!* The message came from fullmealdeal@excite.com, sent on December 1, 2000. It said: "I'm David. I'm forty years old. I live in the Northwest in a city called Lynnwood, thirty minutes north of Seattle." *Why is the distance measured in minutes and not kilometers?* I wondered.

"Where's Seattle?" I asked.

"Washington state," Leonid answered.

"Washington, the capital of America?"

"No, they have a state called Washington." I looked at Leonid, moving his finger on the map all the way across Europe, then over the Atlantic Ocean, then across the United States. He hesitated for a few seconds. "Here it is. Seattle. That's about ten thousand kilometers away."

"Might as well be on the moon," I answered and went back to my reading. "I am looking for a woman who can take care of me." *Huh?* "I love children, so don't worry about them. I want a family and look forward to a day when I have a lady to love again." *Family man?* "My first marriage ended recently when my wife was unfaithful." *What woman would do that?* "I need a lady I can trust. Someone who is romantic, caring, attentive, and passionate." *Don't we all?* "Could it be you? Dare I dream to love again? Take care."

Well, that's different. Open and sincere, perhaps too sincere. Did he really need to talk about his ex-wife in the first letter? Or is he so hurt that he can't stop thinking about her? "I love children" is a strong sentiment. Could anyone love someone else's kids unconditionally without knowing them? I know I can't. Then what's up with him looking for a woman to take care of him?

"Irina," Leonid yelled across the room, getting my attention. "David sent a photo with his letter, but it's not resized correctly, so it's gigantic. I don't think I can print it on one page. The best I can do is to show you one piece at a time." The photo on the screen looked like a broken collage. Leonid moved his mouse from the left side of David's face to the right in an attempt to fit it all in one frame.

"Is that a cowboy hat?" I giggled.

"That must be one of those old-fashioned Western photos. Almost every American has a photo like that in his profile. He says that's a picture of him and his son. I assume that's the boy in the photo with him." Leonid kept moving his mouse and stopped on David's body. "He's a big fellow."

"I can see that. You know what, don't print his photo. Let me send him a message and see how it goes." I wrote on David's letter, next to his name: "Lynnwood, Washington. Plump man in cowboy hat."

The response from David came back the next day.

"Oh, boy!" I said in English and rushed to read his letter, skipping the "how are you" and other pleasantries and going directly for the juice.

"I'm an Internet sales manager at a Ford dealership." *Ford? You can sell cars on the Internet? That's crazy!* "I make pretty good money." *Bragging about money, seriously?* "I think, in a marriage, that both should work unless the woman has babies at home. I respect single mothers, and I'm looking for a family to accept me. I was married, but she was unfaithful, so I'm alone and heartbroken." *Here we go again!* I took a break to reload and moved on to his questions at the bottom of the page:

"Can you cook?" *The road to a man's heart goes through his stomach.*

"Do you keep a good house?" *Looking for a housemaid?*

"What do you think a wife's responsibilities should be?"

"What are your hobbies?"

"What kind of lover do you want?" *Isn't it a little too early?*

"What kind of lover are you?" *That's definitely too early!*

"PS: I'm resending my resized picture, since you said the previous was too big and hard to see. I am here with my son, Derek. He's a good boy, and he comes to visit me often. David."

"You know," Leonid said, when I asked him to open David's photo on his computer, "now that we can see him in a normal-sized picture, he's quite handsome. He's tall, but not as big as we thought."

"Assuming that's a recent photo of him," Sonya interrupted. "I got a photo from a *Pampushka*-man once. Then two months later, when I started pressing him to meet in person, he sent me another photo. The man looked twice his size. Nobody gains so much weight in two months."

"Girls, hearing your stories is like being in a horror movie," I said.

"It could be a horror movie if I'd met him: Giant Squishes Lady Like a Bug." The room exploded into loud laughter.

"All right then," I said when the laughter subsided. "I'm going to write a response to my giant right now, since there are no other brave women around here." I dropped into the office chair, unsure where to even begin.

"Hello, David!," I wrote. "Thank you for your letter. Now I'll try to respond to your questions: I can cook, and I like it. Of course, my cooking is according to my country's traditions, but I can learn a new recipe quickly. It's a tradition in my country that a woman should cook well, and I am such a woman. I can also keep a good clean house. I could say a lot of things about a wife's responsibilities, but I'll name only some of them: A wife should be caring and loving. She should take care of children and her husband. She should also have an occupation outside the house. A husband should have the same responsibilities in addition to earning enough money to be able to take care of a family."

But the last question was the most uncomfortable to answer. *Lover? Is it my Soviet mentality that is blocking any deliberation on this subject? Or is it really a weird question?* Nevertheless, I wrote down cautiously in the end: "I want a warm, romantic lover, not too hot but not too cold." I kept my finger on the backspace button, unsure if I wanted to leave it there or erase it for good.

"Come on, everybody, let's hurry up," Leonid yelled from his chair. "I adore you all, but it's Friday night, and I want to go home to my wife. All these lovers of yours will be there on Monday. Let them rest for the weekend." I hesitated for a few seconds, but my fellow ladies got up, ready to leave, so I quickly pressed "Send" and left with the rest of them.

* * *

But over the weekend, I agonized over my "not too hot and not too cold" comment. *Really? What the hell does that even mean? That was not a smart move on my part.* I tried to guess: What would David think about this? But there was nothing I could do about it right now, not until the agency was open for business on Monday. I should have concentrated on my housework, now that I was finally getting some peace and quiet in the house. The first winter snow covering the playground in front of the house was like a magnet for the kids, keeping them outside to play. Especially Serghei, he only came home if he needed to pee or to change his pants when they got wet from melting snow and made him shiver.

"Mom, Mom!" Serghei yelled, dropping in the house on his

second run of the day. "Are we going to buy a fir tree for New Year's? My friend says they have a tree every year. We haven't had one in years."

"Are you going to eat trees for the holidays? Then, no. We're buying food, not trees."

"No presents for New Year's either?" Lica asked, disappointed. "We don't get presents anymore."

"What are you complaining about?" Mariana snapped. "Your mother bought you new shoes and clothes for school."

"Yeah, but those aren't presents, and that was in, like, September." At an attempt to look serious, he crossed his arms.

A long sudden ring on the home phone interrupted our conversation.

"Pick up!" Mariana jumped. "That's probably Mom from Greece. What if she's sending us presents?" Apparently presents hadn't escaped her mind either.

"Irina." I heard an unmistakable loud, deep voice in the receiver. I looked at Mariana, shook my head, and whispered, "It's not Mom."

"It's Vasily Gramovich," Vasily yelled in my ear.

"I recognized you. My God, how long has it been? Six months?"

"Something like that. I just decided to call you to wish you and your family a happy New Year!"

"It's a little early for New Year's congratulations, but thank you, that's very nice of you." I was skeptical that this call was about a holiday. "What's going on? How's your business coming?"

"That's the other reason I called you. God works in mysterious ways, and *Moş Crăciun* finally got lost in our city and dropped some presents for Christmas in my neighborhood."

"Are you drunk?" I asked, unable to hold my laughter.

"Drunk with happiness! Tomorrow I'm going to rent an office for my new business. It's on the first floor of the building where my mother-in-law lives in the center of the city. Some people were renting it before, but their business went up in flames. Nobody is renting office space in the winter, so I got a heck of a deal. Do you want to come tomorrow to see it? I'm also hiring the other girl, Tatiana. She'll be there tomorrow too."

"My God, every other girl in the city is called Tatiana. Do you really need two people for a business that's not even open?"

"I know, it's stupid, but as I said, Victor needs his secretary. Come and see the office tomorrow."

* * *

To call the empty room with two desks and two chairs "an office" was quite a stretch. The room was unheated and dark, with small windows, and some dusty, old yellowish curtains hanging on a thread. The wooden floors were annoyingly squeaky and bouncy, as if they were about to give in and open a hole under our feet.

"It smells like mold," Tatiana, the other future secretary, said, and shrugged. We had just become acquainted. She was tall and skinny in a light winter coat.

"It's actually the condensation on the windows that smells like that. Once the room heats up, the smell will go away," Vasily said, and moved across the room, as if he was a house inspector. "Oh, Shura! What are you doing here?" he yelled in surprise when he saw a woman in her late forties walk in.

She wore a thick brown leather coat, a long black wool skirt, and a white winter scarf wrapped around her head and neck. She was carrying a see-through bag with groceries in her right hand and a big black purse with worn corners on her left shoulder, like a classic Russian housewife.

"I went to see Mom upstairs and decided to stop by and check out the office. Is that all right with you?" Shura asked Vasily, though it was clear to everyone, she was not asking for permission.

"Irina, Tatiana, get acquainted. That's my wife Shura." Shura nodded, looking at us, perhaps trying to gauge if she could take us both down with one hand.

"Nice to meet you," Tatiana answered for both of us, then turned to me, rolling her eyes as if saying, "God help us all." I smiled back without saying anything.

Shura unceremoniously walked across the room. "I brought some new curtains to hang in the windows," she said. "One of you come help me."

I took the bullet for both of us this time and went to help Shura, while Tatiana stayed behind to ask questions.

"I see only a typing machine in here. Will there be a computer in the office?" Tatiana asked.

"Typing machine is fine with me," I interjected. "I worked as a telegraph operator at the airport before, so I can type very well. I haven't used computers that much."

Vasily coughed. "Eventually, we'll have a computer in the office. When we get all settled in … in a month or two."

"Will we be able to use the computer, like for e-mails and such?" I asked, intrigued.

"I don't know if there is going to be much e-mailing going on. People will probably call, so we need you to answer the phones for now."

"So, is that official then? When will the business open?" When I asked these questions, Shura smirked and looked at her husband. I walked away from her and her curtains. "You see, I can't quit my day care job, which is crappy but stable, for something that may not work out."

"Everything will be okay," Vasily dismissed my worries. I looked at Tatiana, but she, too, seemed unconvinced.

"This enterprise is as certain as my online dating," I whispered into her ear.

"Oh yeah? I've heard a lot of women are doing this online thing nowadays. What's his name? The online man, I mean."

"The frontrunner right now is David from America. We'll see if he can last to the end of the week."

Tatiana giggled. "Looks like this David of yours is more of a certain deal than this job."

"He's not mine yet, but we're working on it," I answered. "Well," I said, louder now, figuring that we were done, "let me know when you officially open for business, Vasily. I have to go now."

* * *

On Monday after work, I took the bus to the dating agency to get my correspondence. To my surprise, I had two letters from David. *Oh, he must have missed me!* I smiled. The first letter was dated December 8, 2000. It said: "Your letter touched my heart. I asked myself: Is she the one?" *Really? I didn't scare him off yet?* "But I must tell you now. I'm a diabetic. Due to complications, my toes were amputated, so I lost half of the bottom of my right foot. I'm not crippled, and I can walk, but it hurts sometimes. I have some other health complications too. If you can deal with that, then we can move forward." I paused, as if trying to catch my breath after a bucket of cold water had been dumped on my head. I reread the letter slowly. *Wow, the hee-hee, hah-hah time is over.* I imagined how I'd feel if that were me, having a disease that I had to disclose, worried that someone would toss me aside because of it. I didn't know much about diabetes, but the half-lost foot seemed very serious.

"You are a very desirable and voluptuous woman," he continued, "and I have fantasized about being with you, and I believe we met for a reason, but I had to tell you the truth. I'll wait anxiously for your response, dear. David."

I needed a moment to think, but my hand instinctively took

the second letter to read. This one was sent on December eleventh. "It has been an agonizing three days since I've heard from you," it said. "Is everything okay? Please e-mail me. Unless you are not interested in me any longer. Dave."

My heart sank. A vivid image of David checking his e-mail inbox for my messages for three days popped into my head. But nothing was there for him day after day. *He must think that I'm just a heartless bimbo.*

Overwhelmed with emotions, I sat down and wrote: "David, dear. Please don't worry if I don't write you for a long period of time. I have no access to a computer, so I can only answer through the bureau, which is not open during the weekends. Also, don't forget about the time difference." I took a moment, then continued.

"You may trust me. Please don't be angry, and excuse me for the delay in my answer. Now I can say: Thank you for your heartfelt and sincere letter. If something is wrong, I will tell you at once, but now I'm fine and looking forward to your answer." I didn't know what else to say.

"Did you bring your kids' pictures?" Leonid asked, seeing me wrestling with the keyboard: typing a line, then deleting it, then typing it again. "Let me scan them. We'll attach them to your letter."

"I don't know if today's the right day for shoving my kids down his throat. We're kinda in the middle of a dilemma right now."

"This is how we separate the seeds from the weeds," Leonid said. "If all the man wants is you, but not you as a package with your kids, then there will be no more dilemma. You'll know what to do."

"You need to be a psychologist, not a dating expert," I said to Leonid and gave him two photos to scan.

"One doesn't exclude the other," Leonid said, very proud of himself.

I went back to my computer to finish my message to David:

"I'm sending you the photos of my children. The first photo is from my daughter's birthday, that's why she has flowers in her hands. In the second photo they are in their granny's garden. Take care of yourself. Goodbye."

I paused to reread my message. It seemed dry and awkward, but I didn't want to give him too much hope, because I didn't know how I felt about David's missing half foot. At least, he needed to hear that he was not abandoned.

* * *

I barely slept that night. I couldn't wait for Tuesday to come, and for work to end so I could get to the agency. There was a new e-mail, sent on December twelfth. "Your children are beautiful, you are beautiful. I think we're on the way to being a family," David wrote. "I'm trying to put some money away so I can visit after the first of the year. Maybe you could show me around the city, and I can spend a couple of days there. And if it all works out, you and your babies can come to the States with me. That would be a dream come true." *What? Was he serious?*

"Okay, more about me. I used to play all sports: soccer, volleyball, football, baseball, and basketball. I have also coached them all. I like movies, music, dining in and out, and crave family outings, family drives, trips to the beach, you name it. I like to play bingo, cards, and board games."

I was learning so much about him, and his willingness to share was refreshing. I wanted more, so I kept reading.

"My family is large: two brothers and two sisters, five nieces and one nephew, plus their spouses and their kids, a total of twenty-six and climbing. My family is very accepting, and all the kids get taken care of at Christmas. The adults don't buy for each other, except for husband and wife. I have no love to buy for, or to buy for me this year. I am so lonely, but my heart sings at the possibility of having you and your children here with me.

"I have a dog, his name is Teddy Bear, nicknamed Ted. He's a miniature schipperke but is built like a toy bear cub. He's jet-black, purebred, very playful, and the smartest dog I have ever seen. He loves kids and playing fetch. I hope to hear from you real soon. Kiss the children for me and keep hope close to your heart. David."

I sat down to absorb all of this. *I guess that answers the question about me and the kids as a package. But who proposes marriage first, then describes himself and his family later? However, if all of this is true, he seems to have a lively big family. I wouldn't mind being a part of that. Oh, David, David, what am I going to do with you?*

"What the hell is bingo?" I asked.

"It's kinda like a lottery or a game of guessing numbers, or something like that," Leonid said.

"Lottery, huh? Did I just draw the lucky number or something?"

Chapter 14

All Sorts of Presents

A week later, David seemed exuberant in his next letter: "Thank you for sending me your phone number. Do you know the Moldova code? If not, I'll figure it out and call you soon. SEND ME YOUR ADDRESS."

"Leonid, he's asking me for my address." I showed him David's letter.

Leonid read the rest of the line. "To send Christmas presents for the kids. How considerate."

"You're missing the point. He's asking me for my *physical* address. I've only known him for a month."

"What's your concern? Do you think he might show up at your door? He's thousands of kilometers away."

"He might fly in. He said he was looking into plane fares."

"What are the other men writing you?"

"They're still at 'how are you?' and 'gorgeous eyes.'"

"There's your answer. It's better to have a sparrow in your hands than two storks in the sky."

"You and your proverbs!" I laughed, but Leonid, as usual, had a point.

Nevertheless, I felt that David was setting things in motion at lightning speed, as if he was in a hurry. *In a hurry for what? Is it normal for American men to date women like this? You tell me what you want, I tell you what I want. Nobody wastes each other's time.* I didn't know.

Know-it-all Leonid was at a loss this time, too, and each woman at the dating agency had her own opinion. Sonya thought it was just perfect to move things along fast. She was on her third attempt in the last six months to start a serious relationship, so if a man was dragging his feet at the end of the first month, she tossed him to the curb and moved on to the next one. Valeria, on the other hand, hated being rushed.

But then the hard-nosed, picky Alyona arrived the next day with bombshell news: "Ladies, you won't believe this! My twenty-eight-year-old, hot online boyfriend from the Netherlands, Alexander, flew in over the weekend and *ta-da!*" She put forward her left hand, showing off a platinum ring with three diamonds on her middle finger.

"That's a nice present!" Leonid took Alyona's hand for a closer look.

"That's actually an engagement ring," she said. "I wear it on my middle finger because it's too wide. He couldn't guess my ring size, and I don't want to lose it."

"Get out of here! You only started talking to him like, what, three months ago?"

"I know, but if you'd met him, you'd want to marry him too. He's built like a god, and the sex was a-mmm-aaa-zing!"

"Too much information!" Leonid pushed her hand away.

I went to bed late the day Alyona came to the office with her ring. I closed my eyes, but I couldn't sleep, replaying the last few days in my head, weighing all the pros and cons of what was happening. I closed my eyes and smiled, recalling Leonid's frowning face when he pushed away Alyona's hand. He could be so dramatic at times. His face flew away in the clouds, floating in the air, making a funny noise with his lips like an annoying phone ring…*zzz-zzz-zzz!*

"What are you doing, Leonid?" I asked him.

"Pick up the phone, Irina, pick up the phone!" he yelled from the clouds.

Am I dreaming, or is this real? I jumped out of bed, following the noise, stepping on Serghei who was sleeping on the floor next to his sister. He *mmm*-ed unhappily. I pulled back, then stepped over both of them to pick up the receiver.

"Alyo!"

"Hello!" somebody said on the other end, in perfect English in a raspy voice. "Is that Ai-Ree-Na?" I didn't recognize my name. Nobody had ever called me Ai-ree-na before.

"Da, Irina (Ee-ree-na)," I answered in Romanian, at the same time correcting my name. "Who's this?" I switched to English, but the minute I spoke, it dawned on me who it might be.

"It's David…from America."

"Ah." I finally opened my eyes wide and looked at the clock. *Three in the morning?* "Nice to meet you. Oy, nice to hear you." I was shuffling through my memory for English words to answer, but at this time of night, they were hard to come by.

"How are you?" he asked, sounding unsure.

"Mom, who's that?" Lica stuck her head out of her blanket.

"Go back to sleep," I whispered to her, then returned to David. "I'm okay, it's just three a.m. here," I said, finally forming an entire sentence in English.

"Oh, I'm so sorry. I must have calculated the time difference wrong. I thought I'd call to talk about the trip that I'm planning to see you."

"What?" I asked, a little confused by so many English words in such a rapid succession.

"Maybe it's not a very good time. I'll talk to you later?" David said, baffled. I was sure that our conversation was not going as he'd imagined it.

"Okay," I answered, trying to buy some time to translate what he'd just said, but David hung up before I finished my thought. *Great first impression!* I dropped the receiver on the hook in frustration.

* * *

When I checked my e-mail the next day, I was greeted with little patience from David.

"You didn't sound so enthusiastic when I called," David wrote me. *No, shit!* I almost said it out loud while reading his e-mail. *What part of "it's three a.m. here" didn't he understand?*

But I wrote back calmly: "I wanted to say so much last night." I paused for a minute. *What do you say to a man you know only through letters?* "I would be happy to see you here, to touch you, to kiss you, to feel that you are real. It will be the best present if you come to visit for New Year's. We have great traditions in my country for this season. Kids go to people's houses and sing and wish them a good new year, and they throw wheat at them, which is supposed to bring lots of money and happiness. The people are supposed to pay something in return with candy and cookies and money. It's an old and silly tradition, but it's fun."

I wanted to include something personal with this one, if only to make him more comfortable and to show that I was serious. "Leonid, can you scan these two photos with the kids for me? And one more studio photo. I think it's time," I told him, choosing from the photos that he put the kibosh on last time. I was betting that David would love this one, where I was sitting on the floor with my right leg stretched in front of me with the left leg crossed over. My long hair was pulled back, almost touching my butt. I had a bright, happy smile.

"As you wish," Leonid answered.

"Ira, Ira," Mariana yelled when I came home. "David called you two times already, but all we could say in English was: "Irina not home."

"Did he say when he's going to call back?"

"I don't know. I don't speak English. It's ringing, it's ringing, that's him again," she screamed when the phone rang all of a sudden.

"I'm so glad to hear your voice," David said to me when I picked up the phone. You could tell he was happy by the way he emphasized each word. I smiled and looked at Mariana and Lica, who were standing right in front of me with their eyes and ears wide open.

"Get out of here." I waved at them with my hand.

"We don't speak English, remember?" Mariana whispered back.

"Get out of here. You're making me nervous." I saw them off with my eyes, while they were walking away unwillingly, making faces on their way out.

"I'm glad to hear … from you … too …" I said, interrupted by the smack of the door behind me. Serghei walked into the house with his schoolbag on his shoulders with a huge hole in the bottom of it.

"Sereoja!" I almost didn't recognize my voice. "What the hell happened to your *potfeli?*" He turned around to see, without taking off his schoolbag, just like a little dog chasing his tail. "Take it off and look!"

"What's going on? Tell me." I heard David's impatient voice.

"Well, my son has a big hole in his rucksack, which wasn't there when he left in the morning." David started laughing with a huge hearty belly laugh.

Lica marched in from the other room. "You used your *portfeli* to slide down that icy patch at school, didn't you?"

Mariana followed her. "Oh, my God!" she said. "Look, your notebooks! They're all wet. And your pens are falling out."

"Is he in trouble?" David asked, continuing to laugh. He didn't understand a word of our conversation, but it wasn't too hard to pick up the clues from our tone.

"Why are you laughing?" I asked David, annoyed. But his laugh was disarming and infectious. I even stopped being angry for a while. "I know it's funny for you. But he'll have to use this"—I was looking for a horrible English word to describe it—"till the end of the year. I'm not buying him a new rucksack."

"Oh, that's harsh." David stopped laughing for a few seconds, but he couldn't contain himself for long and burst into laughter again. "Looks like you have a full house. Is there a better time to call you?"

"It's always a full house around here. No difference to me."

"Well, I want to ask you something. What would you personally like as a present?"

"The best present for me will be for you to be here for the holidays."

"Aw-aw-aw, honey, you'll make me cry."

"Happy tears, I hope? But isn't it expensive to mail presents from America? Maybe you should wait until you come here and bring them in person."

"I still want to send you something for the holidays. Is it okay if I send you some presents from Victoria's Secret?"

"Victoria what?" I asked, but I couldn't hear what he said. Lica was trying to get my attention, pulling down on my hand.

"Can I tell David something? I learned it on TV today," she said.

"Hold on, David. Angelica wants to say something." I tentatively handed her the phone.

"David, I love you!" she yelled.

I could hear David gasp for air. "I love you too," he said.

Lica giggled, satisfied, and gave the receiver back to me.

"Oh, my God, that's so precious. I can't tell you how much that means to me, that your daughter accepts me. She is so adorable. I will be shipping presents soon—to all of you."

"You don't have to, but thank you!" I said in the end.

"The phone call, your letter, and your pictures made me so happy today," David wrote in his next letter. "I cannot imagine the happiness I will feel when I am holding you in my arms. My heart sings with passion for you, darling. We think so alike, you and I.

And your children are so beautiful. I can't wait to meet them. To give your daughter a big hug and a kiss on her forehead for what she said today, and hug and shake hands with your son. That will be the best present for me.

"Right now, it doesn't look like I can make it there by New Year's Day. But once I have the money, I'll be there. I have very serious intentions, darling. I have faith in my heart and in the Lord that we will be together AS A FAMILY!!! (I'm so excited!)

"I will ship the presents today for you and the kids. Hopefully they'll make it there by Christmas."

It was the twenty-second of December. I had no idea why David would think that his international package would make it to us by Christmas. There was little hope that it would even make it here by New Year's. But three days later, I found a bright orange notice in the crack of my door.

"You received a parcel from the United States. You can pick it up at the Central Post Office." *David must have paid for the priority shipping. He's racking up the good points!*

"What's the value of this parcel?" The post office worker, a lady in her late forties with a tight bun of gray hair and smudged make-up on her tired face asked me.

"I don't know. It's a present."

"What kind of present?"

"I don't know. People don't typically telegraph you when they send you presents."

"We need the value of the contents because you have to pay the import tax."

"I've never heard of such a tax before, and I used to work in the post office at the airport several years ago."

"Well, a lot has changed since then. I'm not here to argue with you, lady. You are not the first who has complained about it. You either tell me the value, or I'll charge you the base tax of fifty leis."

"Five dollars for this? I could buy the damn presents here for less money. I have only twenty leis on me right now. You will have to send it back, then. I can't pay for it."

"Somebody needs to pay for it to send it back. America is not around the corner, you know."

No shit! "What kind of a deal is that? I have to pay so I don't get my presents? You'll have to figure out who's going to pay for return shipping because it's not going to be me!"

"We can open it and see if the value is less than one hundred leis, then the tax will be less." She rolled her eyes, but her voice was level. This was clearly a conversation she'd had several times before.

"Do you have a price list for American products?" The woman gave me the look, then turned around, took the letter opener off the counter behind her and poked a hole in the box with a sadistic pleasure. She brought to light a dark-green cloth schoolbag. It was big, with large black straps, and a huge pocket in front and two side pockets. So American! *I'll be damned, Serghei. Looks like David took pity on you!* The postal worker pulled a white plush bear out next. It had a giant red plush heart in its paws with the words "I love you!" So out of place in the hands of a lady with a knife. *That's for Angelica, I assume.*

"What's this?" the lady asked, showing me a pink bag wrapped tightly with tape across it. "It says Victoria's Secret."

"I don't know, but if I knew I'd have to pay fifty leis for these, I would have said I don't need this."

"I'll write you a receipt for twenty leis, and you can take this home." I knew what Leonid would say, "It's the thought that counts," but I was pissed. *I have to pay ransom for some silly presents!*

The kids opened the door as soon as they heard me coming up the stairs, as if they had been guarding it the whole time.

"Can we see the presents? Can we see the presents?" Lica, Serghei, and Mariana were shouting, interrupting each other.

"Can I get in the house first?" I asked them, though nobody was listening. Mariana yanked the bag out of my hands and ran into the room to open it. I stayed behind to take my shoes off and hang up my coat.

"Oh, *kruto*, a schoolbag," I heard Serghei say. "Look how many pockets it has. Thank you, David."

"I want the bear," Angelica jumped in.

"No, I want the bear," Serghei jumped right back in. "You can have the schoolbag."

"The bag is for you. Remember, you got a hole in yours?"

"Foo-oo-oo! What is this?" Mariana shouted with an undertone of disgust.

"Foo-oo-oo!" I heard Serghei saying it too. I rushed into the room to see what the fuss was about. Mariana had already ripped the pink package and was holding a pair of lacy black underpants in her hands and a lacy see-through lingerie top.

"Mom, what were you talking to David about?" Lica asked suspiciously.

"Not about this stuff!" I grabbed the lingerie out of Mariana's hands. "He asked me if it was okay to send me some Victoria store items. I thought he was talking about a clothes brand. What the fuck is Victoria's Secret?"

"Mom!" Serghei pulled my hand. "No cursing!"

"Sorry! Your mother doesn't look like a role model right now!"

"I love my present!" Lica said, hugging her bear. "It's very nice of David to send us presents at all. He doesn't even know us."

"Yes, it's nice that he sent us presents. I just wish they'd been more practical. I wouldn't have picked a white toy. The white plush will get dirty so fast. I don't know if we can even wash white plush without ruining it."

"Yeah, these presents are not very practical," Mariana agreed. "Why do they make schoolbags out of cloth in America? Serghei will stain this cloth bag in a week, and the rain will go right through it. Don't they have leather in America?"

"Oh, look what I found at the bottom of the parcel!" Lica lifted up a middle-sized, bright-red bag of Maybelline makeup.

"Oh! I'm so glad the post office lady didn't see that. Then I would have definitely been screwed."

"That's for me, that's for me!" Mariana claimed it right away.

"That's for all the girls, not only for you, for Mom too." Lica hid the makeup bag behind her back.

"All right, all right, but let's have some fun first, shall we?" Mariana was suggesting some mischief, no doubt.

She grabbed the tube of mascara out of the Maybelline bag. Masterfully, like Picasso, she brushed a few strokes on her eyelashes. She took the giant black brush with a long handle and dumped a layer of blush powder on her face. Then dropped a thick layer of brown shadow on her eyelids and around her eyes. *Why?* That made her look like a raccoon-geisha who had too much makeup on her face. To finish off the look, she added the juicy red lipstick and rubbed her lips against each other to give them shine. *Oh, Mother of Christ!* But she wasn't done. She put on the black lacy lingerie on top of her T-shirt, then pulled up the black underwear over her shorts. "Do I look sexy?" She made a circle around the room, shaking her hips like an underwear model.

"For God's sake, take this off!" Lica and I yelled at the same time. Serghei, on the other hand, was dying laughing. David was way off in guessing my size. This thing would be loose on me, like on a scarecrow. *Did he wish for a plumper woman, maybe?* On Mariana, however, it looked even baggier. The black spaghetti straps fell off her right shoulder, hanging off her like an expensive, useless rag. The panties were flopping around her thighs like two black mini parachutes.

Mariana made a few rounds around the house, then took off

the lacy top slowly, like a striptease dancer, and threw it towards the bed. Serghei jumped and picked it up in midair, wore it on his head and started running around the room in circles. "Do I look sexy? Do I look sexy?" He repeated it over and over.

"Enough! Put that thing away!" I yelled at everybody at once. "We are a House of the Absurd! If poor David could see what we've done with his presents! What a waste! I could have used my money for food instead." I looked at Mariana. "What am I going to do with Davidushka?"

"Look at the bright side," Mariana said. "Serghei needed a schoolbag, and now he has one. Lica got a cool present, an American toy that no one around here has. The neighborhood kids will be jealous for years. And I got makeup."

"And what did I get?" I pointed at the pile of lacy disgrace on the floor.

"You got a man who has potential. He paid for expedited shipping to get the presents to us before New Year's. That counts for something. Have you ever had a man like that in your life?"

"No, I have not. He's definitely one of a kind." An unexpected call made us all jump.

"That's probably David, checking to see if we got his presents. Or maybe it's Moş Crăciun bringing us more presents for Christmas?" Mariana ran to pick up the phone. "Alyo! Mama? Aha, aha. That's the best present ever!" she yelled as loud as she could. "Mama's coming home! Mama's coming home!" Mariana was dancing in the hallway. I grabbed the phone out of her hand.

"Mom, are you coming home for New Year's? Will they let you back into Greece, considering you were without status there?"

"I doubt they will, since I overstayed my visa like four years ago, but I don't care. I'm coming home for good. I'm tired of working here. I've got plenty of money saved. About four thousand dollars, which should be enough for about four or five years."

"Mom, that wouldn't last you a year. The prices have changed a lot since you left."

"It can't be so bad."

"I'm glad you're coming home, Mom, but I'm telling you, it's bad."

"I've made up my mind. I want to be home for my birthday in February. I already bought the tickets, so I'll be home by the end of the week."

This was sudden, to say the least, but when my mother made up her mind, it was rarely changed.

"Isn't it great that Mom's coming home?" Mariana yelled in my ear when I put the phone down. "And she's bringing presents for everybody!"

"Grandma's coming home, Grandma's coming home!" Serghei and Lica chanted. They held hands and started running in circles. "And she's bringing presents, and she's bringing presents!"

"Hallelujah! What a great surprise!" Mariana clapped.

"Yeah, what a great surprise," I answered slowly, trying to process the news. "Mama's going to get the surprise, all right. I know our mother. She won't be able to stay still. She'll get tired of our poverty soon and will want to go back."

"I don't care. I haven't seen Mom in five years. I miss her. Are you going to tell Mom about David?" Mariana asked.

"Not yet. I'll wait until he buys the plane tickets. You know our mom, the eternal pessimist. Just give her one small reason and she'll doubt the shit out of everything. If this thing with David turns out to be a dud, it's better if she doesn't know about it." I sighed. "Or I'll never hear the end of it."

It seemed that we lived in a state of limbo in between the phone calls when, for months at a time, nothing was happening. And only the phone calls were changing the course of our lives. They were bringing joy, or heartbreak, or presents, but nothing was the same before and after.

Chapter 15

The Return of the Matriarch

I was at work the day Mom was going to arrive from Greece, nervously flipping through different scenarios, not knowing what to expect from Mom's return. Mariana, on the other hand, took matters into her own hands and called her father. After fifteen minutes of relentless "No, no, no" from him, and "Please, please, please" from her, he finally gave in and said he'd take Mariana with him to the airport to pick up our mother. He had a new car, used, but in good shape and surprisingly clean. He always treated his cars better than humans, but today I was not going to make any comments. At least our mom would ride in comfort that she was not usually accustomed to.

When I got home from work, I found our mother in her usual place, as if she'd never left—in the kitchen, surrounded by the aroma of steaming chicken soup on the stovetop.

"Welcome home!" I said. She smiled and kissed me twice, once on each cheek. "That's new. Since when you do kiss your adult children? And aren't there supposed to be three kisses, according to Orthodox tradition?"

"Yeah, but in Europe they kiss only twice, so I got used to it." She giggled. Her voice was different than I remembered, softer, more reserved. She'd aged; the brown spots under her eyes had become darker, but her short auburn hair had very little gray.

"How come you have less gray hair than I do?" I was amazed. "Darn Babushka Veta's genes. They went to you but bailed on me!"

"You take after your father," Mama said. "Stubborn like him too."

"Hey, you just got home. Save your criticism for after dinner!" I looked at the tiny kitchen table covered with plates of endless courses. "How many dishes are you cooking here?"

"I thought I'd make some chicken noodle soup with home-made noodles. The Greeks don't like hot soups. It's too warm there year round, so they eat it cold. Yuk! But then I got carried away. Especially because I got to cut the vegetables for the salad in thin slices. Greeks just chop everything in big pieces. You almost choke on it when you eat. Ridiculous." She always got carried away when she talked about food, but now she added a Greek drama component to it.

Once a chef, always a chef. I looked at the plates on the table one more time. Lately, I had become a master at cooking meals out of nothing, but my mother was a master-chef of making food art out of nothing.

"Mama, look what Babushka Katya made." Lica showed me some boiled eggs that looked like piglets with ears and noses cut out of bright-orange boiled carrots with two black peppercorns instead of eyes. The eggs were bathing in some cheap yellowish mayonnaise, sprinkled with thin-cut green dill. "Look how she arranged the *kolbasa* in a circle and made a rose out of a tomato, and these parsley leaves look like real rose leaves. So pretty."

Serghei pushed the piglets with his finger, as if testing if they could break. "I almost don't want to eat them because they look alive," he said.

"I'm sure you won't have a problem eating any of them once you get hungry. You are your mother's son," I joked. My mother laughed out loud, as if she finally got to let out whatever she'd been keeping inside for a long while.

"Let's sit down and eat," she invited us. We all cuddled in the small kitchen like the old times, elbow to elbow.

"Mmm," Mariana said, slurping chicken soup broth. "It's so delicious. Ira, how come we could never make it taste so good?"

"It's magic!" Mama smiled, enjoying the moment. We couldn't tell if she liked the compliment or the fact that we were enjoying her soup.

"So, Mama, how do you feel being home?" Mariana asked.

"It's something. I didn't expect to find my old apartment in such bad shape. The wallpaper is all worn out and outdated; the paint on the doors is chipped; the kitchen ceiling is yellow."

"The ceiling is yellow because we've had to use the gas oven for heat every winter since the central heating was turned off by the city," Mariana explained.

"And the last time the old apartment was painted was two years before you left, which makes it seven years without any remodeling. It's just regular wear and tear." I said my piece.

"But even this apartment. Yes, it looks much better after Baba Era, but this wallpaper that you used is not the best quality. It looks cheap and outdated. But that's okay, we are going to fix that. Once the spring comes, we'll repaint, change the wallpaper for something modern." Our mother was making her big plans without pausing to eat in between.

"Will we get one more bed too? It's kinda cramped to sleep with Serghei on the same sofa," Lica said. "He kicks at night."

"We'll look into that." Babushka Katya smiled, and Angelica clapped, all excited.

"So, Mom, did you find a boyfriend in Greece?" Mariana asked.

"What kind of question is that?" Mama blushed.

"Just a regular, normal question," I answered for Mariana.

"I didn't go to Greece to find boyfriends. I was there to make money," she snapped at me.

"One should not exclude another. You are an unmarried woman, still good-looking, and we are adult kids. We can handle this."

Mama dropped her spoon in her bowl, pretending to be busy stirring the soup. "The Soviet times are over. Parents can talk to their kids about their love life, Mom," I pressed on.

"Really? My parents never talked to me about that."

"Come on, come on, come on, don't be shy. What's his name?" Mariana poked her on the side.

"Nicolas," she finally answered, hiding her eyes.

"Oh, our mama is a sex machine!" Mariana cheered her on.

"I'm not telling you nothing!" Mama shouted back.

"Come on, show us his picture!" Mariana insisted. Mama cracked a crooked smile, then turned around to reach for her purse.

"How come you get your way with both your parents, Mariana?" I pointed my finger at my baby sister. "Mom never listens to me unless you join in."

"Because I'm the youngest, and the adorable one!" Mariana smiled mischievously.

"Here." Mom brought out the picture of Nicolas, a man in his late sixties with gray hair, dark skin, and big brown eyes.

"Mama got a hot boyfriend!" Mariana giggled.

Mama lifted her head up and shook her hips. "I can still do it, you know." We all, even the kids, burst into laughter.

"I, on the other hand, have no time for boyfriends while I'm going to school," Mariana said, looking at Nicolas's picture one more time. Then she tilted her head toward Mom, signaling a question with the corner of her eye: *Do you want to tell her?*

I shook my head: *No.* She looked at me conspiratorially, but didn't say anything. The two of us, the sisters, would have to keep my secret a little longer.

The evening blended into night before we even noticed. It was time to leave all our conversations for tomorrow. The minute Mama put her head on the pillow, she was gone. I dropped on the bed next to her, only then realizing I should have probably been more careful. We would be sleeping together on the same folding *divan* for the foreseeable future. I looked with envy at Mom, who was sleeping next to me so peacefully as I kept tossing and turning, unable to fall asleep.

A reflection from a bleak streetlight was coming through the balcony window, casting ghost-like shadows that played on the walls of the pitch-dark room. It was a little spooky. It reminded me of the summer after my father passed away, and our mom was making her trips to Babushka Veta's on the weekends for food supplies (just like I was making them now, so many years later). She was leaving us at home alone in our old village house in the care of a neighbor. Our caretaker, an old, obese lady, would fall asleep in the armchair every time, with her mouth wide open, looking lifeless in the dark corner. I was six years old, but my father's recent death, happening so suddenly, had made me aware of human mortality.

"Vitalic, let's check out if the old lady's breathing," I had said, then shook my three-year-old brother on one of those weekends. He mumbled, unwilling to get up. I shook him again. "Come with me!" I grabbed his arm and pulled him out of bed. We tiptoed closer to the armchair, and I put my ear as close to her mouth as I could, trying to listen in.

"What if she's dead?" my brother whispered.

"I don't know. We would probably have to wait until morning and then go for help."

"She's scary."

"Dead people can't hurt you. They're already dead. Remember when Papa was lying in his coffin? He wasn't scary, he was just dead." I picked a white goose feather from the table, which I had been playing with earlier, pretending to write on paper, like in the movies. I tickled the old lady's nose with it. She sneezed, and we ran to hide under the covers, relieved that she was alive. We could finally go to sleep in peace. But later that night, my brother woke me up.

"I wanna pee."

"Go pee in your potty."

"I can't find it."

I dropped my feet down from the bed and looked in the corner. *Why wasn't the old lady looking for the potty? Can't she hear him?* But I couldn't see the old lady in the corner or on the bed next to us. I rubbed my eyes, letting them adjust to the dark, then ran to the switch to turn the lights on. The old lady was nowhere to be found.

"She left us alone in our dark, dark house? Oh, I'm so telling Mom about this!" I said, but my brother was jumping from one foot to another, trying to hold it in. I walked into the kitchen and picked up a wax candle and a pack of matches.

"Let's go to the outhouse." I lit the candle once we got to the porch, but the wind blew it out immediately. "Hold on to my pajamas," I told my brother.

I lit the candle again and put my left palm around it, protecting it from the breeze. We moved slowly like a two-car train around the corner, along the wall, walking on the long stretch of *prispa*, an old traditional-style porch with a clay floor that went around the house and was covered by a roof held up by wooden poles. It had brown wooden half-walls just a little taller than my shoulders, but good enough to shield us, though the wind was still sneaking through the columns, trying to kill the light of my candle at every move. But my candle was fighting it bravely, and the bright flames were defiantly playing in my palm, teasing the wind like a tongue stuck out of a child's mouth: "Nana-nana-nana!" But its defiance was short lived. As soon as the prispa's walls ended, the candle became helpless, unable to withstand the pressure of the open yard, and it kept dying on me, until I burned all my matches.

"You will have to pee here in the dirt. We are not going in the back yard for this," I said decisively, looking at the black night staring at us.

"Ps-s-s !" I heard my brother's stream of pee going into the dirt, that was slowly turning into an annoying, loud "bz-z-z-z!" The sound was becoming louder and more insistent. "Bz-z-z-z! Bz-z-z-z!"

"Pick up the phone!" I heard Mom next to me.

What is she doing here? She's supposed to be at Grandma's? But her voice kept coming at me. "Pick up the phone!"

I jumped off my bed, disoriented for a minute. *Am I still dreaming? Yes? No?*

"Where are the matches?" I asked her for some reason, looking for the switch of the miniature nightstand lamp that was next to the phone on the other side of the room.

"What matches?" Mom jumped off the bed too. "Are you hallucinating?"

"Hello!" I said in English when I picked up the receiver. I knew it was David. *Who else?*

"Hello!" David answered cheerfully.

"It's one a.m. here," I said in a sleepy, tired voice.

"No way!" He was genuinely surprised.

Seriously? He's still confused about the time difference?

"I was just calling to see if you got the presents."

"Yes, we did. Thank you."

"Did you like the lingerie I sent you?" David asked very playfully. I looked at Mom. Even in the dark I could see her spooked, angry face.

"No, it's too big." I cut it short.

"You don't like it because it's too big, or you don't like it at all?"

"David, my mom just arrived from Greece tonight, and we are sleeping in the same room, so I can't talk to you right now."

"Oh, say hello to your mom. Did you tell her about me?"

"Well, she knows about you now," I answered impatiently. David laughed with a loud deep rumble.

"Good night, honey. Talk to you tomorrow."

I turned around slowly, awaiting Mom's reaction. She was sitting at the edge of the bed with her hands on her hips. "What man calls you in the middle of the night?"

"His name is David."

"Nice! You're now dating foreigners? Why are you talking in English? So I can't understand you?"

"No. Because that's the only language he can speak."

"Why is he calling you so late? Does he want you for the night or something?"

"He's calling from America. It's really hard to ship me over there for the night."

"What do you mean from America? Where did you meet? Here?"

"No. We haven't seen each other yet."

"How do you know each other, then, if you didn't see each other?"

"We met on the Internet."

"What do you mean 'on the Internet'? How can you meet somebody on the Internet? Like, on the computer? We don't even have a computer at home. How is this possible?"

"You don't have to have a computer at home. You can use any computer to get online, as long you have an e-mail address."

"So they send you letters at your home address without a computer at home? How do you get the letters then?"

"How do I explain this to you?" I started pacing around the room. "There is a system that's called the Internet, like a widespread net of wires around the world." I spread my arms wide, showing how that might look. "If you create your own address from whatever combination of words you want with a provider's name at the end, like 'yahoo,' for example." I was choosing my words carefully, looking at Mom's reaction, trying to figure out if she was still with me. "Then you can communicate with another person who has an e-mail address anywhere in the world. It only takes minutes to get a letter from one end of the world to another."

"This is crazy!" She threw her frustration back at me, clearly not understanding any of this.

"I know. It opens opportunities we never had before," I said slowly, "behind the Iron Curtain."

"Where did you find a computer to get your letters?"

"I went to a dating agency."

"What? This is how you spent the money I was sending you?"

"Would you stop treating me like a child? I would not let my children starve, Mom. I'm not stupid or irresponsible! I've been taking care of all of us for the last five years by all means necessary, while working full time and going to college. Finally, the English that I studied for so long is starting to pay off. It's only smart not to let it go to waste. I took matters into my own hands, and I invested a little money in our future. Was it a risk? Yes. It's still a risk. But what's waiting for me here? You told me yourself that nobody is going to marry me because I'm a divorcee with two children. You know it better than anyone. You ended up as a single mother with three kids with no prospects in this country. And now you have a Greek boyfriend and you're happy. There are not many foreigners coming to Moldova, Mom. The only way to meet them is online."

It was hard saying the words out loud. These were thoughts I'd mostly kept to myself, so saying them to my mother felt strange.

Mom was speechless for a few minutes, then asked, "Do you even know how he looks?"

"Yeah." I turned the big switch that brightened up the room so fast it blinded both of us. I pulled out a printed page of David's photo and showed it to Mom.

"He has a kind face, but he looks big. Was he married?" she said.

"He says he's separated."

"What's separated?"

"That's English for 'divorced,' I guess."

"Does he have kids?"

"He has a son, who is his wife's, actually, but he treats him like his own because he's raised him since he was three."

"How long has this been going on?"

"For about three months."

"And you didn't tell me?"

"I didn't tell you because I don't know how this will end. Now, I guess we'll see him in person soon and judge for ourselves. He said he's saving some money for the trip to come to Moldova to see us in the next three weeks, if everything goes right."

"That's too soon! This apartment is a disaster! We wouldn't have time to remodel it! What will he think about you, and about us? That we are in the slum of the world?"

She didn't know David existed five minutes ago, and now she was worried about impressing him.

"Calm down, Mom. He's not looking to inherit my nonexistent treasures!" I caught myself using Igor's words. "I'm pretty sure he's not making a trip across the world to Moldova thinking: 'Oh, I'm getting myself a rich wife!' He didn't seem shallow. He even sent us presents last week."

"What presents?"

"You don't wanna know."

"Why?"

"Because." I felt my cheeks warm. "Why don't we talk about all of this tomorrow? Can we go to sleep now?"

Chapter 16

Reading the Tea Leaves

When I was seven, I broke a tea cup from my mom's favorite collection of white china with light-blue flowers, a shiny golden edge, and an exquisitely designed handle. It was a present that my father brought from his trip to Czechoslovakia during the height of the Cold War, when almost nobody was allowed to leave the country.

I hid my crime at the bottom of the garbage bucket and agonized about it for two days until the broken pieces were discovered, when Mom threw the garbage away. "You never listen!" Mom yelled at me while slapping me hard on the rear. I took Mom's fury with relief, because my agony was finally over. It turned out that a sore butt was much easier to handle than the constant fear of being discovered.

I felt the same relief when Mom discovered my online romance with David. Now, at least, I didn't have to hide. But just the next day, she reminded me of why I didn't want to tell her too much, too soon, in the first place.

"How serious is David, really?" she asked me out of the blue.

"He asked me to be his wife."

"Yeah, but what does that mean? He's there, and you're here."

As if I don't know that.

"There is a lot of paperwork before it can happen, Mom. He made an appointment with an immigration lawyer, so he'll know more soon. He also needs to find the money for the trip; he's not a rich man."

"Of course, out of all the Americans you found the poor one!" Mom smirked.

"Really, Mom? He sent me a copy of his driver's license and his Social Security number. He says that's a unique number that everyone in America has from birth. That sounds pretty serious to me."

"From across the ocean he can make a lot of promises that he doesn't necessarily intend to keep."

"What's his master plan then? Waste his time writing letters, sending presents, making expensive international phone calls for no reason? Or do you think he's a sadist, torturing women with promises of marriage?"

"He could be a sadist, you don't know. Everybody can be nice on the phone."

"You are accusing him of crimes he hasn't committed yet. Can you at least give him the benefit of the doubt?"

Silence.

* * *

"David didn't call you today. I wonder what happened?" she said casually a few days later, when his call patterns were interrupted by a day.

"That's because he racked up a two thousand-dollar phone bill. He said he'll have to cut down on phone calls and call me every other day now, instead of every day."

"Two thousand dollars. That's reckless! What is he thinking, spending so much money on phone calls when he doesn't have the money for the trip?" Mom was upset, as if David was spending *her* money. "With such spending habits, he'll never make it here."

I knew Mom was right, though I didn't like to admit it.

* * *

"You could save your money on phone calls if you'd just buy me a computer, the smallest and oldest computer in the world, so I could write you letters every day," I wrote in frustration in my next e-mail to David. But his reaction was like a thunderstorm in the middle of a sunny day.

"Your letter kinda left me confused. I didn't know what else to do or say. Remember I told you about a friend who was skeptical about this whole thing? He warned me about women who ask for money. He says this is a scam ... a con game. I told him that you were for real and that we'd hit it off. But he said, 'Watch and see, she'll ask you to buy her something, or ask for money.' I told him you weren't like that ... and now you send me a letter asking me to buy you a computer? Everything was going so well, but now I'm kinda concerned. I don't want to get my heart broken again. E-mail me right away. We need to fix this. Dave."

I dropped in the office chair at the dating agency, reading David's letter over and over again. Cold sweat was breaking on my forehead, though I could feel my cheeks burning. *What the hell?* I had no words. How could he come to this conclusion? Obviously, these thoughts were percolating in his head. He seemed like a strong and confident man in his letters, but apparently he had a boy's heart that flickered at the first doubt. For the first time, I saw our relationship through his eyes. He was as scared about our romantic situation as I was. "What if she is a con?" he was thinking all this time. "What if he's a sadist?" as my mom bluntly asked me yesterday. I needed a moment to process it all.

"David, darling!" I started, cautiously typing my response. "I never asked you for money. I only shared my thoughts with you. If you remember, I never asked, even once, how much you earn. Money couldn't make me happy, if we didn't love each other. If this is because of the computer, forgive me. I couldn't imagine that it would hurt you so."

I stopped for a moment, wondering how this had taken such a turn. I had to fix it. I couldn't lose him over money—it wasn't true to my character.

"I really love you, darling. I don't want to lose you because of one stupid thing. I would be the meanest human being in the world if I took advantage of your feelings. Forgive me. I was just being sincere with you. I can only imagine how you are feeling now. Believe me, please believe me." I hit send and walked out of the office in silence. There was nothing else I could do but go home and live through the next agonizing twenty-four hours before I could hear from David.

* * *

"You see, I told you he's not serious," Mom commented on David's letter.

"You never said that."

"But I meant to. He's just making excuses now."

I wanted to find a place to hide and cry, but there was nowhere to go. I dropped in the armchair in the corner, feeling the walls of our small apartment close in on me.

"You're not Cinderella," Mom kept talking, this time seemingly to herself. "You could be just sitting here, waiting for your prince on a white horse, but he might be courting other women at the same time as you. You don't know what he's doing there in America."

"He doesn't know what I'm doing here either. The point is to trust each other. Without trust, there is nothing."

"M-m-m, trust, wouldn't that be nice?"

"Have you ever thought what a risk he's taking with a woman

with two kids from a foreign country, who he knows only from phone calls and letters?"

"You are not a serial killer." Mom rolled her eyes.

"He doesn't know that for sure. He's obviously trusting me to be a decent human being."

Mom cooled off for a few moments, processing what I'd said, then added, "Let's say he takes you to America. What happens if he's not nice to you and the kids? Then what? How are you going to come back home?"

I felt like I was in the middle of the David and Goliath battle, where David, incarnated as Katerina, was throwing rocks at the giant with her sling, but every time she'd throw one, the rock would hit me.

"First things first, Mom. He needs to get here, and we will see for ourselves who he really is. I'm not a kamikaze. If he acts too weird, I wouldn't go. Or he may decide that we're too much for him and will never go through with the visa process after he goes back home. Or maybe your wish will come true and nothing will happen, because I've not heard from him for over a day."

"I never wished for him not to call you back," Mom said defensively.

"Then what are you wishing me, Mama? All I hear is that I have a bad plan. But if it's not this, then what? What are our other options? Waiting for a prince on a white horse from the neighborhood who's just dying to gallop up the stairs for me?" I barked at her.

"You just need to think about every possibility," Mom was mumbling under her breath, unwilling to let it go. "Maybe we should go to Tonia, so she can read the cards for you."

"Mom, I know that she's your friend, and you think she's a fortuneteller, but Tonia can't keep her mouth shut. The neighborhood will be full of rumors before we even have David here, so I'll pass. Besides, I don't need a fortuneteller! What if she tells me some crazy shit like 'the king of hearts is going to be the death of you'? Am I just going to abort the entire operation because of some fortune-telling?"

"She drew the cards for me many times before, and most of it came true."

"Most of it would have come true even without the cards!"

Tonia, the fortuneteller, as if she'd been listening in to our conversation, stopped by the next evening to see my mother. "Stopping by for tea" was the official term for it. I discovered them in the kitchen with tea cups in their hands, surrounded by two plates with cookies, when I came back from the dating agency empty handed. It had been two days since I wrote David my plea, but he hadn't written back to me. That was not a good sign.

Tonia's loud laughter—and her chatter with a Nordic Russian drawl from the Far North region of Russia, very unusual in our southern country—was always very appealing to me. She was an exotic, Viking-like woman: tall, big chested, a very light-colored blonde, almost white-headed, with lots of freckles and a big round potato nose. She even cursed differently, using hard-core coarse expressions, unheard of around here, with such soft undertones that they were actually soothing. They were funny and affectionate, if she liked you. But they would barrage you to the ground like a machine gun if she hated you. However, today I was not in the right mood.

"Hey, come here!" Mom waved me in.

"What are you ladies up to?" I asked, looking in the kitchen from the corridor, hoping to escape the pleasantries and hide in the other room.

"Come here. Tonia is telling me my fortune," Mom said. "We finished with the tea, and we are about to have some coffee so she can read my fortune in the coffee residue."

"We have coffee?" I asked.

"I bought some ground coffee today and boiled it in the pot, so let's both of us have some reading."

"I thought Tonia only drew the cards for fortune-telling."

"We'll do the cards later. Sit, sit." Tonia pointed at the empty space on the bench next to her.

"Are you going for a trifecta today? Tea, coffee, then cards?"

"Today is a great day for fortune-telling," Tonia insisted.

"I bet it is," I said sarcastically and looked at Mom out of the corner of my eye. She was pouring a thick brown liquid with chunks of small grains out of a red pot with a wooden handle into the last tea cup left from the Czechoslovakian china set. *Must be a very special occasion, indeed.* "What am I supposed to do with it?" I took the cup out of Mama's hands.

"Shake the coffee in the cup a little, then think about the man you want, then you drink it, then we'll look at the bottom of the cup and read your fortune," Tonia instructed.

I smiled, jiggled the cup in my hand, and gathered my thoughts for a few seconds, but all I could think of was how mad I was at David. I didn't know if that was the right ritual for the coffee-reading ceremony. Was I supposed to be calm, or was it fine to be angry? I didn't want to trigger some voodoo shit on poor David. *Let's just get it over with!* I gulped the coffee all at once.

"Wait, wait," Tonia pulled my hand back. "You are supposed to drink it slowly, so you don't mess up the residue."

Pttfu! I spat out the tiny coffee grains that had jumped into my mouth.

"Don't spit it back into the cup! You grazed your brains at the fucked-up pasture or something?" Tonia pulled the cup from my hand. I was breaking all sorts of etiquette apparently. I looked at Tonia's concentrated face, trying to guess what was in her head.

"You see this?" Tonia brought the cup back in front of my eyes. She showed me with her pinky the stain that started on the bottom of the cup and spread all the way to the edge, the result of me drinking it too fast.

"A brown goo? Yes, I see it. What does it mean?"

"What does it look like to you?"

"It's like a stretch of wet dirt road in Grandma's village." I laughed.

"Look closer, you blind milk-less goat!"

I burst into laughter. Weirdly enough, that was the relief I needed right then. "I wondered how long it would take you before you called me names."

"Concentrate! You see this big torso, and this big head with horns? It's a bull!"

"So glad it's not a male goat!" I laughed even louder. "We'd be quite a milk-less pair!"

Mom raised her hands in the air. She was getting anxious. "So what does it mean, the bull?"

"This man that you thought about," Tonia turned to me, "he's a big, strong man, very stubborn, very pushy. He's determined to get to your heart."

I looked at Mom, who was in total awe. "I swear, I didn't tell her anything," she said. "But as I said, she's good at this. Let's read the cards, Tonia."

Tonia pulled the deck of Russian tarot cards from her pocket. I always liked their bright design: the queens and kings of clubs, spades, diamonds, and hearts in expensive outfits with very seri ous faces. We used to play cards in secret in school because it was considered a decadent habit of the bourgeois to gamble, not worthy of Soviet living. How far away had we gotten from our old taboos of just fifteen years ago? Now we were having a fortune-telling ses- sion in our house, for God's sake!

Tonia shuffled the deck four times; then, picking one card at a time, she laid them on the table in front of us in a square formed by four horizontal rows and four vertical columns, sixteen cards in all. It looked like a dysfunctional mosaic. Here was the queen of clubs in the upper left corner.

"That's your card," Tonia said. I already knew that. According to the Russian card-reading rules, the queen of clubs represented a brown-eyed brunette, like me. Then there was a six of diamonds, a seven of hearts, an ace of clubs in the lower right corner, and a king of hearts was right under the queen.

Tonia shook her head with an air of importance. "I'll be fucking damned! That's your man." Tonia pointed at the king. That was a bummer, because according to the same rules, hearts were the symbol for blue-eyed men, but David had brown eyes. The reading was already going sideways. I was not expecting a love triangle with another man in the equation!

"That's a government house." Tonia put her finger on the ace of clubs.

"What's a government house?"

"It could be any official government entity: a courthouse, a registry, or even a prison."

"I can't wait to see a prisoner in my house. Could it be an embassy?"

"It could be."

"So, what does it mean when one card can be something between a prison and an embassy?"

"Shhh! A rush is needed only when you're catching fleas," she said, using an old Russian joke. I started laughing again. I had totally forgotten about that expression. But lucky for us, we had the wild Tonia here to remind us about silly things like that!

"And let thunder strike me right into my heart if this man doesn't have you on his mind!" Tonia pointed at the king of hearts and looked straight into my eyes.

"What man? A blue-eyed blond?" I asked, sincerely intrigued.

"Not necessarily. Sometimes the combination of cards is more important than just the color identifier."

"Are you telling me that my king could be any man with blond or dark hair? Do I have to suspect that any man walking on the street could be The One?"

But Tonia was very focused on her mission. "You see this seven of hearts next to him? That tells me he has a love interest in you."

"Could it also be a love interest in any woman between a brunette and a blonde? If the kings can change colors, why not the queens?"

"The queens' colors are permanent. Queens in general are more consistent in any matters," Tonia said without a flinch. "Look at this six of diamonds." She brought my attention to a card in the middle of the mix. "That's a long road, so that means a trip far away to this government house."

"For me or for him?"

"For both of you, swear on my mother!" To prove how serious she was, Tonia was jeopardizing her family's wellbeing so effortlessly for a tarot session's sake.

After a couple more rounds of card reading and gossip, I realized that getting rid of Tonia, once she had her claws in you, was more difficult than one could hope for. She would sit in our kitchen for days if we let her. Tonia and Mom would find lots of subjects to discuss, so I gently reminded them both it was getting late.

"What good does this card reading do for anyone?" I asked Mom after Tonia finally left. "Do I have to read the tea leaves after a fortune-telling session?"

A distinctive long-distance phone ring interrupted our conversation.

"Pick up, pick up!" Mom yelled at me. "It's probably him."

"It's six a.m. in America, so I doubt that's him. David normally calls me after work."

"Go, you stupid, go!" Mom yelled at me again. "You'll miss the call." I reluctantly picked up the phone, but the familiar deep voice in the receiver left no doubt who was calling.

"Is it him?" Mom asked with her eyes.

"Hello, David," I answered in a trembling voice, having an out-of-body experience. His call was both scary and liberating, as if I was a little girl again, waiting for my spanking so I could finally get it over with. Mom tiptoed into the other room, letting us talk.

"I read your letter," David said. "I had to call you before I go to work. I couldn't wait."

"I'm glad you did. I thought I'd have to wait until tomorrow to find out my fate."

"Your fate?" David asked with defiance in his voice. "Your fate and your kids' fates belong with me. Your letter made me a happy man. I don't care what people say about us and what jokes they make about mail-order brides."

"What's a mail-order bride?"

"Here in America, we joke about men who find wives from abroad online. Those women are called mail-order brides, as if you're ordering something from a catalog."

"Is it what you think I am, something that you order from a catalog?" I gripped the receiver tighter, annoyed by this offensive joke.

"That's just a stupid joke, honey. Don't take it seriously."

"What do they call the men who look for mail-order brides?"

"I don't know, a desperado? I don't really care. You and I are for real! And I will do anything possible to come up with the money for my plane tickets soon and come see you. Okay?"

"Okay."

"I love you."

"I love you too." I breathed out carefully, trying not to burst into tears. I sat down. I had to. My shaking legs demanded it. I needed to let it sink in, unable to believe that the crisis that came out of nowhere had disappeared into thin air in the same way that it started, fast and mysteriously, like Tonia's fortune-telling session.

Mom peeked around the corner as soon as I put the phone down. I was sure she'd been listening in all this time. I didn't know why. It wasn't like she could understand anything. Perhaps she was just listening to my tone.

"How was it?" she asked.

"I think it went okay."

"Is he coming to Moldova or not?"

"He said he's looking into it. He needs to come up with the money for the trip first."

"I told you Tonia is good at this predicting! Here is your love interest, and here's his long trip."

"And what about the government house?"

"With God's help, you'll get to the government house too!" Mom breathed out, relieved, and made a cross with her right hand, the Orthodox style. Three fingers put together touched her forehead, then her belly, then the right shoulder, then the left. "Everything is going to be all right, with God's help." She said it one more time. "But, of course, out of all Americans, you had to get the poor one."

Chapter 17

The Carriage
Before the Horse

"Happy New Year 2001!" David said cheerfully, calling ten min-utes before midnight in Chişinău. After so many phone calls, he'd finally figured out how to tell the time difference. "Happy Ne-e-ew Ye-e-ear! Happy Ne-e-ew Ye-e-ear! I want to make love on Ne-e-ew Ye-e-ear's to you!" he sang to me.

"Well, you're in a good mood!" I responded, a subtle code so my family in the other room would not suspect us.

"Hopefully this is the last holiday we'll spend separated from each other." David sighed.

Lica showed up from the other room, holding a glass of bubbly. She touched my hand. "Give me the phone, Mom."

"David, hold on. Lica wants to say something."

"David, I love you!" Lica giggled, swaying with the glass in her hand like a true lady.

"Awwww! That's so sweet. I love you all too."

"What's that?" Lica asked him when she heard a dog's bark on the phone. "Teddy Bear?"

"Oh, yes, Teddy Bear says hi and happy New Year! Teddy Bear will be so excited to see you all in America." I could hear that David was getting emotional. Lica grimaced. She didn't understand most of what he said, though she tried so hard to decipher it. But she did pick up on a few easy words.

"Happy ... New ... Year!" Lica said slowly, making sure that she pronounced every word correctly.

"Okay, give me the phone back. I think he got the picture." I took the phone from her.

"Here, Soviet champagne for you!" Lica shoved the glass she'd been holding all this time into my hand. It was filled with a cheap sour bubbly drink, and I smiled, as the name for the drink was both ironic and contradictory. If that was really champagne, it couldn't be Soviet. It also couldn't be Soviet, because the Soviet Union didn't exist anymore, though the ever-present ghost of the dead country was still alive and ticking, like the clock on the Kremlin tower, which would ring at midnight. "We're getting ready for the end-of-the-year countdown, Mom!"

"I'm coming, I'm coming!" I brushed her off.

"You have to clink your glass with somebody on New Year's Eve or you'll have bad luck all year!"

I waved at Lica to leave me alone. She walked away disappointed, as if she were my mother and not the other way around.

"What's going on?" David asked me.

"It's nothing, just a stupid superstition."

"I have some good news, honey."

"Did you buy the plane tickets?" I almost jumped.

"Not yet. I went to a jewelry store, and I put some money down for an engagement ring for you." David giggled like a schoolboy.

"Why are you buying the ring before the tickets?" I scolded.

"You don't seem excited." David's mood sank.

"I am excited, because now it's official." I agreed that he had a good point, a bride would eventually need her ring. "But that's like putting the carriage before the horse. What does this ring do for me if both you and the ring are in America? And what's this 'money down'?"

"How do I explain this?" David trilled his lips. "I put some money down now, and I'll pay the ring in installments from my two paychecks next month until I pay the ring off."

"I don't understand. So, you don't have the ring yet?"

"Not right now, but they'll hold on to the ring for me."

"What happens if you don't pay next month?"

"Then I'll lose my deposit, but that will never happen, because I intend to buy it."

"But now, your next two paychecks will go toward the ring instead of the tickets? That's so confusing. Money down, deposit, installments. America is so strange. Here, if I don't have money, I can't go to the store and say to hold something for me. They'd laugh in my face!"

"Then you'll love it in America, honey. When you arrive, I'll take you all shopping."

"Let's get us to America first."

"I'm sure this year will finally bring us together," David said very confidently.

"I hope so," I answered, leaving some room for improvement, in case something went wrong.

"I'll write you a letter after we hang up," he said. "I still like sending you letters, even if we talk on the phone so often. I'll send you some recent pictures too. Just promise that you won't be scared when you see a big guy."

I paused for a moment. "Okay, send me new pictures. I'll send you some pictures of the kids too."

"Let me wish my future mother-in-law a happy New Year," he insisted.

I walked into other room, where Mom, Mariana, Serghei, Lica, and my younger cousin, another Irina, were at the festive table munching away.

"Mama, David wants to wish you a happy New Year."

Mom shook her head. "No, no, no. I don't speak English."

"He knows you don't. Just say hello and listen to whatever he says, and at the end say thank you. That's it."

"No, I can't say that 'thank you, thank you' of yours." She repeated the words a few times as if she was in a phonetics class, but every time it would turn into "sank you." I put the receiver to her ear anyway and whispered to her, "Say 'hello.'" She made a face, bulging her eyes, looking like a scared bird with tattered feathers.

"H-h-he-llo!" She stressed the "h" so hard with her rough Russian accent that the word was barely recognizable. Then she lifted her hands in the air, as if telling me "I don't understand what's he saying" and pulled her head away from the phone.

"Thank you, David. Mom loved it!" I laughed, looking at Mom, who was mumbling under her breath, stressed out by the whole experience, as if she'd just failed her English exam in front of all of America. "We'll have to let you go now. The food is getting cold."

"I love you," David said at the end.

"Me too," I said quickly, glancing at everybody.

"You're not saying it right. You're supposed to say, 'I love you too,'" David corrected me. I rolled my eyes. I could usually get away with "me too." "Love you" was one English expression that everybody, including my mom knew, so I didn't want to say it out loud in front of her. She was uncomfortable with this American style of courtship. It seemed strange to her, as if she was watching two aliens from different planets doing the nasties.

"Okay, okay." I lowered my voice and said, "I love you too."

"That's so cheesy!" Mom breathed out like a tired horse, showing her displeasure.

I put the phone down and said unapologetically, "Americans are cheesy like that. So, where is that champagne?"

"It's too late now!" Lica said, her tone letting me know I'd done something wrong. "It's already past midnight."

"Let's clink glasses anyway," I insisted. "And let's take a photo of our possibly last New Year's at home."

"Hey, hey!" Mom raised her finger. "Don't put the carriage before the horse."

"I just told David the same thing." I pointed at her. "That's scary. I'm turning into my mother!"

"You'll be just fine if you turn into your mother," she said, placing her hands on her hips.

"I don't think so. You worry so much about everything that you drive yourself nuts! I want to be myself, because that's how David likes me."

"That's because he hasn't seen you yet," Mom said defiantly. Everybody started laughing.

"Happy New Year to all of you, traitors!"

* * *

"Hello, my love. It's midnight here and the fireworks are in full bloom," David's letter dated January 1, 2001, said. *Fireworks?* I smirked. *That might be nice.* All we got last night was a few sparkly Bengal lights that Mom bought to entertain the kids. They ran outside after midnight to light them up, for it seemed more logical to light them up in the dark than inside the brightly lit room.

"Our YEAR, my love," the letter continued. "My New Year's resolution is to work hard to make more money so we can have everything we want for our future, and our children. I want to lose weight and eat healthily so we can live a long and happy life together. I feel the distance between us is shrinking, day by day, as it gets closer to the day when I'll fly to you. Below is the information that you need for the embassy." He gave me a long list with his and his parents' information, for some reason.

"Anything you want, my love, let me know. You hold my heart in your hands. Please cherish it. Kiss Lica and Serghei for me. Tell Mariana I said hello, and thank your mother for having you. Your Man, David."

I smiled. His letter was a bit over the top for my taste. *So what? A girl needs some mushy fluff for self-esteem.* The year started on a promising trajectory because David was making big plans. The next day he told me he was looking for apartments for us in America.

"The horse before the carriage again!" I told him. "Concentrate on buying the tickets!"

* * *

On the third of January, David almost cried on the phone, like a child who didn't get his candy. "The tickets to Chișinău are around two thousand dollars. I don't have that kind of money right now. We'll have to wait until I get paid in February, no sooner than the twenty-seventh. I hate this! I absolutely hate this!"

Talking to David day to day was like riding a roller coaster. He was coming soon. No, he wasn't coming soon. He wanted all things at once and seemed to have no idea what to do when things were not going his way. For God's sake, when I was growing up, every kid knew that you couldn't get all things at once. You were lucky to get them one at a time. You just had to roll with the punches!

Can he keep himself together and come up with a plan? Or will he make me wait for him for years? I need to know if this man is for real or just an online fantasy. I was getting angry, therefore motivated and very creative.

I went to a few ticketing agencies to find a way around the damn rock that David had stumbled upon in the middle of his raging river. What other routes were there from America to Moscow, to Bucharest, to Kiev, anywhere that I could travel without needing a visa?

"David, darling," I wrote David later in the day. "It's so terrible that you can't come in January. I was looking forward to seeing you so much. But I'll wait for you anyway." *Not forever!* "I was shocked, though, to hear that the flight to Chișinău costs so much. I found some other information today: In the spring, a two-way ticket— Seattle-New York-Frankfurt-Chișinău —costs $950. In summer it costs $1,100. In winter, it's less. If you come through Budapest, I mean New York-Budapest-Chișinău, it will cost you $560." I was pounding hard on the keyboard. *Where in the hell was he shopping for plane tickets? At Tiffany's?*

I took a break, then continued: "I received your new pictures yesterday. Why are you so hard on yourself? You are so nice, really. And your Teddy Bear also. Yesterday I stitched your dog on a piece of cloth. Above it, I wrote: TEDDY BEAR. Lica painted a new picture for you. It's so cute." That mushy fluffy stuff, I realized, worked both ways. As my babushka would say: "alternate the whip and the gingerbread!" David needed some sugarcoating at this time.

David wrote: "Thank you for the information you sent me. Next week, I'll get my salary and go to the American embassy to find out about the documents we both need for the bride visa. I want to be with you as soon as possible. I feel terrible when I'm so far from you, from your arms, your lips, your body. I miss you. I want you every minute. Let the twenty-seventh of February come sooner. I sent you the photos with the kids that I promised before. Kiss you, dear, everywhere. Irina and children."

I smiled. My gingerbread trick seemed to work for now. But then there was another day, and another challenge.

"It will almost kill me not to be able to call you, honey," David wrote on January seventh. "But I'll have to cut my spending. I'll get prepaid calling cards to call you and pay the phone bill over time. I love you, darling, and please understand that there's nothing that can keep me from you. I am flying to Moscow, even if I have to steal a plane." *Wouldn't that be a scene? David stealing a plane?* I imagined him tripping on the steps, catching his breath. Would he have a gun, or would he just charm the heck out of the pilots with our sob story?

"I've been thinking about you a lot, my darling," he continued. "And I want you to know how much I love you and my future children, Serghei and Angelica. Your children have a special place in my heart reserved." *Awww!* "I love my son, Derek. He's my best friend. He knows how special Serghei and Lica are to me. I have always wanted a daughter. And I'm so glad that your children have accepted me as their future papa. I think, partially, because I vowed to make you and your children happy." *The road to a mother's heart is through her children,* as some smart mothers would say.

"And as far as you are concerned … you are everything I prayed to God for: beautiful, respectful, naughty, sexy, desirable, funny, smart, caring, tender, sensual, a great mommy." *Easy, easy now, cowboy!* "But most of all, you accepted me with all my faults and shortcomings. I am so lucky! Right now, I'm trying to save all the money I have to bring with me to Moscow to pay for presents for you and the kids and your ring—and have extra money in case of emergencies. I LOVE YOU! I LOVE YOU! I LOVE YOU! I LOVE YOU! I LOVE YOU!

"It seems that everything has come down on me ever since **I bought my tickets to you for February twenty-seventh**." *What? He couldn't start with THIS NEWS first?* "Two bills that I was unaware of popped up, and stress is a little high, but I'll be okay. You are my strength, my goal. I'll sell a lot of cars and make enough money to come to you." He was going through so much already, but this news changed everything. I barely made it through the rest. "Please e-mail me every day. I need to feel your love, and I will get some calling cards so we can make love by telephone. Yours only, David. Hugs and kisses."

"He bought the tickets! My God! The horse is FINALLY in front of the carriage!" I yelled. Now I could go back and read over the cutesy stuff that he wrote. *What was he saying about how beautiful, funny, and smart I was?*

Chapter 18

Everything Is Broken

"On the second of February, it will be my fifty-fifth birthday," Mom said, giggling on the phone, making arrangements with her girlfriends to come for her jubilee. "Yes, I'm cooking my specialty dishes. I brought some wine from my brother-in-law's village. We're going to celebrate and remember the good old times."

Good old times, indeed, when Mom's idea of a party was to cook in the kitchen all day, then stress out that the meat jelly turned out too jiggly, and that we didn't roll the cabbage rolls tight enough, according to her culinary standards.

"Mama, nobody will care," I said.

"They know my cooking. They'll notice." Mom was freaking out. "Why are the wine glasses on the table all different sizes? Don't we have some matching glasses?"

"No, we broke them all."

"Oh, my God, everything is broken in this house. I should have bought some new glasses!"

"Nobody will care, Mama!" I huffed. "Go get dressed!" I kicked her out of the kitchen.

"And put on the new lipstick I bought for you," Mariana joined in. "We've got this!"

"Turn down the fire on the oven, the water is boiling too hard." Mom was giving us instructions on her way out.

"We've got this!" Mariana and I yelled at the same time. "Will she ever stop being a head chef?" We listened for more faraway instructions. "All the time?" My sister and I looked at each other. We both knew the answer to that.

Mom's girlfriends—women in different stages of being single: widows, longtime or recent divorcees, or in Mom's case both—were ringing the doorbell and coming in the house one by one. Some I had seen once or twice before. Others I had never seen in my life, friends that Mom made in Greece, as if Mom had an entire secret family that we had no idea about. I was de facto the matriarch of our family for so long, calling the shots, and making decisions that it felt surreal to see how Mom took over her reins back, bringing in house strangers whom she possibly was closer than to us.

"Happy birthday!" the first woman said, kissed my mom on both cheeks, and handed her a bouquet and a set of six wine glasses as a present. The second and third women did the same. There must have been a recent shipment from China on the market, now being sold by all the merchants, because the wine glasses brought by three different women looked exactly the same.

"Well, I guess we'll never have to worry about matching glasses," I whispered into my mom's ear. She pinched my butt cheek, but kept smiling to the guests, as she used to do when I was a kid, forcing me to behave.

"Jenea!" I yelled excitedly when I saw my mom's oldest friend at the door. She was the familiar face we needed, and she cussed when she tripped on the doorstep, so the evening promised to be entertaining.

"Look at you: a new dress, a new hairdo, and pink lipstick! Mama, the beauty!" Jenea hugged my mom.

"All right, all right, everybody, sit down," Mom said, tearing up.

Our mother sat at the head of the table like a queen bee looking at her busy hive: radiant, cheerful. We hadn't seen her like that in a long time.

"Give me that red wine from the country." Mom pointed at it

across the table. She was getting sassy after the one glass of wine she'd drunk earlier. *Out of practice, evidently.*

"Pour that wine!" Jenea cheered her on. "What a get-together! So nice to see you at home."

"Katya, so how is it in Greece?" one of the older women asked. "They pay almost nothing in school nowadays. I've been thinking of going to work abroad. Almost all the teachers in our school have gone either to Greece or Italy."

"Whatever you do, don't go with the same agency I did," Mom answered. "When they got us our visas, they promised us that jobs were waiting for us in Athens at an employment agency, but they dropped us off at the outskirts. We didn't even know where to go or how to get there, because none of us spoke Greek."

Mariana gasped. "Shit, Mom, you never told us that."

"Well, it's water under the bridge. I spent three nights at a church, but I found a job on my third day, before I spent all my money on food. However, the job was on an island. For three months I couldn't even get to the post office to send a letter home."

An unpleasant, guilty feeling overwhelmed me. How scared our Mom must have been? Hungry, out of money, alone in a foreign country. Not understanding a word. Her pushiness and stubbornness, that got her through in Greece, came home with her, causing lots of tensions between us. But now, all little spats that Mom and I had since she came back felt pitiful, embracing even. She went through hell for us and I was arguing with her about little, insignificant stuff.

"When I finally learned some basic Greek," Mom continued, "I asked the son of the old man I was taking care of to mail the letter for me. I didn't want to scare you with my sad story. I just wanted to let you know that I'd made it and everything was fine."

I shook my head recalling that letter. It was short, very specific. Nothing hinted on the drama that was behind the scenes.

"But how was the work itself?" the teacher asked.

"The old man was in his eighties and in a wheelchair, but a little cuckoo. He liked to pull my skirt up when I got near him. I smacked his hands a few times, but he would just laugh. I even told his son, but his father was on his best behavior when his son was around. As soon as he was gone, the old man would do the same thing. In the end, I had to change jobs because the pervert just wouldn't stop."

Jenea looked at Mariana and me and said, "Don't you ever forget what your mother had to do for you to put food on the table." I nodded. *How could I?* She gulped her glass of wine, bottoms up. "Let's sing a song, ladies! Katya, do you still remember the song named after you?"

"*Katyusha?* That was not named after me; that was written before the war." Mama blushed.

"Yeah, *Katyusha, Katyusha!* That was papa's favorite song," I yelled.

"Your father was the singer." Mom laughed. "I can't sing for shit."

"Do it, do it, Mama!" I encouraged her. Mom giggled, but Jenea had already started in a falsetto:

Rastzvetali yabloni y grushi. (Apple and pear trees were blooming.)

Poplyli tumany nad rekoy. (Mist was floating over the river.)

Vykhodila na bereg Katyusha... (Katyusha's walking on the riverbank...)

"Come on, Katya, sing about how Katyusha was waiting for her lover on the riverbank!"

"*Vykhodila na bereg Katyusha...*" Mom started in a high pitch. Her voice broke halfway, like the raspy voice of a goat trying too hard. She was right, she couldn't sing for shit. Now I knew whom Mariana was taking after.

Mom tried the next two lines, but couldn't keep up, and dropped the song at the finish line, waving her hand. "I'm done!"

Well, no surprise there! The singing at the Russian parties stopped as abruptly as they spontaneously started.

"What a pity that your Babushka Veta didn't come for your birthday," Jenea said. "Look what a beautiful party we have here."

"She's too old for long travels. We'll go visit her in a couple of days, during the kids' winter break."

* * *

"Everybody, out!" Mom yelled at the kids and Mariana, gathering the last things they needed for the trip to see Grandma. I had no idea why Mom would want to take the kids to Grandma's in the winter. It seemed like a lot of hustle for just a week, but once decided, there was no turning back, and off they went, leaving me alone in the house. I had to work that week, so I couldn't go, but Mom left me with a list of chores, presumably so I didn't get bored.

Friday night was uneventful. I made myself some tea and watched TV, waiting for David's usual call, but he didn't call that night. *That's strange*, I thought. *He didn't call me yesterday either, but good boy! He's finally saving money for the trip.*

Saturday morning, I took all the rugs out, turned on the TV, and sent myself on an adventure doing some deep house cleaning. Shakira was blasting from the TV screen: Whenever, Wherever.

I shook my hips like Shakira, bent forward dramatically to lift the broom from the floor and spun it in the air like a helicopter blade. I jumped on the chair in the corner, leaned forward on my right foot, lifting my left leg in the air like a ballerina, and swept the giant spider web that was spreading between two walls. Then I jumped down and threw the broom with the spider web on the floor, making it spin on the parquet floor like a break-dancer.

I took the big red rag with holes in it that we used to wash floors and, like a matador in front of a bull, I shook it, then dropped it in a bucket of water: *splash!* I soaked the rag a few times, then squeezed it till no more water came out and threw it on the floor. I dropped down on my knees and started washing the floor old style, like my grandma and mom taught me: reaching into all the corners under the bed, getting behind the furniture, moving it out of the way, then sliding it back. It was actually nice that everybody was gone, and the kids were not getting in the way.

I looked around the room with a sense of accomplishment. It looked spotless. There was one more thing left to do. I brought the pitcher from the kitchen to water the plants on the windowsill. Then I put the pitcher down to pick up the dead leaves. I opened the window to let in some fresh air. A loud noise of a broken glass scared me. *Goddamn it!* I totally forgot I had the pitcher on the windowsill. And now the broken pieces of sharp glass were everywhere. I was so glad Mom wasn't home to lecture me on how I break everything, which was true, but I didn't want to hear about it right then.

Drrr. I heard the sound of the ringing phone. I stood in the middle of the disaster for a few seconds trying to decide if I wanted to run for the phone or sweep the floor so I wouldn't step on broken glass. The second phone ring was long and insistent, so I abandoned the rescue operation for the moment.

"Alyo!" I said in Russian.

"Ho-ney," I heard a slurred voice say—tired, unrecognizable.

"David?" I looked at the clock, which was showing noon in Chişinău. "What are you doing calling so late? Isn't it two a.m. in Seattle?"

"Ho-n-ney," I heard the same word again but even more slurred.

"Are you drunk?" I laughed. "I thought you didn't drink."

"I'mnn … drnk, I'mnn drnk …"

"What are you saying? Are you sleepy or something?" I sat down with the phone on the couch. I put my feet under my butt, giggling, ready to tease David some more.

"I'mm hos-pi-tal."

The fun was long gone now.

"Did you say *hospital*?"

"Ye-e-es."

"What are you doing in the hospital?" Now I was worried, and the distance between us was even more apparent. "Is your mom sick?"

"No. Mom fine. I had … a … stroke."

"You had what? Did somebody strike you? What's a stroke? Are you okay?"

"No, I'm not okay."

"What's a stroke?" I yelled into the phone, gasping for air, as if somebody had hit me hard in the chest, realizing that whatever it was couldn't be good.

David breathed hard for a few seconds, then said slowly, as if measuring every word, "It's when … you … have a … rup-ture … of the artery … in your … head. I couldn't … talk … yes-ter-day … that's why … I didn't … call … Sorry."

I started weeping uncontrollably. "How bad is it?"

"The doc-tor said … it's bad. Doc-tor said … it will take … months to … recover. Sorry … I will not be … coming … soon … Don't cry!"

"How can I not cry when you're in the hospital, and I'm here, and you're in America?"

David took another deep breath, as if gathering his strength. "You are … a … beautiful … woman … Will you … not love me … anymore?"

"What are you talking about?" I wiped my tears.

"I'm afraid, you … won't wait … for me." But before I answered, I could hear a woman's voice, most likely a nurse, saying something to David. He answered something back to her. Then he came back to me. "I have to … go to … sleep now. I'm tired, ho-ney."

"Will you call me tomorrow?" I asked, shivering so hard that I was clenching my teeth.

"I'll try," David whispered, and the phone went dead.

I covered my face with both my hands and started rocking back and forth, feeling an excruciating pain, as if I was in labor but multiplied by a hundred. An unhuman, animal scream came out of my mouth. I had to let it out!

"What am I going to do now? What are we all going to do now?" I was yelling through the avalanche of tears, looking at the pieces of glass spread on the floor. I felt like that glass right now: shattered, unfixable, with no answers and nobody in the whole world to talk to.

Alone! Again alone!

Chapter 19

The Recovery

My heart started racing when my mom, my kids, and my sister returned home from Grandma's. They came inside with the big bags Grandma had stuffed with country goodies, as usual. The kids were pushing and shoving each other in the corridor, as usual. Mariana yelled at them, as usual. Things seemed normal, but I knew that everything would change in an instant when I broke the news about David. I let thirty minutes pass to let everybody settle in and catch their breath, then I said:

"David's in the hospital."

"What?" Mom heard me first. "What happened?"

"He said he had a stroke." Mom looked at me, puzzled. I explained, "It's when a blood vessel erupts in your brain. I don't know how to translate it."

"God Almighty!" Mom made the sign of the cross. "In Russian, it's called *insult*." *What an appropriate translation!*

"What does it mean?" Mariana looked at me, scared. "Is he okay?"

"Barely. He can't even talk."

Mom sighed, shook her head, and walked to the sink to get a glass of water.

"I took care of people after a stroke," she said. "They can't walk, can't lift their hands. He could be paralyzed for months"—she paused—"or forever."

"Babushka Katya, what does it mean?" Lica asked. "Does it mean he's not coming to visit us?"

"I'm afraid not. At least not for now," I answered for her.

Mariana dropped onto the chair. The tears flowed from her eyes. Serghei caressed her head.

"Don't cry, Mariana," he said. "When I'm sick, I get better in a week."

"It's not a cold, Sereoja. It's very serious." Mariana pushed his hand away. "What are you going to do now?" she asked me.

"What can I do? I can't get a visa to America, and even if I could, I don't have the money for a plane ticket. All I can do is wait. I can try to call him."

"Are you crazy? One call to America will ruin us all!" Mom brought me back to reality.

"Then I'll go tomorrow to the dating agency and send him a letter."

"I'll write him a letter too," Lica said.

"Me too," Serghei jumped in. "I'll draw him a picture."

"Will he even get them?" Mom asked me. "Him being in the hospital and all."

"I don't know, but I feel like I need to do something."

* * *

"My honey, my dear, my beloved David," I wrote on the seventh of February. "I am so glad everything is okay with you. Thank God that He gives me you again. Don't worry, dear. I love you so much, nothing can stop me. I promised you I'd be with you when you are well and when you feel bad. I think I've kept my word. I'm very glad you need me, because I need you so much. I was practically dead those days. If I just could be there."

I leaned back in my chair for a moment, thinking I wasn't getting the words quite right, but I had to try.

"Be healthy, darling. I need you alive. You are my handsomest man in the world. I don't need another man. There is no other man like you in the whole fucking world. Kiss you. Irina."

And I left it at that.

"What if he doesn't get better?" Mom asked me the next day.

"Right now, I'm taking it one day at a time," I said. "First, he needs to get out of the hospital. Hopefully he'll get better afterward."

"Honey," David started when he called me three days later. "They are letting me go home today." His voice was raspy, but the words were comprehensible, which I thought was a good sign. "I still want to come see you and the kids in February."

"You do?" I asked with a glimmer of hope. "What does the doctor say?"

"My doctor thinks it's a bad idea. The stress of the flight may trigger another stroke."

"Then don't! I don't want you to die. Let's postpone it. I'll return my train tickets to Moscow tomorrow."

"You are giving up on me?" David said with sadness in his voice.

"I'm not giving up. I'm being practical. We'll need that money later, for when you can travel."

"You are giving up on me."

"David, you are driving yourself crazy over this. They are letting you go home. That's the good news, right?"

"What good will that do? They're not releasing me to work yet, which means I'll be short on my paycheck. And because of my medical bills, I'll probably have to cut back on our phone calls again. I can't imagine doing that. You are my lifeline. If I don't talk to you, I'll go insane. It's the worst time this could have happened to us—the worst time!"

"There's nothing you can do right now, David. You have to recover first, then worry about other stuff later. Recovery first!" I said it stronger this time.

"Tell me you love me."

"I love you."

"Do you really mean it?" I heard David's voice, full of emotion.

"You are my one in a million! You are the man I wished for. Of course I love you."

"Did you wish for a giant with half a foot and a stroke?"

"You got your sense of humor back. That's good." David tried to laugh, but I could hear it was hard for him to even breathe, so I continued, "I wished for a man with a big heart, so I got one. This is how God tests us, by sending us obstacles. Just get better. Okay?"

"Thank you, honey. You have no idea how much I needed to hear this to get me though. I'll call you when I get home."

"Can you afford this right now?"

"You don't want me to call you?"

"Of course I want you to call me, but you just said you have medical bills."

"Screw the bills! I'll figure something out, I promise. You don't understand, I *have* to call you."

I put the phone down and walked into the other room, where Mom was watching TV.

"How is he?" Mom asked.

"They're releasing him from the hospital today, but the doctor said he can't fly at this time." I dropped onto the couch. Mom was quiet for a while then turned to me.

"What if he doesn't get better after he gets home?" she asked.

That was a little dramatic. "He's not dead, Mom." I rolled my eyes. "Give him a few months."

"Sparrow always dreams of corn."

"What does that proverb even mean in our situation?"

"You may have big dreams of America, but that dream is so far away that it may never come true. Get your head out of the clouds and put your feet on the ground."

"I have my feet on the ground, Mama. We both just have to wait."

"Sure, you can wait, but your kids can't." She crossed her arms, her tone growing more serious. "They need clothes and shoes and school supplies every year. I'd say, let's plan for this now, while I still have some money left, because if I run out of it, we may all be stranded here with nothing but your dreams. Did you ever consider what might happen if he gets better but never comes?" I looked at my mother, the realist. This thought had never crossed my mind until she said it out loud. *Indeed, what if he never comes?*

"Then I'll come up with a backup plan."

"It's better to think about it sooner than later. If it all works out with David, great, but if it doesn't, at least you'll be prepared."

"Prepared for what?"

"I talked to a woman who can get us visas for Italy. We can go work in Italy and make some money while David's recovering. You'll need money for the plane tickets for the three of you, and he isn't a big help right now."

"What jobs are there in Italy that let me use my English degree?"

"Don't even think you'll get an office job abroad. First of all, you don't speak Italian. Then you'd have to find a firm that would do the paperwork for you. Good luck with that. There are no white-hand jobs for our women abroad, only the dirty ones: housecleaners, caregivers—"

"Caregiver? So an old man can pull my skirt up? I have a diploma."

"What do the old men here do to you with your diploma? The same thing?" *Touché.* "Housekeeping and caregiving are the cleanest dirty jobs. The real dirty job is being a prostitute! Which some of our younger women resort to."

"Mama, please!"

"I'm just telling you now so you prepare yourself mentally for some hard manual labor. There are no easy jobs abroad for us."

"I get it. Hard manual labor. I'll keep that in mind."

* * *

"I'm so lucky to have you in my life, Irina!" David said on the phone. His voice was strong and cheerful, full of hope.

"You think so?"

"Yes, I think so! I got your e-mail, and the kids' letters. They made me so happy. Lica's little picture with a flower like a heart is so cute, and it says, 'I like you, David. Lica.' Did she write it herself?"

"Yes. I'm teaching her English so she can talk to you when you come to Moldova."

"O-o-oh! That's so sweet. And Serghei drew a truck for me, and a police helicopter. Then there's a sun on the bottom with rays shooting out words. Wait, let me read them. It says, 'I like you,' then 'I love you.' O-o-oh! I'm about to cry. Did he write it himself? Are you teaching him English too?"

"I haven't started with him yet. Lica was helping him with that."

"Does he even know what those words mean?"

"Oh, yeah. He told his sister what he wanted to write. She showed him the English words in her book, and he copied them on his drawing."

"Wait, there's another sentence. It says, 'I want to be your *det-ka.*' What does 'detka' mean?"

"It means a child."

"Does he mean he wants to be my son?"

"That's what it means. I swear, I didn't make him write that. He came up with it himself."

David let out a deep breath. "I am so lucky to have you all!"

"I'm glad that we make you happy." I smiled. "But tell me. How are you doing?"

"My left hand got better. I can finally type with two hands now. I'm going back to work on Monday."

"That's fantastic!" There was no time to waste, not with Mom's preposition lingering in the back of my mind. "So when can you fly to see us?"

"I don't know yet. The doctor said the full recovery may take from six months to a year, so I returned my plane tickets today."

"A whole year?" I almost whispered, trying to think of a good response. "So long?"

"You're not giving up on me, are you?"

"No, of course not," I tried to sound cheerful. "But that's so long." I said it in a more somber voice. The phone receiver dropped out of my shaking hand, as soon as our conversation was over. The gravity of our situation was sinking in fast. *Shit! I hate when Mom is right.*

Chapter 20

The Backup Plan

"Well?" Mom looked at me with an "I told you so" look.

"What?"

"How long?"

"I don't know. It could be months."

"And?"

"I don't know!" I snapped at her and walked away.

For the next two weeks Mom was using her candy-and-whip tactics, pushing me to make a decision, while I was weighing in my options. Should I stay home, put, waiting for David with a fifty-fifty chance of success, or should I leave with Mom for work with, probably, the same odds of success? It was like playing at a casino with all the bad cards, hoping for a miracle. Ultimately, the option of doing something rather than staying still moved the needle. I finally gave in to the idea of a backup plan and went with Mom to the travel agency office near the central bus station in Chișinău to get some firsthand information about job prospects abroad. *It can't be as bad as Mom's painting it.*

"Agency" was a fancy name for a dusty room with one desk and two chairs, which we peeked into whenever anyone walked out the door. The line of ten outside the door was restless. People (from barely out of college to pre-retirement age, from city to country folks) with papers in their hands were loudly exchanging information.

"You don't need that," a woman with bleached hair was telling a man in his late fifties. She was a self-proclaimed expert in everything; he stood behind her in baggy black pants with bulging knees.

"I was here last week," the man said. "She told me to bring my papers for my house in the village to show I have property. It's easier to get a visa if we can prove we have something to come back home to."

"This is for a tourist visa, not for a work visa," the woman replied.

"We're all going as tourists, aren't we?"

"Quiet! I'm on the phone!" the redheaded woman in charge yelled from her office. The queue became mum at once. "Yes, you can apply for visas for Italy, Greece, and Spain with us." Her voice, with its professional tone, carried through the cracked door, but just a few seconds later, she interrupted the caller with the same attitude she'd shushed us with earlier. "What guarantee? We're a tourist agency. Nobody in this business can guarantee you any job. If they tell you that, they're lying to you. What you do with your tourist visas afterwards, when you are in whatever country you go to, is not our problem."

"You see, I told you." A man in line turned to his wife. "She can't guarantee anything."

"Let's talk to her anyway," his wife insisted.

"Come in," the redhead growled at the line, putting her phone down. Both the woman and her husband tiptoed into the office, as if trying not to bother her too much. They handed her their papers: passports, birth certificates, affidavits.

"We want to obtain a visa for Italy." The redhead took the papers out of their hands unceremoniously, looked through them, and said, "Four hundred dollars for each of you."

"Four hundred dollars?" The woman almost gasped for air. "Last month it was two hundred dollars."

"That was last month, now it's this month."

Another man with a full head of gray hair, tall and skinny with tanned skin, unusual for February (probably another fool who came home from Greece too early), had been holding the door open all this time, listening to every word. Now he was agitated. "Four hundred dollars? For what? For a stamp in a passport? Do you even provide transportation?"

"Transportation is separate," the redhead answered without flinching. The gray man stepped away from the door, pacing back and forth, cursing under his breath. This man was speaking my mind. That was exactly what I wanted to say. "What the actual fuck?" He walked out. Four people from the line left with him.

"We don't have so much money," the woman who wanted the Italian visa finally got the strength to say.

"How much have you got?"

The woman untied a dirty handkerchief that she was holding in her hands, got out all her money, and handed it to the redhead.

"Four hundred dollars for both of you? Do you think this is a charity?" She frowned.

"Can you please, please help us out? We beg you. We borrowed this money from our neighbors. We don't have anyone else to borrow from." The woman put her hands together as if praying to God.

"What am I going to do with you, poor people?" She looked at the begging woman with pity. "But if I turned you all down, I'd have no clients. Every year, it's getting worse, I tell you. I'll start the visa for one of you with the money you have here, but I'll need the money for the second visa later." The woman got quiet, as if hesitating to proceed or not. "Look, you don't have enough money to go together anyway," the redhead persisted. "You need bus tickets and money for both of you to live there before you get a job. Besides, it's better if your wife goes there first. It's easier for a woman to find a job as a live-in maid, where she doesn't have to pay for rent. She saves money, sends some home, and you can go next. Many families do that."

"But how am I going to find a job on my own without speaking Italian?"

"Our people always find a way. Don't worry, with your Romanian, you'll start speaking Italian in three months."

"We really want to go together." The husband clenched his palms so tight, they turned lifeless white.

"And I want to be a beauty queen." The redhead smirked. The couple glanced at each other timidly, and finally gave in.

"Mama, let's go," I whispered. "This woman treats people like dogs."

"A bowed head, the sword can't cut," Mom said. "We didn't come all this way to just go home."

"Come in," the redhead said, waving us in after the begging couple left. Mom handed her the passport. "You worked in Greece?" The redhead raised her eyes at Mom after flipping through pages.

"Yes, I came back two months ago. I thought I'd stay home permanently, but the situation is..."

"You and half the country thought that. So many of those who came back want to leave again. Were you in Greece legally?"

"Not at first. But I got my papers later, when they passed the law. When I came back home, I had the legal papers."

"Good, because it's much harder for people to go abroad for work again if they stayed in any European Union country without papers. Once they get in the EU database, they can't cross the border without being stopped. I've heard stories from people who had to go back in cisterns and trucks. Like cattle. It's a desperate world out there. A desperate time." She shook her head. "What can I do for you?"

"I'd like a visa for Italy," Mom said.

"Four hundred dollars. All of it, upfront."

"How long will it take to get the papers?"

"I don't know, it could be three or four weeks. We'll prepare the package, but it all depends on the Italian embassy."

"What happens if we can't get our visas?" I asked.

"We can't control the Italian embassy."

"But will we get our money back?" I asked again.

"The Italians charge for the visa regardless of whether one is granted to you or not, and we have to get all this paperwork for you."

"So, we could pay for it and not even get a visa?" I pressed on.

"We'll do all we can." She smirked. "Are you ready to start today?"

I pulled Mom's sleeve. "Let's think about it, Mom."

"Look, the prices are going up every day. The more you delay it, the more expensive it gets," the redhead insisted.

"I don't have the money on me now, so we'll come back," Mom responded. That was Mom's polite way of saying, "Let's get out of here." I breathed out, relieved, as we walked out of the building.

"I'll call a few more places," she said, "see if I can get a cheaper rate." I didn't say anything.

At home, Mariana was happy to see us. "I got some great news, Mom!" she yelled. "My father got his Romanian citizenship."

"Good for him. How is that great news for you?"

"Because I'm his daughter. I can get Romanian citizenship through him!" Mom was still puzzled.

I stepped in to explain. "Romania is about to enter the European Union. Once they do, Romanian citizens can freely go abroad for work for three months without any visas."

"All right. But how does that help us?"

I continued: "Every citizen of Moldova who was born before the war or has parents born before the war, you know, when Stalin grabbed a piece of Moldova territory from Romania, are considered Romanian citizens. We just need to apply to reclaim our stolen citizenship. Papa was born in 1937, which means that both Vitalic and I qualify. This is the answer to our prayers, Mama! We don't need to hide in trucks like cattle. We can move freely across

Europe if we get our Romanian citizenship. That's excellent news, Mariana. Probably, the smartest thing you've ever said."

Mariana made a face at me, but I was on a roll. "We should definitely look into it."

"How long will this process take?" Mom asked.

"Dad said it's about half a year," Mariana answered.

"Half a year?" Mom was flustered. "We need to get you a job *now*. That's too long."

"Mama, just think about it. I can't go to Italy as a tourist, then overstay my visa like you did."

"It's not that bad. I stayed in Greece for three years without papers."

"And what rights did you have? You told me yourself, you couldn't go in the streets without looking over your shoulder. Besides, I can't be in the EU database as a delinquent. That would mean goodbye to America forever!"

"A friend of mine is now in Ireland," Mariana intervened. "He says it's easy to get work visas there because the Irish farms are desperate for seasonal workers in the summertime. They need people to pick strawberries."

I looked at her. "That's the stupidest thing you've said today."

"What? We've done it every summer at Babushka's," Mariana reminded me.

"Picking a bucket of strawberries from Babushka's garden doesn't make us Irish farmers." I smirked.

"Why not? You speak English." Mariana wouldn't let it go.

"I don't think there's going to be much English spoken in those fields." They still weren't getting it. "I have a better idea. I should get my driver's license."

"What do you need a license for? You don't have a car," Mom dismissed me.

"That could come in handy if I go abroad for work. Or if I go to America. David told me they can start driving in America when they're sixteen."

"Are they crazy over there? Who would trust a sixteen-year-old on the road with a car?"

"What I'm trying to say is that I'll be way behind the times if I don't at least try to get some driving lessons. Besides, everybody says it's cheaper to get a license here."

"Cheaper for whom?" Mom wasn't buying it. "Maybe in comparison with Western European prices it's cheaper, but for us this is not cheap stuff. Besides, where are you going to get the money?"

"One month of my salary should be enough to pay for it," I said.

"And how are you going to feed your kids?"

"I hoped you could help."

Mom rolled her eyes and walked away without saying anything. Negotiating with Mom was like negotiating with meat jelly. It jiggled when you shook it, but it would come back to its original form as if nothing had happened. Her silence was encouraging, though, because it was a form of yes. Something like, "I don't really want to, but if you twist my arm, I might. But I'll remind you about it till the day you die."

Chapter 21

You'll Be There,
I'll Be Here

"What are you doing!" the driving instructor yelled. The poor guy was sweating yellow droplets trying to teach me how to drive the white Soviet Jiguli or, as it was often called, "the soapbox." Three other students sat in the back, impatiently waiting their turn for the driver's seat, while I was frantically jerking the car, trying to get it started.

"I don't know," I said honestly. I put the manual car into first gear, keeping my left foot on the clutch, then stepped on the gas, then let go of the clutch. The car made a scary noise and nosedived a few times, spitting exhaust, but it was not moving anywhere.

"Your driving test is in two weeks. How are going to pass it if you can't even start the car?"

"I don't know!" I yelled at him desperately. What I knew for sure was that yelling at me was not helping. *Tr-r-r-r!* The car growled one more time and finally moved. Driving wasn't so difficult, I thought, even changing lanes while watching for my blind spots, but the minute I had to stop at a red light and do the "clutch, gas, clutch, gas" again, the car turned into a stubborn mule, unwilling to move until the third attempt. *I hope I don't have to pass a driving test before they let me in America, or I'll be screwed.*

Driving test aside, I wasn't fully confident about the written test either, that I'd be taking in a week. Just the thought of it was making me tremble nervously. Unlike in America, however, in Moldova, there was always a way to beat the system.

"If you go to Moraru, he'll pass you for fifty—dollars, of course," a perky know-it-all student at the driving school shared with me the day before. "Raducanu is a bloodsucker, he will ask you for one hundred." So those were the names of bribe-takers at the licensing office.

"Why are you doing this?" I asked her. "You're rewarding corruption."

"They have the power, you know," she whispered and looked over her shoulder. "They can tank you on purpose if you defy them."

"I'll take the test by myself!" I dismissed her recommendations. It felt good to ride my high white horse for a few minutes, until the reality of going through this torture sank in.

Nevertheless, I asked the instructor to drop me off at the licensing office after class to look up the schedule. He dropped me at the curb at the bus stop instead, where the licensing office was hiding in the distance, in the middle of nowhere.

"Whoever thought to put this office at the end of the city, at the end of the road, needs to be shot in the leg," I mumbled, trying to fight the anxiety that this building was triggering. *Why did I have to do it today?*

I regretted my decision even more when I stepped into slushy snow mixed with water. The end of February hadn't decided whether to remain winter or, "to heck with it," go straight into spring. The sun in the sky was signaling that the end was near, but the cold, chilly breeze was setting the record straight: "Oh, yeah, it's still winter!" The sunshine didn't do anything for my wet feet either. My short navy-blue boots, which I was wearing for the seventh season, had cracked leather in places and were letting in icy water. "Careful, careful," I was telling myself, glancing at the door at the end of the parking lot, mindful of the worn bottoms of my shoes.

I was looking for snow patches on the sidewalk to step on, trying to avoid the ice that was sticking out here and there. "Here you are," I said, stepping confidently on the next patch.

Swish-sh-sh. I heard the sound of my right foot slipping on ice hidden under a thin layer of snow. My left foot twisted unnaturally behind me, as if I were an ice skater in a heavy winter coat, doing the splits on ice. I balanced for a few seconds but lost the battle, and my entire body fell on top of my left foot. I heard *swish, swish, crack* first, then I felt a sharp pain.

"Motherfucker!" I yelled as loud as my lungs allowed. I got on my knees, then slowly pushed myself up on my right foot. But as soon as I put my left foot down, the sensation of pain going up my leg was unbearable, as if somebody was poking me repeatedly with a knife. I couldn't stand on my left foot. I couldn't even touch the ground with it.

Why am I sweating? Oh, that can't be good! How am I going to check the schedule? Who cares about the schedule? My mind was wandering. *Somebody, help me! Anyone? Anyone?* I looked around in despair, but there was nobody in sight. There was no telephone booth nearby either. *I can't just stand here on one foot.* I looked at the licensing office in the distance. It was just a few hundred meters away, but now that seemed like a full kilometer. I turned around. The bus stop was closer. I gritted my teeth and went for it: *step, step, ouch; step, step, ouch; step, step, motherfucker!* The distance that had taken me thirty seconds earlier now took five minutes off my life and drained me, as if I had run a half marathon.

When I saw an orange bus in the distance, I almost cried. But the real tears came when I stepped on the first step of the bus. If I thought that walking with a hurt foot was hard, going up the stairs was like climbing a mountain. I dropped down on the first empty seat that I could find and stretched my feet in front of me. *This bus is going to the clinic. Good.* For the first time since I fell, I was thinking clearly. It was amazing what a relief it was not to have pressure on my left foot, at least for a while.

When the bus finally dropped me off at my destination, I looked at the long walkway to the clinic ahead of me. I had no choice but to proceed alone. I pulled together the last of my strength for the final fifteen minutes of a slow, dragging marathon: *step, step, ouch; step, step, motherfucker!*

"Your foot is broken in two places," a young doctor, barely out of medical school, told me, looking at my X-rays. "You said you walked to the clinic? I have no idea how you did that." I shook my head in disbelief. I didn't know either. "We'll need to put a cast on it. That will cost you—" he said, very businesslike, as if he worked as a warehouse cashier.

"Wait, wait." I put my hand up. In the pain of the moment, I had totally forgotten that post-Soviet medicine was "cash first, service second." "All I've got on me is my bus money. Don't tell me that I have to hop back home with a broken foot to get the money for the cast!"

"Can you call somebody? You'll need help to get home anyway, because you wouldn't be able to walk out of here in a cast. Do you know somebody who can bring you crutches?"

"No, I don't know anybody who has crutches!" I said, trying to keep myself together, only now faced with the logistical nightmare of being a person with a broken foot. *What good would crutches do me, going up six flights of stairs to our third-floor apartment in a building with no lift?* I was about to scream. Besides, the numbness in my foot had started wearing off, and the pain was no longer feeling like a knife stab, but like a cut from a rusty chainsaw going up and down my leg.

"You can pay for it when we take the cast off," he said, falling back on his Hippocratic Oath after getting the business part out of the way.

* * *

"What happened?" my mom yelled in shock, seeing me hopping on one foot, trying to get into the house.

"What does it look like?" I asked her, staying on one foot like a stork, leaning on my friend Vlad's shoulder. He'd taken pity on me and picked me up from the clinic in his car. "I fell, woke up, and *gips.*" I used the Russian word "gips" instead of "cast," from an old Soviet comedy, *The Diamond Arm,* about two robbers who hid diamonds in the cast of an unsuspecting tourist by mistake.

"Very funny."

"Thank you, Vlad. I think we've got it from here," I told my savior. "I'll call you later."

"Take care," he said, and left.

"Who's that?" Mom whispered suspiciously, seeing Vlad off with her eyes.

"A friend."

"A *male* friend?"

"Yeah, a friend," I snapped at her, unamused, leaning on her shoulder, trying to navigate the narrow corridor of our apartment toward the bedroom. "He was the only one who answered when I called, so I can call him a friend. One man in the entire damn county who didn't pull up my skirt. Imagine that!"

"Why didn't you call me?" she kept asking, helping me sit down on the bed.

"What good would that do when you don't have a car?" I pushed myself all the way to the wall and leaned on the pillow that she'd fluffed behind me so fast that I didn't even notice when she did it.

"David called twice already, and I didn't know where you were." She was scolding me while lifting my left foot in the cast carefully, then laying it down on another pillow even more carefully. "It's better when the foot is elevated. It won't throb as much," she said like an expert.

"That caregiver job that you had in Greece is coming in handy right now." I tried to smile.

"I picked up a few medical terms in Greek too." Mom giggled. "I even know that the Greek word 'hospital' sounds the same in English, so if I'd known where you were, I could have at least told David, 'Irina, hospital, hospital,' or something."

"Good one, Mama. 'Hospital, hospital' would really put David at ease." I closed my eyes, breathing out heavily.

"Where are the crutches?" Mom finally realized that something was missing.

"They didn't have any crutches. They said I'll have to buy them on my own."

"How are you going to walk around without crutches?"

"I don't know. Hopping, I guess." I cringed.

"It hurts like hell, doesn't it?" Mom asked. "Did they prescribe any painkillers for you?"

"He didn't give me a prescription."

"What kind of doctor doesn't prescribe painkillers to a person with a broken foot?"

"Well, the miracles of Soviet medicine, Mama."

"Here, take these." Mom pulled something from her purse.

"Aspirin? Isn't this for headaches?" I swallowed them, nonetheless. I was in so much pain that I would have taken anything. "The doctor said it will take six to eight weeks to heal, so there goes our backup plan, Mama," I tried to joke.

The next step was telling David, which I wasn't looking forward to, not wanting to deliver such bad news.

"I broke my foot," I told David, after the usual pleasantries, when he called the third time.

"What? I'm so sorry. Honey, I need you to be healthy, at least. Are you okay?"

"I have a cast and I can't get out of the house, but other than that, everything is peachy."

"What happened?"

"I fell on ice. Russian winters are not safe for humans. I didn't know whether I should tell you or not. I didn't want you to worry about me, when you're dealing with your own shit."

"You should always tell me what's going on. I don't want you to keep secrets from me. Especially something like that. Do you need anything? I can send you some money. Probably not much, because I just got back to work, but something."

"No. I'm fine. The medical costs here, I'm sure, are one hundred times cheaper than in America, though the quality is one hundred times cheaper too. You get what you pay for, right? Anyway, I thought I'd tell you, just in case you're planning a trip to Moldova. I wouldn't be able to do much until May. Unless you don't mind me jumping on one foot."

"Now we are a truly matching pair. One with half a foot and one with a broken foot." David laughed.

I lay in bed past midnight, unable to fall asleep. The throbbing pain from my broken foot was keeping me awake. I was tossing and turning, and thinking, and thinking again. Here we were, David and I, two broken people, "a truly matching pair," separated by the ocean, connected only by phone. Everything we'd tried to do was not getting us any closer. Shakira's melody was rolling in my head, like that time I danced to her music, full of hope, but I changed her words this time: "You'll be there, I'll be here, and that's the deal, my dear."

What else would life throw at us? How long could this separation last? Would David have the patience to follow through? Or would he eventually move on with his life and find comfort in someone nearby? *The million-dollar question*, as they said in America, *the million-dollar question!*

Chapter 22

The Curtains

Mom came from the bazar carrying new snow-white curtains with white flower patterns that reminded me of the frosty windows in Grandma's house in winter. A strange choice, considering it was already spring. But Mom was so into them, it was almost funny. She couldn't wait to hang them in the living room, getting up immediately on our old squeaky chair to measure the window and see if the material would cover it wall to wall. Mariana grabbed one end of the measuring tape and walked to the other side of the room, while I watched from the armchair with my cast resting on a short kitchen stool.

"Isn't it nice to have new curtains?" Mom said to me, though looking at Mariana. "When David comes, the house will look like new."

"I'm sure he won't care about our curtains," I said, shifting my cast to the right to find a more comfortable position.

"It's not about the curtains. It's about having a nice, presentable house. How can you not care about this? Don't you have any shame? It's like you weren't even raised by me." A metal plate with two old curtain wires hung from the ceiling. Mom used pliers to yank on it, but the rusty, ugly piece of metal just wouldn't come out, so she cut the wires off the plate instead. "Let's see if we can cover up this monstrosity with our new curtain rod," she said, and put the curtain rod on top of the window. "How does it look?"

"Great," I answered.

"That's good." She turned to me. "I don't want David to think we're savages."

"I'm sure he's not going to think that. We may not have as much money as Americans, but we're educated, well mannered, and have family values. Those are the qualities he's looking for. Not how much crap we have lying around."

"Maybe. But there are also visuals," Mom said, brushing me off and admiring the curtains. "We don't want to scare him off the minute he walks in this house."

"How are you going to hang that curtain rod?" I asked her to change the subject.

"Mariana, give me the screwdriver."

"Mom, these are old Soviet cement walls," I said. "We couldn't hammer even one nail into it. Do you think you can screw anything in there by hand? You need a drill."

"We don't have a drill." As if that meant a miracle could happen, Mom pushed on the screwdriver with all her strength. Her elbow moved up and down, the back of her neck turned red, but the screw didn't move a millimeter. "Mother ... fucking ... piece of shit!"

Mom cursed in front of us so rarely that I thought this was hilarious. *Stubborn, she says? I wonder whom I take after?*

* * *

The phone in the corridor rang with two short rings, and Lica ran to pick it up. "Alyo!" she said with importance in her voice. "Yes, she's home. One minute. I'll pass her the phone." She brought the landline phone into the room, dragging the long cord behind it. "Some Vasily Gramovich for you."

"Alyo!" I answered, somewhat shocked. I hadn't heard from Gramovich since December.

"*Zdravia jelaiu!*" he roared into the phone in his usual raspy voice. I found his greeting amusing, because it literally meant "I wish you good health," but it was also used as a formal greeting in the military.

"Good afternoon to you too. Did your oil company promote you to a captain or something?"

"I wish. We are still waiting for some approvals. Now the hold-up is on our side of the government. In the meantime, Shura gave me a list of projects to do so I don't go crazy. I fixed everything I could around the house, a cupboard door in the kitchen, installed a dish rack, hung some curtains." I shuddered at that last one. "You know, the handyman stuff. Now I'm checking on you and Tatiana to see if you're still interested in the job. She said she can't wait. Her current boss is a total ass. How are you doing? Can I get both of you out to a café or something?"

"It's nice of you to offer, but I can't go anywhere right now. I fell on ice and broke my foot. So I'm in a cast at home…"

"Where did you find ice in April?"

"Well, I've been in this cast for two months now, since February. Luckily, my day care let me take some unpaid time off to recover."

"Jeez! Do you need anything? I can stop at the bazar and buy some produce or something. Who's taking care of the kids?"

"Oh, they mostly take care of themselves. They're big enough. But my mother came back home from Greece, so she's taking care of all of us right now."

"What a coincidence. One of my neighbors came back from Italy for the first time in ten years because his wife is very sick. He used to be a policeman here, a major, but when the whole country collapsed, he couldn't deal with all the corruption. You know, when the bandits can buy their way out of jail, but the regular people can't get justice? I kept teasing him that he was too honest for an officer of the law."

"Uh-huh." I nodded. It was hard to stop Vasily if he wanted to talk, so I didn't try.

"One day, he quit the forces and went to Italy for work. He ended up working in a small shoe factory as a regular laborer. He said he had to be so meticulous and methodical in his new job—I guess the same way he was meticulous at his old job. He got very good at shoemaking. The owner noticed him, and in a few years promoted him to second-in-command. He made me eat my words yesterday. He said he's living proof it's possible to have an honest career without compromising your soul." I nodded again, as if he could hear me. "Anyway, I can stop by your house any time if you need help with groceries or whatever."

"Actually, Vasily, do you have a drill?"

"Of course I have a drill."

"Bring it with you. I have a handyman project for you."

"That's all? No problem. Give me your address. I'll be there in an hour."

* * *

"I can't believe she made you, her future boss, hang up our curtains," Mom said to Vasily, pouring him a second bowl of home-made chicken soup, then giving a joyful glance at her new white curtains, hung perfectly from ceiling to floor. "She has no shame."

"How do you think we survived all this time without money, Mom? We asked kind people for help. If they couldn't do it, there was no harm. But if they said yes, then all of a sudden our washing machine was fixed, or we had a new part for our broken TV—or curtains got hung." I pointed at the window.

"A woman's gotta do what she's gotta do!" Vasily said philosophically. "But please, don't worry. It was my pleasure. Aren't we human beings who just help each other in times of need? I know, nowadays, that's not so common, but my neighbor, the former police major, really inspired me with his story. So let's say I'm just paying it forward, that's all. I'm just glad I could help." He slurped broth from his spoon with such intensity that a green parsley leaf landed on his bushy mustache. "This soup is incredible. Thank you, Katerina."

"Our mother is the chef around here," Mariana said with pride, putting her hands on Mom's shoulders.

Mom blushed. "Oh, please, have more if you'd like."

"That's plenty. You don't want to overfeed the boss." Vasily laughed with a deep belly laugh. "Though, God only knows when our firm will open. I've been to every government and nongovernmental office possible to resolve this issue. I even went up and down my apartment building to all the neighbors who have influential jobs to see if I could find somebody who can push this through without having to bribe all these bloodsuckers. I haven't resolved things yet, but I found out a lot about my neighbors. One of them was a college professor but now works at the Italian embassy as a translator in the visa department. I never knew that. It's amazing what you can find out just by talking to people. I joked with him that if this business of mine doesn't work out, I might get a visa to Italy through him and go work in the Italian shoe factory. But don't mind me, tell me, how was it in Greece?"

"What can I say?" Mom took a deep breath. "It wasn't easy." She stirred the soup in her bowl, trying to find the right words.

"If it's too hard for you, you don't have to talk about it. Do you have anything else you need fixed while I'm here?"

"Since you asked, Vasily"—I raised my finger—"Did you say you know somebody who's working at the Italian embassy?"

"Yes, why?"

"Our mama here is trying to get a visa for Italy, and the firm we went to asked us for four hundred dollars."

"That's outrageous. Italians charge sixty dollars for a visa, tops. The rest she puts in her pocket, no doubt. Give me your passport,

I'll ask my neighbor if we can do something for you." Mom almost lost her breath.

The phone in the corridor rang two long rings. Lica ran to pick it up, as usual. "Mom, it's David!" she yelled.

"I'm coming!" I got up and, holding on to the walls and stepping gently on the cast, moved slowly to the phone.

"Hello, honey!" David sang into my ear.

"Hello! You're in a good mood."

"I wanted to call you so badly last night, but I didn't want to wake you up. Besides, it's a surprise!"

"I hate surprises." I'd had my fair share of them in my life. "What is it? You're freaking me out."

"I got such a good deal on tickets last night. I booked my flight to Bucharest for May fifteenth."

"David, that's exciting," I said carefully, filled with sudden panic.

"You don't sound excited."

"I am, believe me, but I'm still in the cast."

"What? You said they were supposed to take the cast off today."

"They did, but they put it right back on for two more weeks because the X-ray showed the bones aren't healed yet."

David sighed heavily. "I rushed it, didn't I?" he said. "Sorry, honey, I just couldn't wait. That's my fault, but don't worry. I'll carry you around myself if I have to."

"After your stroke? I don't think so. Well, there are three weeks before the fifteenth. Let's hope they'll take the cast off by then. But Bucharest is a long way from my home city. We'll need to take a train or another flight to Chişinău, if you want to see the kids."

"Is it really so far?" His tone changed. "It was such a good deal. Are you mad at me?"

"I'm not mad. I just wish you'd talked to me first. I don't want you to be stranded in a foreign airport because of a surprise."

"Neither do I. I just couldn't help it."

"Okay. Give me your flight information and I'll see what I can do."

I finally calmed down, trying to run all the options in my head, and hopped back into the kitchen with a piece of paper in hand. Everyone was waiting quietly, heads turned toward me. *What?* I wanted to ask, but no words were needed. Their eyes said it all. I raised my left hand in the air, touched the wall with my right, and said as dramatically as I could, "David is flying to Bucharest on May fifteenth!"

"*Ura! Ura!*" Lica, Serghei, and Mariana screamed and started jumping in the kitchen.

"He's coming now?" Mom asked, looking ready to have a panic attack. "With your foot in the cast and everything that's going on?"

I got myself to the edge of the bench, sat down, and shrugged. *What could I say?*

Mom kept talking. "We haven't finished the remodeling yet, as I wanted. And what am I going to do about Italy?"

"With this new development, I think you should stay home until David comes," I said.

"Who's David?" Vasily asked curiously.

"Do you have six more hours, Vasily? Because it's a long story. And you thought you were just stopping by for some soup and curtains."

Chapter 23

David's Arrival

The early May sun was burning through a window of the tiny, old microbus that was taking me to the Bucharest airport to meet David. There were fifteen other passengers packed in together like sardines in a barrel, and the air conditioner was broken, creating an unmistakable aroma of public transportation sweat.

I wore a knit white summer top with decorative holes that let a bit of air from a wide-open top window flow through. But I regretted putting on my new black jeans. With this heat, they were soaking wet and burning my thighs, as if I was soaking in a hot bathtub from my neck down. My left foot, freshly relieved from the cast a few days earlier, was throbbing uncomfortably.

David would get quite the culture shock if I took him back to Chișinău on a microbus like this. Or I might get a shock if I made it all the way to Bucharest and he didn't show up. I shook my head, trying to scare the bad thoughts away and turned to the window, hoping that time would pass faster if I focused on the passing green fields.

I finally spotted the words "Bucharest International Airport" on top of a long building with tall, wide, dark glass doors. When I ran from the microbus into the building, a wave of chilly air conditioning shocked me. *Sweet mother of Jesus.* It was like jumping into a pool of ice. I had to pee immediately. It was smart not to take much stuff with me. Moving through the airport with my little shoulder bag was much easier. I ran into the spacious bathroom: bright, clean, no harsh smell of urine. Such a Western European feel. If not for the announcement in Romanian on the stall door, I might have imagined that I was peeing in some foreign bathroom in a far, faraway world.

While washing my hands, I saw myself in the mirror. *Sweet mother of Jesus again!* I looked like a water creature escaped from a rotten swamp. My long hair was wet and sticky. My red lipstick had smudged onto my cheek, as if I was bleeding from my mouth. I frantically washed off sweat, dirt, lipstick, all of it. Then I reapplied my bright-red lipstick one more time and looked in the mirror again: *Hello, Ms. Irina! This could be the beginning of your journey to America. Or the end.* I felt a chill go down my spine. My hands started shaking. A nauseating feeling hit my gut. I ran into the stall, trying to hold it in. *This was unexpected.* Even during my school or college exams, which always felt like mini deaths, I never got so nervous.

Breathe, breathe! I was talking to myself like my mom did when I was a kid and I'd get car sick on our way to Grandma's. My body demanded something sour or salty to suppress my nausea. *Where do you get lemons in an airport?* That question distracted me for a moment. It seemed that I simply needed to think about something else, and the desire to puke went away as quickly as it appeared. Feeling free but still cautious, like a woman who'd just escaped captivity, I went out.

I went to check David's flight on the arrivals board. *New York, New York.* I smiled. It sounded so American. There were two hours before landing. Good. I had more time to prepare, but also more time to be in agony. Right in front of me, people were coming out of the arrival gate from earlier flights. Some of them passed on to the exit. Others, with their eyes wandering, were looking for someone in the crowd on my side of the barrier. They smiled and waved if they found them. Two teenage girls held a poster in their hands—"We love you, Dad!"—and started jumping when they saw their father. Hugs and kisses, tears and smiles.

The thought hit me then: What if I didn't recognize David? Af-ter all, I'd only seen him in pictures. Or what if he didn't recognize me? What could I do? Just yell his name into the crowd?

I walked away to calm my nerves and, instead, imagined how we could lose each other in the airport, each of us assuming that the other one hadn't shown up. I passed a line of taxi drivers in black suits, holding white cardboard signs with names written on them, probably passengers they had to pick up. *Wait a minute. Of course. I need a piece of paper to write his name on! Why didn't I think of this earlier?*

I dug through my purse, looking for something to write on. But all I could find was an old letter that I'd printed at Leonid's on some yellowish paper. It was wrinkled, with ripped edges. I straightened it out, turned it over, and wrote on the blank side: "David Draisey." It looked too official, impersonal, like I was a taxi driver, so I added more. "David Draisey, I love you!" It was *so* tacky, with uneven cursive letters, but in these circumstances, it would have to do. I looked at the arrival board one more time and moved closer to the barrier.

The arrivals board said that the New York plane had already landed, but the gates wouldn't open for another thirty minutes. *Why was it taking them so long to let everyone out?* I walked back and forth restlessly, then stopped in a spot that seemed to give me the best view, though I couldn't stay still for long. I was tapping my right foot. I was stretching my shoulder blades. I could feel cold sweat on my body. *Come on, gate, open up already!*

Suddenly, it happened. Two large doors parted ways slowly, like old grandmas, making room for the crowd that quickly filled the opening. I scanned the people who rushed out. A big, tall man, towering over the crowd like a giant, stood out. It was strange to see a giant like this wearing regular human black pants and a white polo shirt, pushing a cart holding two suitcases. His big head, with a very short haircut, was shining under the light, betraying a balding spot on the top. His face was stamped with the most standard American smile: wide, cheerful, addressed to no one in particular, like you see in American movies. I immediately recognized David, though I'd never imagined he would be a man-giant like this. He'd mentioned his height in inches to me before, but those inches meant nothing to my metric measurement system. *Surprise!*

I don't know how, but he picked me out of the crowd, then noticed the sign in my hand and teared up. "I love you too!" he said, and left his luggage behind, walking toward me, wobbly, uneven, heavier on his right side. As he approached me, I noticed a black orthopedic boot on his right foot, but I didn't have time to examine it.

"Finally, I get to hold you!" he said, and drowned me in his hug, embracing me with his big, long arms. He kissed me on my lips like a thirsty man who'd reached water after walking through the desert for days. I shrugged. His passionate reaction in the middle of a busy airport felt awkward, as if my fantasy became reality too quickly, and I didn't have time to adjust to it.

He took his lips off mine but kept me in his arms and smiled, exposing braces on his front, slightly crooked, yellowish teeth. So many little things that I hadn't known or realized about him were jumping out at me now that we were so close to each other. I wondered if he was noticing little things like that about me too. Like the brown circles with small white blemishes under my eyes, courtesy of my grandma's genes. I realized right then that all of this would take some getting used to. Though, at least for now, he didn't seem to be overly analytical about my looks.

"You are so much more beautiful than your pictures," David said, finally letting me go.

"You're a little different than I imagined," I said honestly.

"Fatter than you thought?"

"Bigger ... taller than I thought."

"I hope I didn't disappoint you."

"You came all the way from America for me, so I'm not disappointed."

"Funny you should say that. I was bragging about you on the plane to a lady next to me."

"You're talking to random people about us?"

"Of course. I couldn't contain my happiness!" He couldn't contain it, even now, when talking to me. "She asked me, 'What are you going to do if she doesn't show up at the airport?' I honestly didn't know what I would do. This is my first time in Europe. Heck, I've never been outside the U.S., so I'm also glad you made it all the way from Moldova for me." He hugged me one more time, as if trying to make sure I was still there. "So, where do we go from here?" he asked.

"We need to get to Chișinău. However, the night train to Moldova is leaving in half an hour. I don't think we'll make it. We can try to catch a bus. It will take about six or seven hours to get home."

"Seven hours? I just came out of a transatlantic nineteen-hour flight. How long would it take by plane?"

"About an hour or so …"

"That sounds much better."

"Flight to Chișinău … today is … full," an airport ticket agent said in broken English. "We have only business class left for tomorrow's flight. Three hundred dollars each."

"Six hundred dollars for both?" I gasped and looked at David, who was counting the cash in his wallet.

"Do you accept Visa credit cards?" he asked.

"No, no American cards," the agent said.

David sighed, getting more frustrated with each answer he heard.

"That's too much." I touched his hand, trying to give him a way out. "We can take the bus or the train tomorrow."

"No, we're doing this," David insisted stubbornly and paid cash for the tickets.

"Are you hungry?" he asked me when we were done with the tickets, as if buying tickets was so exhausting it had starved him to death. "Oh, my God, look. McDonald's." He giggled like a kid when he saw the red and yellow stripes in the nearby eating area.

"You just came from America. Why McDonald's?"

"It's American comfort food," he explained and walked up to the counter, almost salivating. "Can I have a Big Mac and a large Coke?" he ordered. "What would you like?" he asked me.

"I don't know. Aren't they all the same?" I looked at the board with pictures of burgers.

"No, they are not the same!" David was almost offended, a true McDonald's connoisseur!

"I don't care. They all look the same," I answered.

David shook his head. "Okay, then. We'll take two Big Macs with French fries and two Cokes," he told the young blond girl working at the counter.

"What's 'French fries'?" I asked. "The fried potatoes?"

"Yes, the fried potatoes." He smiled, amused by my confusion.

"Why are they called 'French'? I thought that was a classic American food."

"I honestly don't know." David laughed. "Americans are weird like that. Making shit up."

"Big Mac hamburger and Coca-Cola," the cashier repeated the order back to David with a smile, poking the keys on her register enthusiastically. I imagined that's exactly how an American girl taking Big Mac orders would look.

We took the far table on the left and rolled David's luggage into the corner, while a second girl, barely sixteen, brought trays of food to the table and two plastic glasses with our drinks.

"They don't have lids on the cups here?" David noticed, sipping from the glass. "Ah-ah-ah! Nice and cold, just the way I like it! Wait, wait, don't start eating," he told me, getting a video camera out of his suitcase. "Let's say hello to my family first!"

"Here?" I asked.

"Yes, with McDonald's in the background. It's perfect!"

I rolled my eyes and took a sip of my drink while he was getting the camera ready.

"This is so sweet." I stuck my tongue out. "How do you drink this?" I put the cup down.

"Say hello!" David told me. I lifted my hand to wave to the camera. *Splash!* I heard it first, then I saw it. The sound came from my cup, which I'd knocked down, and now it was rolling off the table with an impressive summersault, spreading sticky brown fluid everywhere: on the table, on the floor, on David's pants. *Shit!*

I looked at David, terrified and embarrassed, expecting him to jump up and try to clean himself. But David was sitting in his chair, laughing hysterically, with his camera rolling. He pointed it at the spill on the floor, where the teenage server was trying to clean up my mess with a mop. "Look at this beautiful picture," David was commenting.

"Stop filming!" I yelled, jumping over the massive brown lake.

"We are so sorry," David said to the waitress, who didn't look enthused. He finally put his camera down. "You gotta admit this was hilarious." He looked at me and giggled again, covering his mouth with his hand. His laughter put me at ease. The spill didn't seem to be a big deal to him.

"Do all Americans laugh when they make a mess?" I asked. "My mom wouldn't ever laugh at this, that's for sure. She would smack my ass if I'd done it as a kid."

"No! That's cruel." He looked at me sympathetically. "In our family, we don't sweat the small stuff. Can we get a refill for that?" he asked the waitress.

"You want to buy one more Coca-Cola?" she asked in English.

"You have to pay for refills?" He was dumbstruck.

"Yes," I told him, surprised by his confusion. "You don't have to pay for refills in America?"

"No." David looked at me. "It was an accident."

"We pay for our accidents here," I said. "So, no, I don't want another Coca-Cola." I looked at the waitress.

"Let's take a picture together," David suggested, when we finally got out of the airport. "The immigration lawyer told me to take lots of pictures for our profile. See. I borrowed a digital camera from a friend of mine." I smiled. *He'd come prepared, ready for the next step.* "Also, we need to preserve this historic moment. It's still very surreal to me."

"Very surreal to me too," I said with total sincerity. David prepared the camera and looked around, like he owned the place.

"Sir, can you please take our picture?" he said to a man smoking nearby. The man looked puzzled or, perhaps, annoyed that this foreigner assumed he spoke English. But David didn't get flustered. He said it slowly one more time—first pointing at the gentleman—"Can … you …?" Then he pointed at the camera—"Take … a photo …?" And finally he pointed at himself and me while saying—"Of us?" The man reluctantly put his cigarette down and took David's camera. He flipped it a few times in his hands, then put it to his left eye.

David raised his finger and turned to me. "Tell him it's a digital camera. He doesn't need to put it to his eye. He can look at the image on the screen."

"What's digital? And where is this screen?" I asked him. I was feeling as puzzled as the smoking man and struggled to translate David's words into Romanian, which was difficult since I didn't understand them myself. David took the camera back, turned it around, and pointed the camera at a tree.

"See?" He pointed at the image of the tree on the screen of his camera.

"Whoa!" both the stranger and I said in one voice, like two Amazons who'd never seen an electric light before. Even more intriguing was observing David find ways to communicate, when all had seemed lost. The smoking man, now curious, took the camera and stepped back.

"Cheese!" he said in English. David put his arms around me, hugging me from behind, and squeezed me tight in front of him. I tilted my head to the left, worried I would cover his face.

The man, smiling like he'd just become the best photographer in the world, ran back with the camera and showed us our photo on the screen. "Good?" he asked, and I glanced at it, getting my first visual of how I looked engulfed in David's arms. His face— with an infinite smile—was clearly visible above my shoulder. In fact, his head was way above mine, making my maneuver with a tilted head unnecessary.

"Thank you. We look so cute," David said, and gave two thumbs up to the man.

"What's next?" he asked me.

"If we stay overnight in Bucharest, we'll need to find a hotel," I said. "The city bus stops over there."

"I'd rather take a cab. My suitcases are very heavy." He raised his hand at two parked taxis, but the drivers were taking a smoke break outside, with their backs turned to us. "Fwee-ee-eet!" I whistled at them loudly with a long trill that even surprised me. That got their attention. One of them jumped in his car fast and pulled up.

"You can whistle?" David looked at me with curiosity.

"If I have to."

"You and I, we'll get along just fine." He laughed.

* * *

The taxi driver was a chatty young man with decent English, who asked David all kinds of questions about America, while driving us to what he described as "a nice and reasonably priced hotel." It put David in such a good mood that he gave him a tip. But as we walked into the hotel, the dynamic changed.

"No American credit cards," the hotel desk clerk said dryly, looking at David as if he'd just landed from Mars.

"How much for the room?" I asked him in Romanian.

"Three hundred dollars for foreigners."

"How much for locals?"

"Fifty dollars," he said shortly, as if doing me a huge favor. "Are you booking a room?"

"Yes," I said defiantly, almost slamming my passport on his desk.

"What's going on?" David looked worried, listening to our back and forth.

"I'll have to book the room in my name," I explained, "or he'll overcharge you six times over because you're an American."

David opened his mouth wide in disbelief. "Is that normal around here?"

"I'm assuming that's an adjustment for foreign income. Give him fifty dollars. Today, you're under my jurisdiction." It felt good to protect my American man from a double standard.

"Irina? From Moldova, huh?" The clerk looked at me with suspicion. In his mind, obviously, there could not be an innocent reason for a Moldavian girl to check into a hotel with a foreigner. Nevertheless, he took the hundred-dollar bill that David got out of his wallet, processed the booking in my name, but gave David only forty dollars back.

"No more change," he told him.

"You better find that change," I insisted. He was not getting any tips today with such an attitude. The clerk gave me a look, but obeyed, like I knew he would. He wouldn't want to upset the American guest. To David's amusement, he pulled a ten-dollar bill out of his pocket and handed it to us. *Look at that, he found the change!*

I enjoyed that little mental dance with the clerk. I could pull the American card on him, when he crossed the line with me, then go back to my Moldavian card, when he tried to pull a fast one on David. I took our room key, and before we even turned our backs to the counter, the clerk casually took David's hundred-dollar bill from the till and put the money in his pocket.

"Did you see that?" David whispered, still amazed that he'd landed in a different world.

"Welcome to the Wild West," I said, and walked away, pulling one of David's suitcases.

The hotel room was spacious and clean, but dark-green curtains covered the windows almost entirely, making the room unusually grim. David dragged in his last suitcase, passing a cozy armchair in the corner, puffing like a person who'd just run a mile. I couldn't believe how heavy his cases were. *What the hell did he pack in there? Half of America?*

To the left of the room there was a large bed with a sparkly white cover and four pillows, also white. I'd only seen beds like that in foreign movies, so I giggled. David, on the other hand, sighed heavily. "This is a queen size. I only sleep on king-size beds," he said, visibly disappointed.

"What's this queen and king size? I don't understand," I said, totally confused.

"The queen-size bed is smaller than the king," he explained. "Can you call downstairs and see if we can change rooms?"

"This is a small bed?" But as the words came out of my mouth, I measured him with my eyes against the bed. "Okay, I'll call them."

But it was in vain. I could clearly hear the pleasure in the clerk's voice when he answered shortly, "We don't have king-size beds in our hotel." That bastard had to get his last hurrah!

"It is what it is," David said, finally accepting his fate. He dropped his silver, hard-shell suitcase on the bed and popped the latches. The lid swung wide. The clothes jumped out like a jack-in-the-box, spitting out shirts and pants everywhere, exposing an old camera underneath.

"Is this a Polaroid?" I asked him, surprised that I recognized the brand, though its distinctive shape was hard to miss. "I first saw one of these at the end of the eighties. I don't know anyone who still has one around." I laughed.

"I know, it's a little old-fashioned, but it's still fun to take pictures with it, so we'll use it later." *He did bring half of old America with him.* "I have a present for you," he said, digging through his clothes. He dropped onto the bed, holding a thick book with a brown cover in his hands.

"You brought me a book?"

"No!" He laughed. "That's the Harry Potter book I was reading on the plane." He set the book next to him on the bed and kept looking inside the case. I glanced at the cover, which showed a boy with round glasses wearing a black cloak and riding a broom.

"Is this a fairy tale? Do adults like to read fairy tales in America?"

"No, it's not a fairy tale. It's about a magic school."

"Magic is not fairy tale?"

"You haven't heard of Harry Potter? It's a big hit in America." I shook my head. David opened his mouth in disbelief again. *Some of us have to live in a real world*, I thought, though I didn't get offended. I was sure that wouldn't be his last shock. *David is into stories about magic schools? How bizarre!*

"They're making a movie based on this book," he continued. "We'll have to go see it as a family, when you come to America."

"Okay," I said, without giving it a second thought. At that point, Harry Potter was not exactly on my priority list.

"I brought your engagement ring with me." He finally dug out of his suitcase a small, black jewelry box, tied with a white bow.

"Oh!" I sat down in the armchair in front of him, still a little in awe of how it was all finally becoming a reality. I watched him take the ring out of the box. It was half platinum, half golden, with one tiny diamond on the top, embedded in a metal square with sharp edges. One wrong move, and I'd catch and rip my clothes with it!

David stretched out his right hand, held the ring in front of me, and asked me very ceremoniously, "Irina, my darling, will you be my wife?"

"Yes, yes, yes," I answered anxiously. *Who cares about the sharp edges? This a magic ring. It opens doors to America.* I gave him my left hand, and he put the ring on my finger, pushing it hard until it hit my knuckle. The ring got stuck helplessly and was not moving anywhere. He hadn't guessed my size again. This time in the opposite direction.

"Sorry." David looked at me, scared. "I asked the lady at the jewelry store to try it on her middle finger. I thought it would fit you." *Middle finger indeed.*

"Do American women have tiny hands?" I joked.

"Ha-ha-ha. I don't think so." He laughed, covering his mouth like a little boy, trying to hide his teeth. "I'll have to exchange it when I go back."

"Or we can find a place here to make it bigger." I was not willing to let it go. I twisted the ring around my ring finger a few times until I could finally pull it off, then slid it on my pinky.

"That's a brilliant idea. We'll fix it when we get out in the city. But wait, let's record this: you with the engagement ring on your hand to show my relatives that you are real."

"They don't believe I'm real?"

"You have to admit it's quite a fairy-tale love story you and I have. Some believe me more than others." *Funny. They'd rather believe a book about a magic school. How many realists advised him not to come here? But he flew in anyway!* "We don't need to prove anything to nonbelievers," David continued. "This video is mostly for my family and my son, Derek. He's really curious about the whole thing. Here it is!" David extracted the video camera from the bottom of his suitcase.

"What do I say?" I asked, choking up, panicking.

"Say something from your heart."

"I don't know … I need to think. This recording is forever."

"Ready?" He gave me a short warning, then turned on the camera and spoke first. "Hello, everybody in America! This is Irina, the Moldavian woman I'm in love with. She wants to say a few words to all of you."

I breathed out heavily and waved at the camera. "Hello, David's family! I'm glad I finally met this man … And he's here with me now … I don't know what else to say, besides, that I'm real."

David laughed loudly, wholeheartedly, and stopped the camera. "That's good for now."

"I need to call home, so they don't worry," I said.

"Of course, of course." He pulled the hotel phone closer to me so I could dial Chişinău. My sister picked up.

"Mariana, tell Mom I got to Bucharest all right."

"Did you meet David? Did you meet David?" she asked with a curiosity she couldn't contain.

"Yes. I'm at the hotel with him right now."

"Hallelujah!" Mariana yelled. Then I heard her asking Mom: "What?" Then she said to me, "Mom's asking if he's really big."

I looked at David. Luckily, he couldn't understand Romanian. "He's ginormous, big and tall."

"Oh, my God!" She laughed. "Did he squish you like a bug?"

"We haven't gotten to that part yet," I shushed her. "We bought airplane tickets for tomorrow. We should be in Chişinău at one o'clock."

"Mom," Mariana yelled away from the phone, "you better be ready. Your American son-in-law is coming tomorrow!"

Mom took the receiver from her. "What should I cook for him? I don't know what Americans like to eat. Does he eat soup?"

"Just cook your usual dishes. You don't need to make anything special for him. I'm sure he'll find something he'll like."

"Is he really big?" Mom asked me, toning her voice down, trying to be discreet, as if David could overhear us and object.

"You'll see him tomorrow. Bye now," I said, and hung up.

"What did they say?" David was curious.

"Mom's worried about what to cook for you." I told him half the truth.

"That's so sweet." he smiled. "But I'd like to take you out for dinner tonight."

"Do I get to dress up?"

"You can do whatever you want."

"Good. Because I brought my green dress from home, the same one that's in my photo from the dating agency. Remember?" I said, while putting on my turquoise dress, which had a split going up the front of my left leg. I turned around to show off.

"Wow! It's just like you jumped out of your photo!" he said. I turned to the mirror and put on my bright-red cherry lipstick, then turned around one more time. "*Mamasita!*"

David whistled. I laughed, detecting a Spanish word I wasn't familiar with, but I could guess what it meant by the cat-like look David gave me.

"We have a restaurant upstairs in the hotel," said the friendly woman who'd replaced the earlier jerk at the counter.

I didn't like the idea. I was all dolled up and ready for a walk. I hadn't been out on a dinner date in a while, but David jumped on it. "That will be perfect," he said. "I can't walk far with my half foot." *Oh, yeah, I'd totally forgotten about that!*

We took the elevator to the top floor, where the restaurant was located on an open terrace. The city spread out before us in semi-darkness, flickering with occasional starburst lights, resembling the magic carpet that I'd seen in a cartoon about Ali Baba and Jasmine when I was a little girl. Candles in jars were placed on bright ruby table cloths, matching my lipstick, and a light wind was shaking the flames.

"So romantic!" David said when we took our seats at the table. He was absorbing the whole experience like a child encountering the sea for the first time. "What would you like to eat?" he asked me, flipping through the menu.

"I don't know. It's been ten years since I ordered a meal in a restaurant. Now I don't even recognize the names on this menu." I looked at it a few times until I realized that the menu was in English. I switched to the Romanian page, but that didn't help either. Half the dishes on the Romanian page were also in English: "rib eye," "sirloin," "baby ribs." *Aren't there equivalents in Romanian?* I wondered. How many food categories have we missed, for God's sake?

"Would you like chicken or beef?" David tried to narrow my confusion down.

"Chicken." I pointed to a dish on the menu that had the Romanian word *pui* in it. "This one."

"A New York steak for me," David said to the waitress a few seconds later, evidently feeling more at home than me.

"What would you like to drink?" the waitress asked.

"I'd like some Coke," David said first.

"Coke?" The waitress looked worried.

"Yes, Coke or Pepsi."

"Oh, Coca-Cola!" the waitress said, relieved.

David laughed, his belly jiggling. "Funny, the server at the Mc-Donald's in the airport said the same thing: 'Coca-Cola.' We just say 'Coke.' Sorry, I didn't mean to scare you. I just need to be more careful with what I say around here, so people don't think I'm asking for cocaine." He laughed.

The waitress turned to me, likely only grasping half of what he'd said. "What would you like? We have an excellent collection of wines and cocktails."

"My grandpa used to make three barrels of wine every year. I'm not sure I'd like bottled wine after that."

"Look at you, a wine snob." David winked at me, amused. "They have margaritas here. I think you'll like that."

"What's a margarita?"

"It's a cocktail made of tequila and lime juice," the waitress explained.

"That sounds exotic. I've never had tequila, or lime juice. I think I'll try that."

"With the salt or sugar on the rim?"

"What? They put salt in drinks?"

"The traditional American margarita is served with the salt on the rim of the glass," David explained.

"Then I'd like a traditional American margarita," I said, finally making my decision. The waitress wrote it down and left to fulfill our order.

"Excuse me, can you take our picture?" David addressed the English-speaking older couple sitting next to us. He gave them his Polaroid. My heart dropped. *Polaroid, really?* The couple laughed at the antiquated photo equipment, but the older man knew exactly how to handle it.

"Cheese!" he said, and snapped our photo. The lady giggled, looking at how the camera spat out the photo of us cuddled together.

"The quality is not the best, because it's dark in here," the lady noticed.

"I know, it's a dinosaur, but I found this camera in my dad's closet after he died, with a full case of film that he'd never used. This photo is a tribute to my dad. He would love the story of how Irina and I met. Let's take another one, with the digital camera. This one is for immigration paperwork."

"How did you two meet?" The man had grown curious. I cringed, but David couldn't wait to tell them.

"We met online. We wrote each other letters and talked on the phone for about six months, and I just flew in from the U.S. today to marry her. Today's our first real date."

"Oh, yeah?" The woman looked at us with her big, inquisitive eyes.

"What are you doing here?" David asked them in return.

"My husband and I are here on vacation," the woman said. "Romania was such a closed country during communism, so we were curious to see how it looks now. We've found it to be beautiful and friendly. Good food, great wine. It's amazing how times have changed. Before, as Americans, we couldn't even peek behind the Iron Curtain, and now we're vacationing in Eastern Europe and marrying each other." The woman smiled. "Congratulations to you both. You seem like a lovely couple."

"Thank you," I said, sincerely moved by her words. It was nice to hear that I wasn't judged. Maybe Americans were like that, with open minds. We clinked our glasses together.

"Let our countries always get along! No more Iron Curtains! No more Cold Wars!" the American couple said.

The world had indeed turned upside down. I, a woman from behind the Iron Curtain, was sharing a toast with an American woman, clinking my margarita glass against her glass of Romanian wine.

* * *

"Can I take a shower first?" I asked, when we got back to our room after dinner.

"Of course," David said. "I'll unpack the rest of my stuff in the meantime."

I turned on the faucet in the bathroom and let warm water run through my fingers until it filled up more than half the bathtub. I lay down in the tub to soak a little bit and let my mind rest from all my anxieties, anticipating what was going to happen next. *Will we have sex? Will we not have sex? What if I don't like him in bed?*

I was half listening to the noises in the other room, behind the closed bathroom door. But they suddenly got quiet. *What if he knocks at the door and I'm naked in here? Do I let him in? Do I tell him to wait out there?* I rushed to get out of the bathtub quickly and wrapped myself in the soft, white bathrobe that I'd discovered in the bathroom and cracked the door open. *How can he unpack so quietly?* I wondered.

I looked toward the bed against the wall. David was lying there diagonally, still in his clothes, with one foot on the bed and one foot on the floor. His arms were spread wide, body surrounded by stuff that hadn't made it to the nearby closet shelves. He was snoring loudly, with his large chest rising, then caving in like a bagpipe. *He must be dead tired from the flight.*

I tiptoed to the bed, picked up the clothes lying around him, and dropped them on a chair. Then I lay down next to him in a corner of the bed, curling up like a child. David felt me moving and turned to me. "Sorry, I fell asleep," he said. "How rude of me."

He hugged me from behind, but in just a few seconds, he was lost to sleep again. I breathed out, relieved. *What a long day!* And I closed my eyes too. Tomorrow was going to be another long day, so we both needed to rest.

Chapter 24

We're Going Home

"Are you ready? We're going home," I said cheerfully, looking at David. He was recovering his two suitcases from the trunk of the taxi, setting them on the pavement at the Bucharest airport's entrance, in the same spot where we took our first photo yesterday.

"I was born ready, baby!" David hugged me and gave me a smooch, showing no worries whatsoever. *If he only knew what my mother and I talked about yesterday.*

"That's a propeller airplane," he said, and looked with disappointment at the small regional plane that was getting ready for boarding. It had two large propellers in front. "I didn't even know these were still in use."

"It doesn't look like any of the other Soviet planes I've flown on before."

"These are very loud," he said, seemingly not only to me but to everybody else in line. The people closest to us smirked without saying anything. I knew what they were thinking: *Arrogant American!*

"Okay," I answered matter-of-factly, giving him the same smirk. Not like the airline was going to swap the plane for him. "The flight is just an hour long. We'll be fine."

"Business class!" the ticket lady called with a thundering voice. She didn't even need her speakerphone. We could hear her just fine.

"That's us." David hurried. "I've never flown business class before."

"Neither have I," I said, and followed him, feeling excited. The plane might be ugly, but at least we got the good seats.

My smile faded as soon as I saw our seats. They were in the

front row of the area that was, absolutely mistakenly, called "business class." There was nothing business-like about it. It didn't even have a curtain to separate it from the rest of the plane. The comfort promised by business-class seats was also misleading. The puke-green cushions, pressed by thousands of butts before us, could not provide much comfort. The only benefit was additional leg room.

"These are just two seats in the front row," David said to the stewardess who was trying hard to keep her smile.

"This is our business class," she explained. "Please take your seats."

I giggled, looking at David's face with its open mouth, full of "what the hell just happened?"—words that never managed to get out. "Take your seat, David," I said. "You are about to have the ride of your life!"

David huffed but dropped into his seat, then looked out the window. "The propeller is right next to us. These must be the least comfortable seats on the plane. I don't understand how they can sell these as business class." He sighed again. "Do you provide food on this flight?" he asked the stewardess.

"No. You'll get snacks when we take off," she replied.

"Not even for purchase?"

"No," she said shortly and moved away to help somebody put his luggage in the overhead bin, though the man didn't seem to need her help. Mostly likely she was eager to get away from David. I didn't blame her. If I were a stewardess, I'd want to get away from a passenger with a demand list a mile long. But I couldn't get away from him. He was now my official fiancé, whom I was taking home to my mom, and my sister, and my kids.

"We should have gotten breakfast before we left," he said.

"We'll have plenty of food when we get home." I tried to calm him down.

"You don't understand. With my diabetes, I have to eat when I'm hungry, or I'll fall into a diabetic coma."

"Now you're telling me this?" What if he dropped dead in mid-air? I imagined what I'd have to do to get his big body off this airplane. And how would I call his family back home with the news? Then what? How did you ship a dead body back to America? *For God's sake, can we just take off already?*

Vr-r-r-r! I heard the cranky propeller blades as the airplane tried to start. *Vr-r-r-r!* They did it again, then made a third noise, reminding me of a protective mama-chicken trying to warn her chicks about the danger of flying. Bo-o-ock, bo-o-ock, bo-o-ock! Finally, slowly, the plane started moving down the tarmac. David was right: the darn propellers were unbearably loud, irritating my ears with a screeching and annoying woo-oo-oo.

"What?" I yelled when David asked me something. It was impossible to decipher his words. He repeated it again, but I couldn't understand him, so he finally gave up. As soon as I got acclimated to the noise, the plane started shaking violently with some insane up and down moves. One minute it was pressing my bladder to the seat, and the next it was lifting my stomach up to my throat. I raised my hand and called for the flight attendant, though my words were drowned in the noise. She didn't hear me, but saw me, and came flying with a brown bag. She clearly knew the drill.

"Ho-o-ney, are you okay?" I saw David's lips moving.

"No." I shook my head.

"Lean on me," he said, squeezing me with his right hand. I unbuckled the seatbelt and lay down on my left side with my head on his belly, covering my ears with my hands. This propeller plane was shaking me down to my last bone, unlike any other flight I'd been on in my life. *Of all days, today?* My body was sweating so intensely that it created a wet spot on David's shirt. I put all my effort into holding back my gastric juices, which were threatening to pop out of my mouth at any minute. David squeezed me tighter, caressing my right hand. "Everything is going to be okay," he whispered into my ear.

When will it be okay? I wondered. *What if he has to carry my dead body from the airplane to my house? Now wouldn't that be a scene?* Before I even finished my thought, the plane took a nose dive. Were we landing? I couldn't tell. I was afraid to lift my head or open my eyes or move at all. Then all of a sudden, we hit the runway, and the plane bounced a few times as if we were on a rollercoaster. The crowd started clapping and cheering loudly, "We made it!"

"Do people do this around here? Chant that we made it? Was there a chance that we wouldn't?" David asked.

I raised my head. Finally, I was able to hear what he was saying, though I still felt like my head had been dipped in water.

"These airplanes are old. Anything can happen," I answered, feeling that my blood was finally returning to my cheeks.

"That's it! When we head back to Bucharest, we're taking the train," David said passionately.

"Okay, American," I answered with a weak smile. "Let's get you through customs. I'm a local, but you'll need an entrance visa."

"They didn't ask me for a visa when I landed in Romania."

"Moldova is a different country. Americans don't get a free pass here."

"We're a little spoiled, aren't we?" David laughed.

"A little?"

We got out of the plane on the runway and boarded a bus that took us to the airport's entrance, where a sign showing the city's name—Chișinău—had a chipped "u" at the end.

"Wow!" David said. "That's a tiny airport." I used to work in this airport as a telegraph operator in a small post office right after high school. It had a restaurant upstairs and two cafeterias, where I'd stop for food on my graveyard shifts, so the two-story building seemed big to me. This was also the place where my ex-husband, Igor, and I met, when he was on patrol rounds from the military base nearby. Therefore, this airport always had a nostalgic feeling to me. But now, after flying in from Bucharest, I had to agree with David. Chișinău airport, and by extension my native city, looked incredibly provincial.

The line going to the exit was dissipating quickly. People with Moldavian, Romanian, Russian, and Ukrainian passports were going through the checkpoint and leaving the arrivals area. David and I went to the farthest customs window that said "visas." There was only one person before us in line, a short man with dark skin and jet-black, bushy hair.

"What is this?" the customs officer asked when he took the man's passport. The man said something in Arabic, but corrected himself. "Visa, visa."

"Where's your entry visa?" the custom's officer asked him in Romanian. The man shrugged and shook his head, obviously not understanding a word. The officer repeated the same sentence in butchered English, then angrily continued, "You no enter Moldova with Emirates' passport and no visa. You need visa before enter Moldova."

"Not understand," the Emirati man responded. "Always have visa here."

"This changed a month ago. You now need visa before you enter country." The man flipped through the pages of his passport and showed one page to the officer, saying something in Arabic. The custom's officer switched to Romanian with a cursing tirade. "I don't care what your page from last year says! The fucking rule changed a month ago! I'll put you back on the plane and send you back where you came from!" He walked away from the counter with the man's passport in his hands.

The man raised his hands in the air, as if praying to Allah, powerless, emotional. Then he started frantically looking in his pockets for cash.

"What's going on? What's this officer saying?" David asked.

"He's threatening to send the man back because he doesn't have a visa."

"Should I be worried?"

"I called them before you arrived. They told me that Americans can get a visa at the airport for sixty dollars. The officer's just playing games. Probably looking for a bribe."

"That's not very reassuring."

"If he tries to extort one extra dollar from you, you're going to tell him that you'll call the American embassy and create an international scandal."

"You want to get me arrested?"

"He'll poop his pants before he arrests an American."

"Damn girl! You're stirring the pot! That's sexy!"

From the corner of my eye, I saw the officer return to his desk. When the Emirati man handed him money, the officer took it all, mumbling, put it in the till, stamped the passport, and gave it back. "That's the last time I stamp your passport," he said. "Next time, I send you home!" The Emirati man bowed and rushed to the exit.

It was our turn to come to the window. I told the officer in Romanian, "This American is visiting Moldova. He needs a visa."

"He didn't get a visa before he came?"

"No," I said sternly and put exactly sixty dollars in front of him. I'd made sure he didn't have to search for change. He took David's passport, glanced at David, head to toe, then looked at me with a long, judgmental look, like the hotel clerk in Bucharest. I stared right back at him. I could hear the Zorro soundtrack in the back of my head. Forget Catherine Zeta-Jones, I was Antonio Banderas today, ready to zip a giant Z across his face with my black, oversized whip. We stood in front of each other for a good minute without saying anything. Finally, he stamped David's passport with a ninety-day entry visa and returned the document to him.

"Welcome to Moldova!" I told David instead of the officer.

"Oh, yeah. Welcome, welcome!" The officer squeezed out a smile.

"Thank you very much," David said cheerfully. Then he turned to me and whispered, "That was a Mexican standoff, and he blinked first."

"What's a Mexican standoff?"

"I'll explain it later." David giggled and walked toward the exit.

Outside the airport building, taxi drivers eyed David right away. Not like it was hard to do, as he towered above the crowd by two heads.

"Let me talk to them," I said. "They can read on your forehead that you're a foreigner, and they'll rip you off in a heartbeat." It was exciting being David's guide in this way. "How much to Bubuieci?" I asked the first brave driver who approached us.

"Bubuieci is on the outskirts of the city," the man said, starting his negotiation while looking up at David, unable to take his eyes off him.

"The airport is at the outskirts too. From here it's closer to Bubuieci than to the center," I said.

"The roads are not very good there." He turned to me, finally figuring out that I was the main negotiator.

"We're going to the apartments on the hill, and that's literally the first stop in the village."

"All right," the driver said, "one hundred leis."

"How much in American dollars?" David asked.

"Ten dollars, man," the driver answered in English with a smile, softening the "l" sound like a true Moldavian.

"That's not too bad."

"David, I'm negotiating here," I shushed him. "I can see there are six cars parked over there, and we're the only people taking a taxi. I bet if I ask another driver, he'll take us home for sixty leis."

"Fine! I'll take you for sixty then."

"Why didn't you say sixty in the first place?"

"It's the first time I'm driving an American. You don't see them often around here, and I thought he wouldn't mind. As you said, there are more cars here than there is work, and we have families to support." He fetched our luggage nimbly and shoved it into the trunk of his tiny soapbox car.

"That's his car?" David asked. "I won't fit in there."

"Is he talking about his feet?" the driver asked, understanding David's tone more than his words. He opened the front passenger door and slid the seat all the way back.

"Sit, sit," he said in English.

"In America, passengers don't normally sit in the front seat of a cab," David said. "This will be something to tell my friends about." He laughed, but nevertheless dropped into the front seat as the driver told him to. He pulled in his legs, trying to slide in his right foot with the stiff, leather boot. Finally, he managed to get all of himself inside. From the back seat, I looked at him sitting in front like a child, with his knees almost to his chin.

"I can't buckle my seat belt. It's too short," David said.

I translated it to the driver, and he looked at us strangely. "That's all right. You don't have to," he said, taking off.

"He's not wearing his seat belt either." David turned to me, terrified. "Won't he get a ticket for both of us?"

"If they stop him, he'll probably pay off the police."

"What? Is that normal around here?"

"I wouldn't say it's normal, but it's very common. Welcome to the Wild, Wild West!"

The taxi driver was swerving in traffic, making David gasp a few times.

"Down this road," I said, showing him the way when we got to our boonies. "But be careful of the big pothole at the bottom."

"Ay-ay-ay!" the driver said, looking for the best way to navigate the narrow path with smaller potholes, trying to avoid the big one. *Thump!* We heard the bottom of the car hit the asphalt, when a back wheel dropped into the hole. The car shook as if we were driving in a small earthquake. I sank in the backseat. David's head hit the top of the car. The driver cursed. I didn't realize how stressful it was to own a car in my country.

"How much farther?" the driver asked.

"Not far. It's the second entrance of this building," I said. The driver, relieved, stopped at the bottom of the steps.

David crawled out of the taxi and stood there for a minute, observing the so-called playground in front of our apartment. I shrugged uncomfortably, looking at it with David's eyes. Stuff that I hadn't noticed before, or had gotten used to, was now so obvious. The ground was uneven, with patches of grass here and there, but mostly covered with holes dug by kids playing with dirt in the absence of sand. The giant metal globe that we used to climb on as kids was all rusty and tilted to the right, now shaped more like an egg than a sphere. Two metal uneven bars were the last pieces of sports decor still standing from the good old times. One teenager was doing pull-ups on the higher bar. A little girl was hanging upside down on the lower bar like a monkey, swaying back and forth. She looked at us curiously, then grabbed the side bars with both her hands and disembarked, flipping in the air. *How old is she? Five?*

David turned around, examining our four-story apartment building. It had a light-blue mosaic still holding on in some places, but for the most part, it showed the gray cement underneath. The flat roof was rusty, and the pavement that led to the building was broken. *Ghetto.* Wasn't that what they called it in an American movie? I was waiting for David to say that word, but he looked at the grape branches covering the entrance, climbing up the balconies, all the way to the top of the roof. Green clusters of tiny grapes were sticking out from under their leaves.

"Is that a decorative grapevine?"

"Decorative? Those are real grapes. They're just green right now because it's early in the year. When they ripen in August or September, we pick them and eat them. People living on the first floor even make wine."

"Wow, you are really resourceful around here."

Of course we are.

I could tell that we'd paused in the front yard for too long, because the neighborhood kids, who'd been playing earlier, had started gathering around us, abandoning their games. Three of them were bluntly staring at David; the other two were whispering to each other and pointing.

"Hello!" David said to them and smiled. The kids giggled and waved back. Their parents were more discreet, staring from afar.

"They haven't seen a big man like me before, have they?" he asked.

"I don't think so. Let's go. We need to take the stairs to the second floor."

"No lift?"

"No. It's an old house. They weren't installing lifts in buildings with four floors back then."

"Are you saying that people on the fourth floor have to walk up to their apartments every day?"

"What's the big deal?"

"My luggage is heavy."

"Do you want me to ask these kids to carry it for you?" I teased him and put my hand on one of his suitcases, ready to pick it up.

"No. I can do it," he said decisively, and lifted both of his suitcases fast in one jerky move. He went up the stairs slowly, struggling to put one foot in front of another, heavily leaning to the left, relying on the rail for balance or from not falling backwards.

"Mama, we're home!" I yelled from the hallway. The kids and Mariana ran to the door.

"Hello!" Mariana said, looking at David still climbing upstairs with his suitcases, breathing heavily and stumbling. The kids started jumping like playful baby goats.

"Hello, David! Hello, David!" They were interrupting each other.

"Hello, everybody!" David smiled, setting his suitcases down.

"Angelica?" He lifted his finger, pointing at my daughter, then at my son, pretending he couldn't guess who was who.

"That's me, that's me," Lica jumped and pointed at herself.

"Me, Serghei." Serghei jumped in front of him.

"And you are? Mariana?" David asked my sister.

"Yes!" Mariana screamed. She was too old for these silly games, but she laughed along anyway.

"Mama!" I called. My mother peeked from the kitchen, then slowly, as if petrified, approached David.

"Hello, Katerina! So nice to meet you." David spread his long arms and gave her a big hug. She looked so petite in comparison, almost drowning in his arms.

"We set the table in the living room for him," Mom said when David finally let go of her.

"For him?" I asked. "For all of us!"

"Yeah, yeah, I'm finishing up in the kitchen, and I'll be right with you."

"Well, come in!" I told David, showing him the open door. He walked slowly into the living room, where the table stood in the middle, covered with a white tablecloth. It held our festive dining china set for six, along with two crystal stem-bowls containing baked sweets and four small plates with homemade salads, which were decorated with bright-colored roses carved from boiled beets and carrots.

"Wow! Was your mom cooking all day?" He took the first seat at the table, salivating. The snow-white curtains that my mother was so excited about went unnoticed. Mariana came in the room with a bowl of water and a towel.

"Mama said this is for David to wash his hands." I translated it for him.

"Is that some sort of a wedding ritual?" He put his hands in the water and washed them carefully. "Am I supposed to wash my face too?"

"I don't know. Go ahead and wash it just in case."

When David was done, I took the bowl from him and brought it back to the kitchen.

"Mama, David's asking what kind of water ritual is that? I've never heard of this before."

"There is no ritual! I just don't want him to come here to wash his hands when my kitchen is a mess from all this preparation."

"You're ridiculous! This is not a competition for mother-in-law of the year." She looked at me with a frown, shook her head, and made a cross.

"What's this for?" I asked.

"My God, he's really huge! Like a *velikan*. I don't know what you call it in English."

"Giant?"

"Yeah, like a giant of giants. What will people think about him?"

"Why would I care what people think about him? They're not marrying him." Mom got quiet, as if measuring the words she was about to say.

"Do you really think he's going to take you to America with two kids?"

"He came all the way from America, didn't he? He seems happy to be here. He might be big, but he's a normal guy. As a matter of fact, he was comforting me on the plane when I felt sick."

"I just don't want you to put all your hopes on him, seeing him have his fun for a week, then go back home and forget about you. It will be heartbreaking for you and for the kids. And people will gossip about you for years how—"

"How stupid I was to believe in him? Can we all, at least for one week, act normal? And not be paranoid?"

I left the kitchen irritated. *What else should David do to convince my mother that he's serious? Jump off the plane?*

"What's going on in here?" I asked when I saw David's suitcase wide open, with stuff spread everywhere on the floor. He didn't appear to worry whatsoever about the mess that he'd created. I was sensing a theme.

"Presents!" Serghei yelled. "David brought us presents." David's arrival, which was worrying my mother sick, had turned into a carnival. The two disasters, separated by one wall—one in the living room and one in the kitchen—looked somehow parallel and similar.

"Mom, look what David brought me," Angelica said, modeling a long pink dress with flower patterns and a little chiffon vest on the top. "It's so cute. I love you!" She gave David a hug and a kiss on the cheek. David was melting in his chair.

"That's a scooter for you, Serghei," David said, getting a silver metal scooter with red wheels out of his suitcase. Serghei grabbed it immediately, flipped it back and forth in his hands, trying to figure out how this thing worked.

"Put it down, Serghei." David pointed with his finger to the floor. "Now put your foot on the ramp." He stomped his foot, showing him how to do it. Serghei climbed with both his feet on the ramp, wobbled for a few seconds, and fell over.

"What is this?" I asked. "A bike without a seat?"

"He needs to put one foot on the ramp, then push himself along with his other foot."

"Like this?" Mariana volunteered to demonstrate. She rolled the scooter on the parquet floor but tripped on the carpet, almost knocking one of the chairs down.

"Stop! Stop!" I yelled. "You need to play with this thing outside!"

"I'll go outside." Serghei took the scooter from Mariana's hands and stormed out of the apartment.

"Me too, me too." Lica followed.

"Mariana, would you do me a favor?" David asked. "Can you take the camera and film them?" David handed her the video camera on her way out.

"What were you thinking?" I asked David. "You've seen our roads. This scooter won't last a few days."

"Sorry, I didn't know the roads were so bad around here, but look how much fun they're having. It's totally worth it."

"Where is everybody?" Mom asked, showing up from the kitchen with a plate of steaming chicken legs.

"They're all outside, trying the scooter David brought for Serghei."

"Now? When the food is on the table? Those kids of yours have no manners." After quickly scolding me, she asked, "What's a scooter?"

"It doesn't matter. Serghei will break it in a week."

My mother rolled her eyes, unwilling to unleash her frustration in front of David.

"Your godmother called," she said. "She prepared Tamara's apartment for you and David in the city. She asked when you're coming, so she can give you the keys."

"We'll go there after dinner. Right, David?" I smiled at him.

"I didn't understand a word you just said, but okay."

"Get used to it. You won't understand much of what people say around you for the whole week you're here." I laughed. David shrugged and laughed too. *He wasn't expecting that, was he?*

Chapter 25

Redefine Breakfast

I opened my eyes and looked at the window with thick golden curtains. A bright sunray was coming through the crack between them, ricocheting from the wallpaper's golden stripes and dancing on David's face. He was lying on the bed next to me in our rented studio apartment. Tamara, my godmother's daughter, was renting it to us for a hundred dollars a week. It was a bargain in comparison with hotels in the city. Besides, I liked the idea of privacy, away from the judgmental eyes of know-it-all post-Soviet concierges.

But *surprise*, it turned out to be located on the fourth floor of the five-story building with no lift, so David had found something to complain about.

"Are you trying to kill me?" he'd asked last night, walking up the stairs with his suitcase.

"It's good practice for you," I'd told him unapologetically, "because we're going to walk everywhere in this city. No more cabs." I thought he should get the whole cultural experience.

"Where are you going?" David asked me now as I dropped my feet onto the floor, ready to get up. He was having a hard time adjusting to the new time zone, so every little disturbance was waking him up.

"To make breakfast," I answered, standing over him.

"You're spoiling me already?" He laughed. "But wait, we didn't buy any produce yesterday."

"Mom said that my brother will drive her to the bazar today.

She'll buy some produce for us before they all come here tonight. In the meantime, I'll find something in Tamara's kitchen. We won't need much for just two of us."

"You wanna bet?" David looked at me with a smile.

"Since you're awake anyway, get up. Let's cook breakfast together."

"Oh, our first couple's breakfast." David pushed himself off the bed. "What are you going to make? Pancakes or French toast?"

"What's a French toast? Another food that Americans made up? Like a regular toast but somehow French?"

David laughed and shrugged. *No comeback?*

I walked into Tamara's large newly remodeled kitchen, which was so different from our outdated one that I seemed to be somewhere in Western Europe, not in my home city. It had all types of modern appliances, including some I didn't even know how to use. I opened the stainless-steel refrigerator in hopes of finding something for breakfast, but it wasn't packed full. I found four eggs, an onion, a bunch of spinach, fresh green dill, and something wrapped in foil at the back of the fridge.

"We have no bread," I finally concluded, after looking for bread in every cupboard. I found only a small bag of flour instead.

"There goes our French toast," he said. "We need bread for that. I guess we can go out for breakfast."

"Restaurants don't open until noon around here."

"Do they have McDonald's in this city? In America they're open twenty-four seven."

"They opened one a few years back, but we're not going to McDonald's for breakfast!" I had my limits.

"But there's nothing here to make breakfast with."

"If there's no bread, we make bread."

"Wouldn't it take hours to bake it?"

"We'll make a *lepeshka*. That doesn't take long."

"A what?"

"It's a piece of dough that I'll flatten with—I don't know what you call that stick—until I make it round." David looked at me, confused. "You'll see. There are things that I can't explain in English."

"Wait." David lifted his finger. "Let me get my camera."

"You're going to film me doing this?"

"Yeah! My woman is making homemade bread! That's unheard of in America." David wasn't joking. He brought his camera from the other room and gave me the command: "Action."

All right then. Hollywood in my kitchen. I dumped most of the flour into a large glass bowl, broke an egg, added baking soda and salt, and poured a glass of water. Then I mixed it all up with my right hand, while rotating the bowl with my left, just like my grandma taught me. The gooey substance stuck to my palm but oozed out between my fingers, like four skinny, white sausages. I kept kneading it, adding a little more flour until the dough became firm enough to stop sticking to my hands. Then I dropped the heavy, gorgeous dome of dough out of the bowl onto the table, and cut four little rolls from it.

"What do you call this stick?" I asked David, holding up a wooden tool that I'd found in Tamara's kitchen drawer.

"A rolling pin."

"I understand rolling, but why 'pin'? Isn't a pin something that you can poke things with?"

"I have no clue." David was as amused as I, discovering all these double meanings of words he'd used his entire life, while never questioning their origins.

"Anyway. I'm going to roll these pieces of dough with this pin."

"Rolling pin. Just 'pin' doesn't make sense."

"Okay. I'm rolling," I said, and started on my mission. "I'm going to fry these rolls, when I make them flat and round. Put the pan with the oil on the fire, please."

"Do you mean the frying pan?" he asked, putting his camera down.

"I didn't realize there are different pans. Good thing you asked."

"I think we need to make a rule to ask each other 'What do you mean?' Just to make sure there are no misunderstandings."

"Good idea."

We were new at this, but a system was forming. David got up and approached the stove to do his part. "When you said, 'Put the frying pan on the fire,' you literally meant 'fire,' right? Is this a gas stove?"

"Yes," I answered, concentrated on my rolling.

"Okay," he said, and twisted the burner knob a few times. The smell of natural gas filled the room almost instantly.

"Why isn't this flaming up?"

"What are you doing?" I jumped to the stove to turn it off. "Where are your matches? You need to light the fire with matches."

"In America, gas stoves have built-in sparks that light a flame when you turn them on."

"This is not America! You are going to blow us up!"

"Crap! Do you know where the matches are, then?"

"No-o-o!" I was frantically looking through the drawers.

"Too bad I don't smoke." David laughed. "I guess we're going out for breakfast after all."

"Not after all this preparation. No, no, no. That will not happen. Do we have any electric appliances in the house?" I looked around. Nothing stood out. Even the teapot was the kind you warmed up on the stove.

"Do you mean something besides the refrigerator? What are we looking for?"

"Something we can use to light up a piece of paper."

"Why?"

"I'll show you a trick I learned from my ex-husband when we

ran out of matches in the middle of the night and needed to light the fireplace in winter. I saw an iron somewhere around here."

"What?"

"Hold this. Face up." I handed him the plugged-in iron. I ripped off half a page from a newspaper, rolled it up, and put it on top of the hot iron.

"What are you doing?"

"Shhh! Don't breathe at it!"

The paper curled up, turned black at the edges, and finally lit up in a big flame. Swiftly, like a circus flamethrower playing with his torch, I turned around to the burner, twisted the knob, and brought the burning piece of paper to the hissing gas. The burner lit up like a mini bonfire, with red sparkles in the air. I also lit a second burner for the teapot, then dropped the burning paper in the sink to put out the remaining fire.

"And you were worried that I would blow us up?" David said.

"Hey, I'm a professional! I know what I'm doing. Now, mister, you're in charge of frying this *lepeshka*," I said, putting the first piece of dough in the frying pan. "Just make sure you flip it over on time so you don't burn it. Okay?"

"Oh, that looks like pita bread. What are we going to have with that?"

"I'm going to make us an omelet."

"Do you mean like scrambled eggs? I didn't see any ham or cheddar cheese, or anything else to make an omelet with."

"As I said, I'm the professional here." I smiled, chopping the onion on the cutting board.

"I've never had omelets with onions." David grimaced.

"There's always a first time," I answered, dropping my onions into the frying pan with sunflower oil. I broke the last three eggs and mixed them up with a fork, then poured the golden mass over the fried onions.

"It needs more substance," I said, pulling the foil from the fridge to see what else was in there. "That will work." I took the white salty cheese out and grated it over the frying pan.

"My God, what kind of stinky cheese is that?" David said, covering his nose.

"It's from sheep's milk."

"Do you mean, like, feta cheese?"

"Is that what it's called in America? Then yes," I said, continuing with my plan, undeterred, arranging the spinach leaves on top of the omelet and sprinkling the fresh-cut dill on top to finish the dish.

"I've never had an omelet with feta cheese." David made a face, taking a bite of my omelet with caution. "Wow! That's actually delicious. You totally redefined breakfast. This is so much better than McDonald's."

Now it was my turn to make a face. "They can't even be compared. Besides, it's not like you had a choice. 'There is no special cooking for you, princess,' as my grandma would say."

David laughed, jiggling his belly. "I'm liking your grandma! Is she coming for lunch too? I'd really like to meet her."

"Unfortunately, she doesn't travel to the city because she doesn't have anyone to take care of her chickens while she's away. Unless you want to walk two kilometers to her village to see her."

"You want me to walk? For over a mile? You're joking."

"What's the deal, big guy?" I was baby talking, pulling on his cheeks. "You can't keep up with this Moldavian anymore?"

He squeezed me. "You'll whip me into shape," he said, giving me a smooch. I couldn't tell if he was concerned or happy about the prospect of me being his fitness instructor. "My doctor actually said that I should exercise more if I want to stay alive."

"Okay then. After breakfast, we're going out for a walk."

Chapter 26

The Knight of the Buzdugan

"Ready?" I asked David, taking seriously my task of keeping him alive.

"I don't want to walk just for the sake of walking. Can you take me to a store? I want to buy some souvenirs for my mom and my friends."

"Okay, as long as you're walking. I'll take you to the arts and crafts market downtown. I'm sure you'll find something there."

"What a beautiful day! What a wonderful life!" David said, raising his face to the bright sun in the sky, as if making it down our stairs and out of the building was the biggest accomplishment of his life. Sunshine poured on his head from above, forming a white halo. *Pure Jesus walking on concrete.*

"Let's see what you say after you walk for a kilometer." I smiled.

"A kilometer? Aren't we going to take a bus or something?" David made a face.

"We'll take a microbus."

"What's that?"

"It's a minibus, more convenient and faster than a regular bus because you can stop it anywhere on the route, not just at a bus stop. And it only costs one lei, that's ten cents per person."

"Is that what we're taking?" David pointed at the microbus that was approaching the stop. "It looks like a van."

I hadn't realized how short and tiny the microbuses were until I saw David next to one. Five people got off, and three people got in, but David was still standing by the open door, trying to figure out the best way to climb in without hitting his head.

"Come on!" the driver said unceremoniously, encouraging David to finally get himself inside. "I don't have all day."

"Get in," I echoed the chauffeur's sentiment, pushing him from behind.

David bent his torso in half and moved slowly, like an injured grasshopper, to the closest open seat inside, then dropped down. He squeezed the passenger next to him to the window with his wide shoulders. His head, on its long, thick neck, was touching the roof. I gasped. He looked like a folded inflatable giraffe that, for some odd reason, was taking public transportation.

"You want to sit down?" he said, trying to get up, when he noticed there were no more empty seats.

"No. It's better if I stand." I put my hand on David's shoulder. Two men, sitting behind him, shook their heads, then whispered something to each other, looking at me with disparaging looks. So much for gratitude. I'd just saved these two asses from the trouble of squeezing themselves around David to the exit. I imagined these two with stretched-out arms, trying to pull themselves out of the microbus, while their legs were stuck behind, pinned by David's big body. *Tom and Jerry live! I should have let it happen.*

"They don't have air conditioning in this thing?" David wiped the sweat off his forehead.

"Just open the window in front of you. You'll be fine."

"How much longer? I'm boiling over here."

"Can you hold on for two more stops?" *Oh, my God!* My patience was running out. How had we even survived without air conditioners all this time? Must have been our "don't give a fuck" attitude that pushed us over the line!

The street arts and crafts market stretched for over one block, right in the heart of the city. We walked along the lines of paintings with breathtaking landscapes mixed up with regular everyday pottery and wooden toys that hung from bushes and tree branches or simply lay on pieces of cardboard under our feet.

"Your mother would like this." I showed David a sophisticated crocheted white tablecloth spread across three bushes.

"One hundred dollars," said a countrywoman. She spoke in Romanian and wore a headscarf tied in back.

"How much?" David asked me. I translated.

"That's a little too—" But before David even finished his thought, the woman addressed me again.

"Tell him I worked on this thing for a month. I'm not letting it go for less." I translated to David and looked at the woman, who was watching us defiantly with her hand on her left hip. "I might as well keep it for myself than give it away for free."

"She's not budging," I summarized her speech to David.

"I sell cars, so I get it, but the price is set by supply and demand," David responded. "The price depends on how much the buyer wants something, and not by how much time the seller spent on making something." He talked to me like he was teaching an American economics class. "But I respect a person who knows the value of her work. She'll just have to find somebody else who absolutely has to have it."

"He's not buying, is he?" the woman asked without waiting for me to translate. I shook my head. "That's fine. This tablecloth will look fantastic on my Christmas table."

"Then let's buy something else for your mother." I pulled David away. "How about this decorative cutting board? It has yellow corn, flower seeds, brown beans, and rosehip. What else is glued to this thing?" I lifted it in the air, holding it against the sun, trying to imagine how it would look on my future mother-in-law's wall in the kitchen. *Would she like it? Would she even hang it there? Or would she laugh at it instead?*

"This good luck," the older gentleman selling the board told David in English, touching the rosehips glued to the board.

"You see, it's for good luck," I said, turning to David.

"That's pretty darn neat. She'd love it." David gave him two thumbs up. "How much?" The man lifted both his palms in the air, spreading his fingers like a hand fan, exposing dark hardened calluses on his hands.

"Ten? Dollars?"

The man nodded with a surprised expression on his face, as if saying, "What other currency is there?" The local markets adjusted to dollars a long time ago.

"Oh, look at these cute rag dolls." David pointed to where they lay on cardboard.

"Those aren't rag dolls, silly. They are ... they are ... What do you call them? Dolls dressed in our national costumes. You see, this doll has a white blouse with traditional red embroidery and a roll-up red skirt, and this scarf wrapped around her head. That's how our ladies dressed up for national holidays. And the man is wearing this white man's shirt with a sheepskin jacket and a winter hat made of black lambskin. That's also a national costume."

"So, these are like cultural dolls? What are those funny shoes made of?" David pointed to the two pieces of brown leather, sewed with rough white thread, that the male doll was wearing.

"Sheepskin again. We were big on sheepskin back in the old days. Well, we still are. My grandpa has a hat just like that. It's very warm, very suitable for winter."

"The lady doll, with her long black hair, looks just like you." David put the two dolls together. "Look, that's you and me."

"If you ignore that the man has a black mustache and you don't." I laughed.

"Irina, have some faith!" David pushed right back. "I can grow a mustache like that in no time."

"And if you ignore that he's much, much thinner than you. Then sure, these two dolls look just like you and me."

"I make," the younger man selling the dolls interrupted our conversation. "Tell him"—he asked me to translate—"I'm an artist. I graduated from the art school. I work as a costume designer at the local theater. But they haven't paid us for four months, so I make dolls in the meantime and sell them at the market. Tell him it's good quality. I don't make bad dolls." He waited for me to translate, then turned to David. "Buy," he said in English. "I make good."

"Here you go, man!" David pulled the money out of his wallet without much hesitation, asking him to pick out, from the stack of bills, how much he thought his dolls were worth.

"You said that buyers are not sentimental," I told David after the purchase was finalized.

"They could be, if it's something they really, really want." He winked at me. "You and I together forever." David held the dolls next to each other, pretending they were kissing. The artist giggled.

"For God's sake, we're in the middle of the market!" I showed him people pointing fingers at us, trying hard not to laugh.

"What? Am I embarrassing you?"

"That's what a kid would do."

"What's wrong with that?" David was unabashed.

"Give me that." I took the dolls out of his hands. David's laugh was loud and rolling, attracting even more attention. But he moved on to the next toy, as if nobody was watching. Mom was right, we drew a lot of looks, which I would need to get used to.

"Wow! What's that?" David pointed at an ornate artifact hanging from a tree branch on a long handle. It had a wooden bulge with spikes on the end.

"That's a kind of old-time weapon used to crack shields or human skulls in battles. I don't know what it's called in English. We call it *buzdugan*."

"It's a mace. This thing is cool as hell. How much?" he asked the seller.

"Why in the world would you want to buy that? It's just a toy. Buy something practical."

"You don't understand. My friends and I play Dungeons & Dragons. We can use it as a weapon in our game. The Knight of Darkness! Or the Knight of Bu-zu...? How do you say it? Bu-zu-gun?" He lifted the wooden mace above his head. The seller laughed. I blushed.

"You pretend to kill dragons? As adults?"

"No, it's not like that. It's a board game with role play."

"Is that a theater play?"

"It's not like that either. I don't know how to explain it to you, but I'll teach you when you all come to America."

"I can't wait," I said. *The Knight of the Buzdugan! Oh, help me God!*

"I'll also take this." David pointed at an old-fashioned bag made from two pieces of tapestry with red, green, blue, and black stripes sewed together. It had a long, green twisted handle going around both sides. He put it on his shoulder to try it on.

"That's a *torba,* a peasant's bag. The last time people used one of those was in the last century. That's mostly for decoration nowadays, and you're wearing it wrong. They used to put it across their chests."

"Like that?" David shoved his head and right hand through the opening, but the handle was too short for his big body, so the *torba* was cutting into his left armpit.

"You look so ridiculous." I couldn't hold back my laughter.

"You said to buy something practical, so I did. I need a bag to carry all my souvenirs, don't I?"

He put his possessions in the newly purchased bag, then asked me, "What are we doing for the rest of the day, honey?"

"I'm taking you out of here. That's what we're doing. You can't be trusted around knick-knacks," I said. "We'll go to the park. It's just a block from here—if you can make it." David huffed but didn't resist.

"Hey, what's that?" David pointed at a white horse carriage near the Arch of Victory in Central Park. Its large wheels had painted white spokes on the inside with a black rim outside, making the carriage look like it had dropped by from a movie set. Its seats were covered with ruby-red plush material that was supposed to give a fancy look, but it was failing. The cushions looked worn out, even from afar. An ash-gray horse dappled with white spots—or as we called it "white apples on grey"—looked bored. He only came alive when snorting and flipping his long, bushy tail, trying to chase off the flies that were relentlessly attacking him.

"That's just a carriage with a horse," I told David. "My grandpa in the country had a real working horse carriage. He took us for rides as kids. His horse Lidia understood human language. This one is just for tourists."

"I want to take you on a ride in that carriage!" David got excited like a child who'd just spotted Santa's Christmas bag with treats.

"Why? A ten-minute ride in that carriage is like half my monthly wages. And I just told you I rode my grandpa's horse carriage for free. Why would we pay for a horse ride?"

"Why are you quarreling with your man?" yelled the coachman, an elderly man with an old-fashioned Moldavian brown, felt hat.

"I'm not quarreling with him. I'm just trying to keep him from wasting money."

"Ah! Where did you find a giant like that?"

"In America."

"And what, in America they don't have money to take their ladies for a carriage ride?"

"What's he saying?" David got curious.

"The old man is good at guilting." I cracked a smile.

"Maybe he has a point. Pretend I'm your prince, taking my Cinderella to the ball." *David was doing the old man's bidding too?* "Come on, my princess, that will be so much fun and so romantic."

"Hardly a Cinderella carriage. Look at that horse. He couldn't give a shit. Besides, don't call me a 'princess.' My grandma called me that to say things like: 'Look at her, princess, waiting for someone else to wash her dishes.' I hate that word!"

"Then, pretend I'm Knight of the Buzdugan"—he finally said it right—"and you are my queen." He gave me his hand.

"Fine, as you wish." I finally gave in and climbed into the carriage.

David couldn't contain his excitement. He sat next to me, raising his head up high, then took my hand in his and squeezed it, giggling. He was watching in fascination how "white apples on grey" pulled our carriage out of the park into the street, clattering with his hooves on the road. *Clop, clop, clop.*

The horse flipped his long tail a few times, still fighting the flies. The tail went to the left, then to the right, then froze in the middle, rising above the horse's butt. *Oh-oh!* I knew exactly what it meant. I instinctively pulled David back, though I knew it couldn't reach us. Without even missing a step, the horse dropped five big turds on the scorching hot asphalt. *Clop, clop, clop.* He kept on going, leaving the mess behind. The old man didn't move a muscle, pretending that nothing had happened.

"That's nasty!" David gave me a distraught look.

"What's the matter, Knight of the *Buzdugan*? Isn't this fun and romantic?" I laughed at David, enjoying every word.

Chapter 27

Like a Child Again

"Oh, my God! Finally!" Mariana and the kids yelled in unison when they saw David and me approaching the bus stop. We were picking them up for a "family day out," as David put it.

"We've been waiting forever," Serghei said as he pulled on my hand.

"Forever? Really?" I asked Mariana.

"Maybe for fifteen minutes, but still. What's that on him?" Mariana pointed at the bag across David's shoulder. "A *torba*?"

"I took him to the arts and crafts market yesterday. He wanted to buy some Moldavian souvenirs to take home."

"And that's what he bought?" It was hard to tell if she was amazed, disgusted, or both. "Why is he wearing it like that?"

"He thinks it's cool." I rolled my eyes.

"What? Are you guys talking about me? About my bag?" David picked up on our eye rolling.

"Y-y-e-e-e-s!" Mariana and I said, laughing simultaneously.

"You don't like it?"

"No-o-o!" Mariana and I said, together again. David laughed. He enjoyed embarrassing us in front of other people. He even made eye contact with a young couple standing at the bus stop.

"I'm with them," he said, and the couple looked away. They either didn't understand him or didn't know how to react. Guaranteed, this scenario was not described in any colloquial English dictionaries they'd studied at their universities.

Angelica started jumping up and down, showing her braided

hair with a white ribbon neatly tied in the back. She wore the long pink dress that David had brought from America.

"Why are you still in this dress?" I asked her. "Were you wearing it all week?"

"She just wouldn't let it go." Mariana sighed. "As soon as Mom washes it, she takes it from the clothesline, even if it's not dry yet, and puts it on."

"What? I like it," Lica said defensively, then turned to David and said, "David, I love you!"

"I love you too." David leaned over to give her a kiss on her forehead.

"And where did Serghei get this ugly green shirt with white stripes in the middle?" I asked Mariana again. "Looks like the colors ran or something."

"He picked this shirt because that's David's present."

"David, did you really bring this shirt from America?" I asked him.

"Yeah. What's wrong with it? It's a very cool hippy shirt."

I shook my head and looked at my sister. "I told you David wants us to take family pictures for our immigration file. You couldn't dress him up a little? He's going to look like a bum. *Ujas, ujas!*"

"What's *ujas*?" David asked.

"Terrible, that's what it is. How are our pictures for immigration going to look? The lawyer will probably think that we've got a clown in the family." I was scolding my sister for not thinking it through.

"We'll be fine," David reproached. "The lawyer will probably get a kick out of it. Everyone in America knows what a tie-dyed shirt is."

I gave him the look, confused by the unfamiliar word "tie-dyed" but as long as Americans were cool with it, it all that mattered. Besides, it was too late to make any changes now.

"Let's go." I grabbed my kids' hands.

"Where are we going?" Lica asked.

"We'll go to the park first, and we'll see from there," I said.

"Are you going to make us walk all the way there?" David whined. I smiled at how smoothly he snuck up an "us" in his pity party.

"We'll take this bus," Mariana answered for me, interrupting my long silence, designed to make David guess a little longer.

"Can we go to the fountain?" Serghei jumped on the step of the bus first. "It doesn't cost us any money to look at the water, right?" He was shouting, looking back at me, while I was letting David, Angelica and Mariana climb up the bus before me.

"Are you going to behave or try to jump in?" I took the first seat to the left, looking at my son.

"I'll be good," he answered after a delay, as if trying to figure out how long he could keep his promise.

"Aha!" I answered in my Grandma Veta tone. "I've heard this before."

The park opened in front of us with its trimmed and well-maintained grass and flowerbeds full of spring flowers bathed in sunshine. The leaves on the trees were shaking in a light breeze. A long alley, called the Alley of Writers, had two rows of sculpted busts down the middle, breaking the entrance of the park into two parts.

"Who are they?" David asked, staring at the sculptures.

"They're the soul and consciousness of our nation. Our writers of the last two hundred years," I said, reading their names one by one as I passed them: "Alexandri, Eminescu, Creangă."

These names didn't mean anything to David, but they brought back childhood memories of my long-gone school years. Our teachers used to make us learn their poems by heart. How much I hated that exercise as a student, but I appreciated it now as an adult. I tried to think of an equivalent English-language writer to draw some parallels for David, but comparisons failed me. How do you compare two different cultures that have never met?

"These two"—I pointed at Alexandri and Eminescu—"are very different poets. One was an educated and very wealthy man. The other one was a poor country boy who ran away from his village with traveling actors, so he could get to the city and pursue his passion for poetry. But both of them wrote the most romantic love poems of their times."

David smiled. "Romantics, like me!"

I smiled back. "You are more like this one: Ion Creangă. He's the author of a memoir called *Childhood Memories.* He was a troublemaker and a rebel. He once got his ass whooped by an orthodox priest for using the Bible to kill flies. He was also a thief. He stole cherries from a neighbor woman's garden. Then while running away from the poor woman, who saw what he was doing, he destroyed her garden by stomping on her harvest."

David burst into laughter. "Yeah, that sounds like me. I was always getting in trouble for making a shortcut over our neighbor's lawn with my bike."

"Wait, we're not done. Once, as a boy, he snuck up on women bathing nude in the lake. They got back at him good, though. They stole his clothes when he went swimming there, so he had to run home naked through the village, hiding in bushes where he accidentally sat on poison ivy with his naked butt."

"Oh, my God! Poor boy. But what young man doesn't like to see a naked woman?" David laughed and winked at me.

"Watch out. There's plenty of poison ivy growing wild in this part of the world. I bet there's some waiting just for you somewhere around here." David laughed even louder. *Ha! Everybody's a hero until they get some poison ivy in their ass.*

"Mom, the fountain's not working." My son pulled my sleeve when he noticed that the old -fashioned fountain, shaped like a giant stone flower, had turned into a rusting statue, with no water shooting from its pool.

"Well, crap!" I said, disappointed. "Nothing works right in this country."

But there was no disaster that Serghei couldn't turn into a farce. He jumped into the empty pool and started running laps around the dead fountain.

"Get out!" I yelled.

"Let them all get inside so I can take a picture," David said.

"David, don't encourage that. People aren't allowed inside the park fountains."

"Really? Kids always play in our fountains." David winked at Lica and Mariana, holding his camera up, encouraging them to go for it. "Let them be kids and have some fun."

"Yeah, fun!" Serghei yelled, recognizing one English word.

"As I said, you're just like Creangă, ready for mischief."

"What mischief? Nobody's naked," David reproached.

"Well, thank God." I looked at David. "Okay. We take one photo. Then, everybody out!"

The kids rushed to the fountain before I could change my mind, jumping, climbing, and causing a ruckus. I wondered what an American park would be like—and how many working fountains they had.

"Look. Isn't this a fun photo of them?" David showed me the kids on his camera screen. "But now we need to take some good family photos." David turned to my sister. "Mariana, you are our photographer for the rest of the day."

Mariana jumped, as if she'd been put in charge of making the world a better place, and grabbed the camera out of David's hands way too eagerly. She took her task to heart by immediately bossing us around.

"Stop, right here at that tree," Mariana said.

David understood her finger pointing more than what she'd said. "Here?" he asked.

"Yes, yes," Mariana answered in English, but then switched to Romanian to tell us: "This huge old tree will look great in the background." By the time Mariana finished her sentence, Serghei had climbed up one of the gnarly branches.

"Don't climb too far!" I yelled. "We need you in the photo frame."

He reluctantly came down halfway, then waved at his sister to join him. Lica lifted her right foot, but her long dress got in the way, so her climb was not going to happen. Serghei sighed and climbed farther down. He put his head on his sister's shoulder and smiled. I wrapped my left hand around David's neck, desperately trying to reach his shoulder on the other side, but all I could feel was my palm hanging in the air instead. He was too tall for a shorty like me.

"Cheese," Mariana said in English, like a professional. We all laughed, mostly because she sounded ridiculous. But she was too busy to notice that.

"Let's take another photo at that sculpture with the big bear," she commanded. It didn't take long for Serghei to climb on top of the bear too.

"How did you get up there so fast?" I was amazed.

"He's like an unruly monkey, always climbing everywhere," Lica said in frustration. She stomped her foot and took her place in front of the bear, like a proper lady. David and I hugged her from behind.

"Cheese!" Mariana said again.

Serghei jumped from the bear onto the grass underneath and started rolling.

"Get up. You'll get all dirty!" I yelled, but David loved the idea.

"Hey, let's all sit down in the grass, like we're on a family picnic."

"We don't have anything to picnic with. And how exactly are you going to sit down and get back up with your boot?"

"There's always a way," David said, and went down on one knee.

Then he rested his hands on the grass and rolled over onto his back. Serghei started giggling and rolled onto his back too.

"Look, Mom, we're like dogs lying in the sun."

"You're going to be like two filthy dogs," Lica said, and squatted behind David, unwilling to sit down and dirty up her pretty dress.

"Come on!" David waved, inviting me to sit next to him.

"Well, what the heck?" I said, and lay down in front of him.

Serghei, restless as usual, ran two circles around us, trying to find a good spot. Finally, he dropped down on me, then stretched his body and grabbed David's neck and mine.

"Let me see," David said after Mariana finished our photo shoot in the grass. "They're perfect!"

"You call these perfect? Are we looking at the same photos?" I asked him. "Look, in the first one, we're all over the place. Serghei is too far up in the tree, and Lica is too far down. I look like I'm hanging from your neck. In the second one, Serghei is too far up again, on the bear this time. And the three of us are too far to the right. It looks like Mariana took a photo of the bear, and we just happened to be nearby. That one on the grass will have to do. But overall, it's a mess. We definitely look like we're from the circus!"

"What's wrong with that? We're in our natural element." David smiled. "I think we've had enough pictures for the day. Let's have some real fun." He winked at the kids.

"Yeah, fun!" Serghei jumped to his feet.

"Don't they have some kids' rides in this park?" David asked.

"There's another park across the street," I told him. "It has a bigger square. They used to have some kids' rides and carousels when I was growing up, but they're gone now. There's a street flower market there instead."

"Mom, look. Little cars." Serghei pointed at a four-year-old boy sitting in a yellow ride-on toy. The boy's father was holding his foot on the gas pedal, simultaneously steering for him, since the boy couldn't quite figure out what to do with the handles. A second toy ATV, a green one, was parked near a flowerbed with blooming yellow, red, and orange tulips.

"That looks like a lot of fun!" David's eyes sparkled.

"Fun! Fun!" Serghei jumped again. This word was triggering some uncontrollable happiness in him.

"How much?" I asked the man handling the electric toys.

"Twenty leis for ten minutes," he responded.

"Wow!" I turned to David. "That's a pair of shoes for Serghei, but it's two bucks for you, David."

"We'll take it," David said. Serghei ran to the ride-on toy as soon as the money exchanged hands.

"Serghei," David called him back. "You'll have to let your sister go first." I translated it for him. He got off. His head down, his lips pouting.

"You go!" David said to Lica, who was still looking at us cautiously, unsure if it was a done deal. She sat down in the green toy car with her back straight, listening carefully to the man's instructions on how to handle it.

"Press the pedal here if you want to go. Take your foot off if you want to stop. Steer the handle to the left if you want to go left. Steer the handle to the right if you want to go right. Understood?"

"Yes," Lica said, and pressed the pedal. The car jerked, pushing her way back since she didn't have her hands on the handles yet. But she quickly recovered, rolling around us in circles with a proud and significant posture like a queen in her carriage. Serghei ran after her, trying to outrun the slow-moving car, unable to stay still for just a moment.

"Go away!" Lica stopped. "You keep running in front of me. I'll run you over. Go get the other car. That little boy is already done with it."

"Can I go? Can I go?" Serghei jumped twice.

"Go, go!" David took out his video camera. "I'm going to film you guys racing each other."

The car renter ran through the same briefing for Serghei. "Gas here, turns here."

Serghei was bouncing up and down like an antsy tiger closed in his cage, half listening, half watching his sister pass by. Finally, he was able to take off. In a few swift moves he caught up with Lica, then turned around, driving toward us, showing off for the camera.

"Lica's driving like a grandma." David giggled, waving to both of them. Serghei turned around again and went after his sister.

"Stop driving like a maniac!" she yelled at him as he flew by.

"What?" Serghei yelled, standing on his feet and turning his body to the right to hear her better. His ATV's handle turned slightly to the right too.

"Stop! Stop!" Mariana and I yelled at once, rushing to Serghei's toy car, which was heading toward the flowerbed. The yellow tulips went down first, then the red, then the orange. The man renting the cars cursed and jumped to turn off the ATV-turned-bulldozer, dragging Serghei's vehicle out of the flowerbed, where the colorful tulips were lying lifelessly under its wheels.

"I got him on video!" David yelled, wiping his eyes, which were tearing up from rambunctious, uncontrollable laughter.

"That's evidence." I pulled his hand down. "Let's get out of here. Quick!"

"We're so sorry! We didn't mean to!" David yelled at the renter. "But that's great material for *America's Funniest Home Videos*." He turned to us. "Look"—he replayed the last few seconds of the video—"isn't this hilarious?"

I looked at David, unsure how to react. I would have already scolded Serghei for not paying attention, but David's laugher made it all less dramatic. Mariana and Lica frowned at first, but started laughing when David replayed the segment for the second time.

Serghei was laughing too because David thought it was funny, but mostly because he was getting a pass. The car renter was smoking angrily at the side. He had reasons for not thinking this was hilarious. But what was he gonna do? Fight with the giant?

"Are you all hungry?" David asked all of a sudden. "Where do you want to go eat, kids?"

"Eat?" Lica asked, and made a gesture with her hand, pretending to hold a spoon to her mouth.

"Yes, eat." David repeated her gesture, confirming that she understood him correctly.

"McDonald's!" Lica said unequivocally.

"McDonald's! McDonald's!" Serghei and Mariana joined her immediately.

"Why?" I resisted. "That's just processed food. There are plenty of good restaurants in the city."

"I want to go," Mariana said, "because I was there only once with my college friends, not to eat, but just to check it out. It's so foreign and cool. Even their bathroom smells nice. Besides, I want to try a McDonald's burger at least once."

"Raise your hand if you say 'yes' for McDonald's," David said, and raised his hand first. Mariana and the kids joined him in just a few seconds. "Sold!" David concluded, looking at me, the only one who hadn't raised her hand. "Looks like you've been overruled." He smiled. It was a strange concept, being overruled by my own kids. But I'd have to fight that fight on a different day. I was getting hungry too.

"Oh! That's so pretty," Lica said, walking into the restaurant. It was my first time entering McDonald's in Chișinău, too, so I was looking at everything with my daughter's eyes, and I could agree with her. The restaurant was much bigger and more presentable than the little dinky airport McDonald's where we'd eaten in Bucharest. It was bright and clean, without foul smells, despite the kitchen being wide open in front of us. It felt chilly and crisp, especially walking in from the hot, dusty outdoors. Air conditioners seemed to be blasting cold air from every corner.

A young cashier greeted us in perfect Romanian: "*Buna ziua!*"

"Hello!" I said, totally confused. "Is that a Bucharest accent?" I asked her.

"Yes!"

"Are our servers so bad that McDonald's had to import Romanian workers?"

"We are here for just a month to provide training," she said, diplomatically avoiding my question.

"Welcome to our city! How do find our accents? Confusing?"

"A little bit different, but not confusing. I struggle with Russian speakers who don't speak Romanian. I had no idea that fifty percent of the population here doesn't speak Romanian or English."

"What? What's going on here?" David asked.

"She speaks English," I said, trying to sum it up.

"Oh, cool! Everybody, pick a burger you like," David said, showing the kids the board above the counter with bright, colorful photos of burgers.

Serghei pointed with his finger. "This one. No, that one. I don't know." Lica looked at the board with the same result.

"Just order the same kind for all of us," I said.

"What if somebody wants something different?"

"How would they know what they want if they've never had a burger before? Don't worry. They'll eat anything."

"Can I have that one?" Lica finally pointed at the third burger from the left.

"Yes, you may," David said, and looked at me. "Let them choose."

I felt that David was changing my kids' behavior by letting them decide on where to go and what to do and what to eat. *Is that normal in America?* I wondered. *What would it lead to? Chaos and anarchy?*

"Not many people here," David observed, picking a table where we could sit.

But before we'd even settled in comfortably, the cashier yelled from the counter, "Order number twenty-five is ready."

"What?" I was surprised. "Done so fast?"

"That's why it's called fast food, honey," David said, grabbing the tray with our order. "It comes in fast." He tossed the wrapped burgers first to Lica and Serghei, then to Mariana and me. Serghei giggled, following the burgers that were landing perfectly in front of us one by one like flying saucers.

"Slow down, buddy," David said, looking at Serghei ripping the wrapper with his teeth, after losing his battle with unwrapping it naturally. Lica gave her brother a look and shook her head like a disappointed high-class lady who'd just discovered that savagery exists. She unwrapped the burger slowly and ceremoniously, as if wanting to impress the teacher of an etiquette class. Those two were polar opposites, even in McDonald's.

"Stop it!" I slapped Serghei on his wrist when I noticed him sneakily stealing fries from Mariana's tray, after finishing his own very fast, almost without chewing.

"You're like that writer. A thief!" Mariana slapped him on the back of his head. "I should smack your hand with poison ivy to teach you a lesson."

"That's not cool, buddy." David looked at him, disappointed. "If you want more, here, go buy yourself another one." He held out twenty leis.

Serghei grabbed it and ran, but halfway, as if remembering something, he came back. "Lica, do you want one too?" he asked his sister. She tilted her head in defiance, with an air of "Now you're asking me?"

"Okay?" She turned to David, asking for permission. David put both thumbs up, approving the deal, then scuffled Serghei's hair.

"Good boy!" he said. "That's the way to take care of your sister."

"You know, on the second floor, they have a playground for kids with a slide and a pool with plastic balls," Mariana said, after chewing her last piece.

"I wanna go." Serghei jumped.

David looked at me, waiting for a translation. His face lit up when I told him what Mariana said.

"Go. Have some fun," he told the kids immediately. "Let's all go. Where's the elevator here?"

"No elevator," Mariana said. "Only stairs."

"No elevator?" David got this part without translation. "Even in McDonald's? How do handicapped people get around this city— no elevators, no accessible sidewalks?"

"They don't have many options, I assume," I said, having not really thought about it before. "But you don't have to go upstairs if you're tired. We'll be right back."

"No, I want to see them play." He got up with a heavy sigh. "You go first. I'll be up eventually."

The kids and Mariana fled as soon as they saw David's hand waving them to go.

The playground was largely empty. One five-year-old girl wearing a cute, short dress was sitting in the middle of a sea of colorful plastic balls. Red, blue, yellow, and green, all mixed up together. She was throwing one ball at a time as far as she could reach, and laughing every time she'd throw one.

Serghei jumped into the pool away from her, digging into the balls, pretending to swim. Then he lay on his back, flopping his arms like a butterfly. The mother of the little girl looked at Serghei, worried, and finally pulled her daughter away, unwilling to take any chances with my wild child.

"No kids here?" David asked, when he finally made it to the second floor. "In America, McDonald's playgrounds are full of kids."

"This place is mostly for foreigners or young people with good jobs. It's too expensive, so families don't come here often," I said.

"Wow! Everything is upside down here. McDonald's in America is for the poor, and here it's for the rich."

"I want to go up there," Lica said, showing us the yellow plastic-tube slide beside the wall.

"Me too, me too," Serghei yelled, and headed for the ladder to get out of the pool. By the time Serghei reached the surface, Lica was already at the top of the slide, getting ready to go down. She hesitated for a minute, but rushed down the tube once she saw her brother was about to reach her.

I followed her with my eyes, then watched the end of the tube where she was supposed to come out. What was taking her so long? Serghei was already sliding down, and she still hadn't come out. I heard Lica saying "push" to her brother somewhere in the middle of the tube where he'd caught up with her. A few seconds later, she finally dropped out of the plastic tube. Serghei followed her.

"Go up, slide again with your brother," David told Lica, who was standing in the middle of the pool, surrounded by plastic balls, watching her brother climb up the ladder, getting ready for his second slide. "Go, have some fun!"

"Fun!" Serghei yelled sliding down the slide again.

"It's too narrow in there. It's for little kids," she said, getting out of the pool. She sat down on the chair next to me. "Too bad David didn't come here sooner," she said, "when I was a kid. Now it's too late." *Too bad, indeed. We'd have a different life now.*

Chapter 28

The Red Dress

"Can we stop at the bank?" David asked the next day, walking slowly from the bedroom of our rented apartment to the kitchen. "My paycheck should have deposited last night. I need to withdraw some money with my debit card."

"Do you mean, like taking money out of the bank? You can't do that unless you have an account in Moldova."

"Well, I'm running out of cash. I'm on my last one hundred dollars. How can I get a money transfer here? Can it be transferred into your account?"

"I don't have a bank account. We get our salaries in cash. Honestly, I don't know many private citizens who have a bank account. We don't trust our banks very much. After the crash of the Soviet Union, money in our banks was devalued by one thousand percent. My grandma had twenty thousand rubles in her bank, that's like ten years' wages. Overnight it became twenty rubles. Basically, she lost all her life savings."

"Jeez! Was it as bad as the Great Depression in the thirties?"

"It was worse because we've had nonstop depressions since. So, no banks. The best way to transfer money to Moldova nowadays is with Western Union."

"Western Union operates in this part of the world?"

"Yeah, there's a Western Union on almost every corner here. That's the one thing that hasn't disappointed us, so far."

"Okay. Let me call my friend Ilya and see if he can help me out."

"Ilya? Is he Russian?"

"No. His father is actually of Greek descent. But he was a literature professor, obsessed with Leo Tolstoy's *War and Peace* and a bunch of other Russian novels, so he gave all his kids Russian names. Ilya has a brother named Alex and a sister named Nadia. Besides that, there were a few girls named Natasha at my school."

"What? I didn't know Tolstoy was so popular that Americans named their daughters Natasha! And now you're here, so we're moving toward making more peace than war."

"Well, you know what the Beatles sang: 'Make love, not war!'" He smiled and lifted his eyebrow mischievously, implying some action, while dialing Ilya's phone number. I rolled my eyes. *Now? When you're calling your friend?*

"Ilya! What's up, my brother?" David yelled in excitement. "Are you asleep? It's only eight p.m. in Seattle! I'm calling from a home phone, so I'll be brief. I don't want to rack up a huge international phone bill. Can you, please, wire me a few hundred dollars via Western Union?" David got quiet for a few seconds, listening to Ilya's response on the other end. "No, Irina's not sucking out my money! She's not like that. I just underestimated my expenses. She's for real, dude! And, by the way, she looks better in real life than in her photos. Your concerns that she might have posted old photos didn't come true." He winked at me. *What! Ilya thought I was a cheat?*

"But other than that," David said, "I'm having the time of my life. It's a different world over here, let me tell you. They walk a lot, like *everywhere*! No wonder they're all so skinny. Also, people eat healthy, and the food here will blow you mind. Irina cooked a delicious breakfast the other morning from virtually nothing. It's freaking unbelievable." He laughed at something Ilya said, and my cheeks warmed.

"And women here are hot!" he continued. "It's like you walk in the streets among supermodels. They dress up like some Greek goddesses: colorful outfits, makeup, high heels. When I get back home, I'm telling everybody looking for a wife to come here and look no further. Women here go above and beyond for their husbands. It's like paradise for men."

I shrugged uncomfortably. What the hell did that mean: paradise for men? I pictured David sitting on a couch like a padishah, waiting to be served. *Did he travel all the way here to fulfill his fantasies? Where would that fantasy leave me? And the kids?*

"Once I get the money, we'll go buy you a pretty dress," David said, putting the phone down.

"Are you trying to buy me with gifts?"

"I just want to do something nice for you. What's your favorite color?"

"Red."

"Then red it is! I have my last one hundred dollars still. Let's find something fun to spend it on."

"Maybe you should wait until you get your money from Ilya first, just in case. We still need to buy your train tickets to get you back to Bucharest airport."

"I'm not worried. Ilya always comes through."

"As you wish, but I'll make you walk for your money. I'll take you to a Western Union in the center that's two blocks away from the bus stop."

"I feel better already," David joked, "because you're trying to keep me alive."

* * *

As soon as we got to the city, I realized that I'd made a mistake having David walk for two blocks. He had to stare at every store window and kept dragging me inside just to look.

"Why are we going inside if you're not buying anything?"

"In America, it's called window shopping."

"Here, we call it a stupid waste of time."

"What's Cricova Cellars store?" he said, looking in the next window.

"It's a wine shop."

"Are those local wines? I should buy a few bottles for my friend Bill. He's Italian. He loves wine."

"I don't want to carry heavy bottles all the way to the Western Union. If you really want them, let's buy them on our way back."

"All right, all right," he said, walking away reluctantly like a kid being dragged from a toy store.

"Excuse me," said a waiter from a nearby restaurant who'd popped up in front of us. He was dressed in black pants, a white shirt, and a black bow tie, and he addressed David in English, sensing a foreigner, no doubt.

"Sorry," I answered and pulled David away. "Don't even think about. We're near Central Market. This place is probably too pricey for locals," I said to David. "That's why he has to lure customers in."

"Our food is fantastic." The waiter wasn't giving up, putting on his sweetest voice. His charms weren't working on me. But he was betting on David. He even pulled the menu from behind his back with a smooth move, like a magician pulling a rabbit from his hat, and handed it to us.

"This lunch will cost us maybe twenty dollars," David said after looking up and down the price list, simultaneously converting the prices from leis into dollars. *If only he were as good with his money as he was with his math.*

"That's insane!" I said.

"Why?" David pressed on. "In America, a lunch like this would be double the cost."

But I was doing my own math in my head. Here, I could buy five pairs of shoes for my kids.

"I want the two of us to have a nice lunch together in a fancy restaurant," David said, suddenly full of emotion. "At least once before I leave." The closer he got to his departure, the more emotional he became.

"You get distracted by shiny things so easily." I sighed. "But let's have lunch, if you wish. We're getting your money from Western Union today anyway. Right?"

"Damn right we are." David cheered up, as he always did when he talked about food.

The inside of the restaurant was not what I expected. I thought we'd find an upgraded version of a rundown facility from the old-Soviet era. But the dark, polished wood pillars combined with snow-white walls gave the restaurant a fresh, modern look. The empty room with only one more couple at the end of it gave us a feeling that we'd stepped into a hidden oasis in the middle of a desert. Though, the light background music put me at ease.

"It's pretty!" I whispered, taking a seat at the first empty table—and thinking I should have gone out with David more often.

"I don't like to say, 'I told you so,' but I told you so!" he teased me.

"Anything to drink?" the waiter asked. "Here is our wine menu."

"Water with lots of ice, please," David said right away.

"Unfortunately, we don't have ice. It's not very customary around here," the waiter said.

"What?" *My God, the suffering on his face!*

"But the bottle is from the refrigerator, so it should be cold." I sensed the waiter's panic.

"Okay," David settled.

"I'll take some grapefruit juice," I said, putting the wine menu down. Ten dollars for a bottle of wine—in a country where every village household makes wine—was just absurd. I couldn't allow David's money to be wasted like that.

He looked at me. "You order for me. I don't understand what any of these foods are."

"I think you'd like this chicken dish." I pointed to the entrée, and then noticed something strange. "But wait, it's stuffed with pineapple? That's so weird . I've never heard of this in our cuisine. I suppose times are changing, but that will be really sweet. You probably wouldn't like that."

"Pineapple in the chicken? Yum, yum, yum! I want that." David raised his hand.

"Great choice." The waiter smiled. "It's a very popular dish with Western European tourists."

"Why?" I asked him. "Why would anyone like sweet meat?"

"What are you talking about? We have pineapple on pizzas too. It's called Hawaiian style."

"That's just wrong." I shook my head. "But if that's what you want, have it. I'll go for this fish dish." I pointed at the menu, letting the waiter see my choice.

"Mmm! Smells so good," David said when the waiter put the chicken and pineapple dish in front of him. "My God, what's that?" He pointed at my plate. "A whole fish?"

"That's a tiny river fish."

"I mean, it still has its head, with eyes, and skin. Don't they have to clean that up?"

"They've cleaned off the hard shells on top of the skin. What are they called?"

"Scales?"

"Yeah, scales. But we don't throw away the skin. We eat it. Don't you?"

"No! I don't even eat fish."

"Well, we do. I know, I know, we're savages!"

"You said it." David laughed, then turned to his plate, cutting deep into the chicken. His fingers slipped, dipping in the white sauce on the plate. A piece of chicken flew out of his plate and landed on his shorts. He picked it up with his hand and put it in his mouth, licking his fingers.

"Who's a savage now?" I looked at him with disgust on my face.

"I guess we're a perfect pair, aren't we?" David said, and touched my nose with his dirty finger.

I smacked him on his wrist, pulled back, and laughed. Then shook my shoulders to the Moldavian pop music floating in the air. "Two dirty pigs we are!"

David turned around and called the waiter over. "Can you take our picture?" he asked. "You just press this button." He handed him the digital camera, showing him where to press.

"Wait, let me wipe my face and put my lipstick on." I grabbed my bright Bordeaux lipstick from my purse. "You'll be showing me off to your family and who knows who else, so I need to look good."

"That's right, baby. I'll be showing you off to everyone."

A little posing didn't hurt either. I put my right hand on David's shoulder and leaned closer to him, touching his head with mine. Then pulled the vase with light-purple flowers closer to us and smiled. I didn't bother to tell David to smile. I knew he had his smile on at all times.

"Perfect," David said when he looked at our photo on the digital screen.

"Definitely better than the one we took at the park yesterday," I said, pleased with what I saw. Besides, we both looked more relaxed and natural today. We were getting used to each other. Finally!

* * *

"You know, I'm glad you dragged me in there. It was a very nice place," I said when we left the restaurant. "Just don't tell me 'I told you so,' or I'll punch you."

"I told you so-o-o," David teased me again. Almost instinctively, I made a fist and punched him in the gut, hard. But he'd tensed up, making my fist bounce off his belly. I felt the pain in my wrist. My teeth clenched.

"Ah!" David bent over, pretending to be hurt. "That's all you've got?" He straightened up and smiled. "Oh, honey, did I hurt you? I'm sorry." He spoke to me like I was a little girl. "Let's go pick up the money and head off to the market to buy you a dress."

"You think you can fix everything with gifts?" I asked, looking at David who was obviously enjoying being the hero and the anti-hero at the same time.

"It always works with women," he said as a matter of fact.

"What women have you been hanging out with?" I asked, and walked away.

"Honey, wait. How far is it?" He sped up to catch up with me.

"Western Union is right in front of us," I said. "You see that yellow-and-black sign?"

We walked into the bright, spacious foyer of the tall apartment building where Western Union was located. I let David go first as we approached the window, where a cashier in her early twenties was on duty. She had dark-brown hair, neatly twisted in a bun, and wore a stylish black skirt and a buttoned-up white silky blouse. Her name tag—saying Anna—shone from a golden frame pinned to her chest.

"Is this where I can receive a money transfer from America?" David asked Anna in English. I jumped in to translate, but the cashier made a gesture with her hand.

"That's okay," she said. "I speak English." *Of course she does! With her job, it would be weird not to speak it.* She turned to David and answered with a slight, barely noticeable accent. "Yes, you can receive money transfers here. Fill out that yellow form over there with your Western Union tracking number, please."

Her manner of speaking was so polished and polite, it threw me off a little bit. She sounded like that Romanian girl from McDonald's—much different from all the grumpy cashiers in dinky "hole in the wall" Western Union offices I'd dealt with before. I didn't know whether it was a new Western Union requirement to treat customers like this, or Anna was just naturally a decent human being. Either way, it was refreshing. She couldn't have behaved more professionally if she'd tried. Was my city stepping up to Western European standards?

David returned his form to Anna with a smile and handed her his dark-blue American passport. "My name is David. I'm waiting for five hundred dollars from my friend Ilya from the United States."

"Okay," Anna said, and took the form, also with a smile. She keyed in the tracking number on her computer, then opened David's passport to verify his name with her computer screen. She repeated the same ritual twice, her face looking more concerned the more she typed.

"I'm sorry, sir, but this transfer says that David is the one who sent the money from the United States, and Ilya is the recipient in Moldova. I can only release the funds to the recipient." That hit David like a thunderstorm in the middle of a bright, sunny day.

"Are you kidding me? We can't be in two places at once, because I'm in Moldova now, and my friend Ilya is in the United States."

"Maybe Ilya accidentally messed it up," I interfered.

"He couldn't have. He knows better. The error is most definitely on the Western Union side," David insisted. His face was red. His lips were trembling.

Anna stepped back, as if David's words could physically hurt her if she stayed too close.

"I'm sorry, sir, but since the error occurred in the States, it can only be corrected in the States."

"You need to make it right for the customer and fix this! Now!" David's neck swelled up from nervous tension.

"David, stop it! You'll give yourself a heart attack." I pulled him away from the window. "Besides, you're yelling at her."

"No, I'm not. I'm just exercising my rights as a customer. In America, the customer is always right. Everybody knows that, and nobody takes it personally."

"This is not America! Okay? Even if it was America, you should not treat people like this." I was getting offended for poor Anna, who was standing up stoically, like a tiny matador in front an enraged, giant bull. "Stay here. I'll handle this," I said sternly and went back to Anna.

"Sorry about that. Now, how do we fix this clusterfuck?"

"He'll have to call his friend Ilya," Anna said, softer this time. "Have him cancel the transfer and resend the money the right way. If his friend fixes this by tomorrow, David could get his money tomorrow as well."

David's arms were crossed as he stood far behind me, and I had a feeling he wasn't going to like this.

"One more day? I need my money today!" David exploded when I told him the news.

"Why? Why do you need your money today? You're not starving; you have a place to stay; you have plenty of time before you leave. You'll have to wait until tomorrow. And that's the reality."

"I promised to buy you a dress today, so we're going to buy that dress today!"

"I can wait," I said simply, losing my patience. Why was this such a big deal to him?

"But I don't want you to wait. We're going to the market right now."

I looked at David's furious, unrecognizable face. The blood in my head was beating like a loud boombox. If this fight was over the phone, I could just hang up on him, and if I wasn't able to forget about it, I could at least switch it off for a while. But now I couldn't. He was right in front of me. I wanted to yell: "You spoiled, childish brat!" But my mother's voice was playing like a recording in my head: "You couldn't keep your mouth shut just this one time?" I pulled away to take a breather. I couldn't hang up the phone, but I could walk away.

"I'm sorry, honey." David followed me. I looked at him with distain, still silent. "I'm really, really sorry. Will you forgive me?" He took my hand.

"Don't you yell at me like that. Ever!" I pulled my hand back.

"I won't. I promise. But I really, really want to buy you your present today."

"No present is going to fix this, David."

"I need to buy you your present today, or I'll feel guilty all day."

What about how I feel?

"Let's get out of here," I said. "There is nothing else we can do here today."

*   *   *

"How was your day?" Mariana was chirping playfully on the phone when I called her that night from our rented apartment.

"Full of adventure, I guess." I tried to sound upbeat.

"What did you do?"

"David and I went to a fancy restaurant today. The food was really good, and the music was nice. We had such a great time."

"Oh, I'm so jealous."

"Then he bought me a red dress." I said, as the memories of that day flashed rapidly in front of my eyes.

"Wow! You had a *great* day, then?" Mariana asked cautiously, sensing a change in my voice.

"Well, that was after we had a huge fight because he couldn't get his money from Western Union, and he insisted on spending his last bit of cash on my red dress." My emotions were boiling up to the surface, shooting my words out of my mouth with a fury of a machine gun.

"I don't understand. Why would he spend the last of his money on your dress?" She latched on to the least logical thing that caught her attention.

"I don't know. It was so stupid." I paused. "What if I made a mistake?"

"About the dress?"

"Yeah." I sighed. "About the dress. There were like rows and rows of them, and we were walking and walking forever, and I just wanted to get it over with, so I picked the first dress I could fit into."

"Do you like it?"

"Does it matter? It's too late now. No returns."

"Do you think you made a mistake with David?" She finally caught up with my metaphor.

"I don't know," I whispered.

"What are you going to do?"

"I don't know." I paused. "What can I do? Just wait and see how it goes, I guess. Tomorrow is going to be a brand-new day."

Chapter 29

When the
Last Bell Rings

"Are you coming home for the last bell-ring ceremony today?" Mom asked me.

"Do you mean for the kids' last day of school?" I said. "Yes, we're coming home. We got David's Western Union money, finally, so we're going to the train station right now to buy our tickets to Bucharest. He's leaving in two days."

"All right then. I'll start lunch so it's ready when you get here. Then I have other news."

"What news?"

"It's a lot to discuss. There is no point in talking about this over the phone. We'll talk when you come home."

Thanks for the cliffhanger.

"Is it bad news or good news?"

"It's a good thing … for the family," Mom answered.

The train station was packed, as if everyone in the city was either leaving or booking summer vacation tickets at the same time.

"Which line is ours?" David asked me, pointing at five different ticket lines. He raised his head to look at the board above the ticketing agents' windows. It listed schedules for the international routes: Moscow, Kiev, Bucharest.

"It doesn't matter. They sell tickets in all directions. Let's pick the short one," I said, and stepped toward the closest line.

"How long will it take?" He looked at the serpentine of people in front of us with impatience.

"If we're lucky, we'll be out of here in less than an hour."

"An hour? Don't they have a handicapped line or something like that?"

"There's no such thing in Moldova. If you're tired, go sit down on the bench outside. I'll stay in line for you."

"Can't we just go outside together and come back later?"

"That's not how the line rules work around here," I said. "You have to stay in line, or you lose your spot."

"There are rules about lines?"

"Yeah. Another rule: you don't cut in line." I pointed at him. "I can see what you're thinking."

"What if I ask nicely?" David smiled.

"You see that old man who looks like he's ninety? He's staying in line. The pregnant woman, and the woman with two small children? They're staying in line too. Who are you going to cut in front of? We're staying in line!" I said sternly. "Go to the exchange window over there and exchange fifty dollars in leis. The tickets are sold in local currency only."

"Okay, okay. I'll be back," he said, then walked away.

A man who stood two places in front of me turned around and asked, "Is he American?"

"Yeah. The shorts give him away?" I said sarcastically.

"That, then his English, then the attitude." The man smiled in response. "He's probably not used to staying in lines. When we get closer, I'll let him go first. I don't want him to have a bad impression of our country."

"That's all right. He pissed me off yesterday, so he's staying in line. He needs to learn that he can't have everything he wants instantly."

The man nodded, agreeing with me. Then something grabbed his attention behind me. "Hey, look over there."

I turned to look where he was pointing and saw David, holding a one hundred-dollar bill. He was talking to a man in a black leather jacket, who was swiftly counting the twenty-dollar bills in his hands.

"Shit! Hold the line for me, please," I told the man and ran toward David. "Hey, what are you doing?" I pulled on David's hand as he reached out, ready to give his money to the man in the leather jacket.

"This gentleman offered to exchange my hundred for smaller bills."

"I bet he did." I waved at the man to leave us alone. "These are railway crooks. They're looking for suckers like you to take your real dollars and give you back fake dollars. I told you to go to the official exchange office." I took his hand and pulled him there myself. "I can't leave you alone for a minute."

"Do we need to call the police?" he asked.

"And report what? A robbery that never happened? Besides, I've seen this dude here before. He wouldn't be at the train station every day, if he didn't have police protection. Here." I gave David the exchanged money. "Don't put them in your back pocket." I smacked his hand as it moved to the back of his shorts. "Somebody will pull them out, and you won't even feel it. Always keep your money in the front pocket of your shirt, so you can see it."

"Wow! So many things to watch for. Hey, you left the line," he said, finally noticing. "Aren't we going to lose our spot?"

"There's a five-minutes rule. You can step away to go to a bathroom—or save somebody from being robbed." I gave David the look. "Don't worry. The person in front of me is keeping my spot."

"My God! How many rules are there for this railway station alone?"

"Listen," the man who was holding our spot said, "go buy his tickets. You've got to get him out of here before he gets himself in more trouble."

* * *

"Oh, good, you're finally home," Mom said, opening the door for me and David. "V-velcome!" She smiled at David, proud that she'd finally learned an English word she could say to him—close enough.

"Good afternoon, Mother!" David smiled at her too.

"Who are the flowers for?" Mom asked me, looking at the bouquet of yellow asters that I was holding in my hands.

"That's for the teachers, for the last day of school. You know, our stupid traditions."

"Ah! I know, I know. The kids are in class right now. Lica said the last bell will ring at one o'clock. You should probably go there now. There are only ten minutes left."

"David," I turned around, "I have to go to school. I'll leave you here with Mom, but I'll be back in about an hour."

"You don't want me to go?" he asked, obviously hurt.

"It's a long walk. You'd have to stay on your feet the entire ceremony. And nobody speaks English there. You wouldn't understand a word." I tried to dissuade him.

"Are the kids getting an award?"

"They should."

"Then I have to go. They need to know their parents are proud of them." *Well,* I thought, *technically, you're not their*—"I understand," David said quickly, as if reading my mind, "that I'm not their real dad. But I'm proud of them the same way." I kept quiet, trying to process what he'd just said. "Unless you don't want me to go," David pouted.

"What's he saying?" Mariana asked me impatiently.

"He wants to go with me to the kids' last bell ceremony."

"Why?" Mom asked. "For God's sake, you don't want to show up at school with David. Everybody's going to stare at him and at his boot. You couldn't tell him to put some pants on?"

"It's hot outside. He insisted on wearing shorts," I said.

"I'll go with you," Mariana said. "At least you won't get all the stares by yourself."

"So, what's the verdict?" David asked me when Mariana, Mom, and I stopped talking.

"If you insist, we'll go."

"Oh, I insist."

David walked uphill slowly, going around the potholes and stopping to take breaks. The bright sun was making him sweat. He looked like an old man who was stubbornly putting on a brave face, insisting that he was fine when he wasn't. Finally, we reached the corner of the school building and the schoolyard opened in front of us.

The students, in their uniforms, were standing outside in a tidy lineup. Boys in black suits and white shirts, girls in black or blue skirts with white shirts. Two lines of children were facing each other. A third line faced the school's front stairs, which served as a podium for the principal, a woman in her late fifties, wearing her best dress for the occasion.

Mariana, David, and I approached the schoolyard as the principal walked to the stand for her speech. We took a sharp left, trying to get behind the lines of children. But there was no such thing as sneaking anywhere with David, who stuck out of the crowd like a giraffe. A few older kids in the front rows locked their eyes on him, looking like meerkats, curious about the giant. They turned their heads in unison as he made his way across the yard.

The younger kids started fidgeting and whispering into each other's ears, disturbing the orderly lines. A teacher tried to calm them down. But one kid pointed his finger in our direction, and when the teacher turned our way, she looked stunned. She moved her hands, making the sign of the cross, as if she'd just seen the devil.

"That's so awkward," Mariana whispered into my ear. I looked for David's reaction, but he was just his usual self.

"He's either unaware or pretending, because it's impossible for him not to notice," I whispered back to Mariana. "But he's smiling, like nothing's happening, so we'll keep smiling too."

The principal, oblivious to the staring contest between the entire school and David, fixed the microphone at her stand and lifted her right hand up, addressing the crowd with the solemn voice appropriate to her position: "I hereby declare the official closure of the last day of the 2001 school year! Ring the last bell!"

"I thought the award ceremony started before the last ring," Mariana said. "Are we late?"

"I don't think so," I said, but my answer was drowned out by a long and loud ringing, floating from the open door into the yard.

"Is that all?" David asked.

"Not yet. By tradition, a graduating student and a first grader are supposed to close the ceremony together."

"They don't separate the students by elementary, middle, and high school age here?"

"No."

"That's very different. Not to mention that, in American public schools, kids don't have to wear uniforms. When you all come to America, Angelica and Serghei can wear jeans to school if they want to."

When we all come to America, I repeated to myself. In the meantime, we followed our school's rules. My thoughts were interrupted by the principal calling for someone to start the ceremony. The teenager in charge lifted up a tiny first-grade girl and placed her on his left shoulder. She wore giant white bows in her hair and held a shiny golden bell in her hand, which was tied with a red ribbon. When the boy started his march around the perimeter, she was spooked for a moment by his fast pace and grabbed at his head with one hand, trying not to fall. She lifted the other hand and shook the bell hard, over and over. The bell's sound came closer as the girl's handler was approaching the spot where we were standing, but it faded away as the boy passed us, moving to the other side of the schoolyard. I looked at the girl with some sadness. I'd wanted to be that girl when I was in school. To be on someone's shoulder like that, ringing the bell. But my turn never came.

It suddenly got quiet. The bell stopped ringing, and the boy dropped the little girl off his shoulder. As if waiting for this signal, the crowd of students dispersed in every direction, like a bunch of overjoyed bunnies.

"Mo-o-om!" I heard Lica's voice running toward us. "They were supposed to give us awards during the ceremony in front of everybody, but they decided to give them out in class, so we can go home faster. That's so unfair."

"That explains why the ceremony was so short," I answered.

"David, look, I got a diploma for good grades." She showed him the paper in her hands.

"A diploma? Is that an award?" David asked me. I confirmed. "You know what?" He caressed Lica's head. "You deserve to be rewarded for your hard work." He pulled twenty dollars out of his pocket and handed it to her. "This is your money. Not Mom's. Yours." He pointed his finger at her. "You can spend it however you want."

"I never get money for good grades," Lica said, looking at him in shock. "I love you, David." She gave him a hug and started crying.

"What about me? What about me?" Serghei ran up right in the middle of the money changing hands.

"Do you have a diploma for good grades too?" I asked.

"They didn't give me one," Serghei pouted.

"No diploma for him?" David asked.

"He didn't get an excellence award, but he still has good grades."

"You know what, Serghei?" David leaned forward. "You'll have to promise me that next year you'll get an excellence award, like your sister. Here's the deal: This year, I'll pay you forward the same amount as your sister. But if you don't get an excellence award next year, you get nothing, since I already paid you this year." He pulled out another twenty dollars and gave the money to Serghei.

"Thank you! Thank you!" Serghei yelled, grabbing the money before I even had a chance to translate the conditions.

Mariana gave me a look: *What's he doing?*

I gave her the look back: *I don't know.*

"I wish you'd talk to me before you give money to my kids," I told David with annoyance in my voice.

"Are you mad at me? What did I do wrong?"

"We don't pay our kids for good grades. We expect them to be good students. Some things just don't need to be paid for with cash. Why is it always about money with you?"

"It's not about money, it's about rewarding hard work. There's a long tradition in American families to pay cash to our kids for good grades. In the family I grew up in, for excellent grades, you could get a hundred dollars. For just okay grades, you could get fifty."

"There's a cash scale for grades? That's just wrong." I shook my head. Our traditions made more sense than his.

A girl from Lica's class finally got up the courage to approach us. "Who's this man?"

"That's David," Lica answered quickly. "He's from America."

"Ah. Is he giving money to everybody?"

"He only gives money if you have good grades," Lica answered as an expert. "Though I don't understand how come I have to have a diploma to get twenty dollars and Serghei doesn't?" She looked at David. "That's unfair."

"Indeed, David. How do you explain this? I'm very confused by your logic," I said, and translated Angelica's concern.

"Technically," David said, "he should have gotten less, but look at him, he's so happy."

"Can I have some?" the girl standing nearby asked. "I have good grades."

"Unfortunately, he's out of money," I answered. "You see what you've done?" I asked David, noticing that a few boys had gathered around Serghei, who was showing off his dollars. "We're in the middle of a school full of students, most of whom have never held such a large amount of money in their hands. That's like rubbing it in their faces."

"I'm sorry. I had good intentions."

"Serghei, Lica!" I yelled. "Let's go home. Grandma's waiting for us with lunch."

* * *

"Come in, and go sit down at the table right away," Mom said, letting us all in the house. "The food is getting cold." Mariana and the kids passed me in the hallway and went to sit on the couch, while I waited for David, who was trailing behind. Serghei swirled around the table like a little hurricane, reached out to a tray, and grabbed a baked roll dusted in powdered sugar from it. Mom smacked his hand.

"Soup first, sweets later," she said.

"David, meet my brother, Vitalic." I pointed at the corner, where my brother was sitting. He stood up to shake David's hand.

"Finally, someone as tall as me." David smiled wide like a giant who had just found a long-lost sibling.

"Hardly, a match," I said, looking at them. I had always considered my brother to be tall. After all, he was the *shpalera* of the family who took after Babushka in height and skinniness, but not next to David, who was a head taller.

David shook Vitalic's hand. "Nice to meet you."

"He's big," my brother said in Romanian, as if speaking to me in code, then turned to David with a smile: "V-velcome, la familia!"

"Fa-mi-li-a?" David asked. "Is he saying: 'Welcome to the family'?" I nodded. "Tell him thank you." David smiled back.

"He understands 'thank you,'" I said. "Are you hungry?"

"I'm starving after all this walking." David took the closest chair, ending up right by a bottle of wine. "I can't have wine." He pushed the bottle away. "Do you want wine?" he asked my brother.

"No," Vitalic said. "I quit drinking."

"That's really good news," I told him, then turned around. "Mom, what's the other good news you promised to tell me about?"

"Here." She gave me her international passport.

"What's that? You got yourself a new passport, I can see."

"Look inside."

I flipped through the pages. "What am I looking for?"

Mom grabbed the passport from me, flipped through the pages herself, and pointed at the last page. "See? Visa for Italy."

"You have a visa for Italy? How come?"

"Vasily Gramovich, your wannabe boss, brought me back my passport yesterday. His neighbor who works for the Italian embassy pushed it through."

"He actually kept his word? I'll be damned. That's exciting!" I almost jumped off the chair. "David, look. Mom got her visa for Italy."

"Is that good?"

"That's more than good. Do you know how hard it is for us Moldavians to get a visa to go anywhere outside this country? It's almost impossible." I smacked his shoulder when I saw the look on his face. "Of course you don't know. You spoiled Americans." I turned to Mom. "When are you leaving and for how long?"

"I'll wait until David goes back to America, and I'll pack for Italy too. It's been too long. I need to go back to work and make sure this family stays afloat." I got quiet, unsure what else to say. "If David keeps his word and takes you and the kids to America, then thank goodness. If that doesn't happen, you'll now have me in Italy. I'll find you a housekeeping job."

"What?" David asked me curiously.

"Mom's asking if you're really taking us to America," I said flatly.

"Of course I am," David said, and pulled me into his arms. "I can't imagine being without you guys."

"I guess the American bells are calling for me." I smiled back. "Italy will have to wait."

"What about Italy?" David asked.

"Nothing. Let's eat."

Chapter 30

David's Departure

"Honey, I'm leaving tonight," David said, poking his food with his fork.

"I know. You said it twice already. Technically, you're leaving tomorrow morning. Tonight, we're just taking the train to Bucharest, so you can get to the airport tomorrow."

"Why do you have to be so technical? In my mind, I'm already on my way back. I'm sad. Aren't you?"

"I'm sad too. But we have a lot to do. We need to pack up your stuff. I need to clean the apartment before we leave, because that was the deal. We need to meet with the kids for the last goodbye. We've got shit to do, so we can be sad, but we need to keep moving." I noticed he had stopped eating, which was rare. "Are you done with that plate?"

"I've lost my appetite." David pushed his plate away.

"You need to finish that. I don't want you to have a diabetic episode right before your flight." I pushed the plate back to him. David sighed, but put another piece of omelet in his mouth.

"Go pack. I'll clean up," I said, taking his plate away to get him out of the kitchen. I really didn't want to come back here and clean up after Bucharest, like my godmother suggested. I wanted it to be done with.

I turned on the hot water, sprayed soap on the dishes, and scrubbed them with the sponge front and back. Then I rinsed them and stacked them on the dish rack one by one. The running water was pleasant to the touch. I let it run through my fingers, washing bubbles off my palms until they faded away. *Here goes my time with David. Gone down the drain.*

"Irina," I heard David calling me from the other room.

"What?" I asked, drying my hands with a towel.

"Come here, look." I went reluctantly. "Aren't we cute?" David was sitting on the bed, looking through the photos that we'd taken in the park with the kids.

"Yes, we are, but you're supposed to be packing. And I need to wash the kitchen floor."

"How can you think about floors right now, when I'm leaving? Spend some time with me," he said, and pulled me closer to him.

"We'll have an entire night on the train together. Right now, you need to pack. We can't miss that train," I said softly.

"You're right. I'll start packing. But it looks like my things have multiplied. I don't think I can fit it all in my suitcases."

"Of course they multiplied. You bought souvenirs, remember?"

"Oh God, I totally forgot about those. Now I have even less space than I thought."

"I'll go finish the floors. And you keep packing. If you can't fit it all, I'll go to the store and buy a small bag that you can take on the plane. That's why I want you to pack, so you know what else you need before we leave for the train station."

"Okay," David said, wiping a corner of his eye.

I walked away to my duties. I couldn't deal with a man crying like a child right then.

* * *

I convinced David to take a microbus to the train station instead of a taxi, so he could save his money for the road.

"How far is it from the bus stop?" David puffed, getting out of the microbus. "My suitcases are heavy."

"It's not far," I said.

"It's not far by your measurements or by American measurements?"

"You'll make it," I brushed him off.

But the minute I saw David trying to drag his suitcases across the uneven, patched-up asphalt, I felt for him. The three hundred meters to the train station became an exhausting distance with multiple stops at every curb that was not designed for luggage on wheels.

"A person in a wheelchair would not survive here," David said, lifting his two suitcases up the stairs to the station.

"Well, there's only one more day for you to suffer. Tomorrow, you'll be home and back to normal."

"Is that supposed to cheer me up?" David said, breathing heavily. "When are the kids coming?"

"Mariana left the house with them at the same time as we did. They should be here soon. Let's go to the platform so we don't miss them."

I pulled David to the end of the crowded platform, passing an endless row of people: two grandmas with live chickens in their bags, three men with cigarettes in their mouths, a group of students with duffle bags, mothers with small kids everywhere. I looked at a ragged line of people crossing the tracks from the other side, trying to get to the platform where we were standing. My attention locked on a young lady in Bordeaux pants and a pink shirt walking with two kids. The kids' clothes looked so familiar. *No way!*

"David! David!" Lica and Serghei yelled, and ran towards us, jumping over the tracks, then climbing up onto the platform.

"What the hell are you doing?" I yelled at Mariana. "Why are you crossing the tracks on foot?"

"It's closer to come from the bus stop on this side than to go all the way around and come from the front. It adds ten more minutes to our trip."

"Ten extra minutes wouldn't kill you, but an oncoming train might."

"Chill! Everybody's doing that, and so far, everybody's alive," Mariana answered dismissively. "Hello, David." Mariana turned to David and went for a hug, as if asking for protection.

David covered her with his big, long arms. "What's she chewing you out for?" he asked. "For walking on the tracks?"

"Yes, for the tracks," I answered, impressed that he understood what we'd talked about. A few more weeks and he'd be fluent in our sisterly intonations.

"Are you guys hungry?" David asked.

Lica and Serghei jumped excitedly. "Yes, yes!" By now they'd learned what those words meant. David was going to buy them some food.

"What's that woman selling?" David pointed at a woman walking on the platform with a plastic see-through bag. "Piroshkies?" He waved the woman over.

"How do you know this Russian name?" I asked him.

"We have a bakery in Seattle called 'Piroshky' near Pike Place Market. I love piroshkies," he said, salivating over the smell of the patties as the woman pulled them from her bag. "I'll take you guys there when you come to America," he said, getting out the last Moldavian coins left in his pocket to pay the seller. I supposed he might as well spend them now. He wouldn't need them anymore.

The kids bit into their piroshkies like hungry wolves, munching on them so fast that they got oil and crumbs all over their faces. *Slow down*, I wanted to say, but I stopped myself. *They should enjoy themselves now. We won't be buying piroshkies again soon.*

"Hey, the train is coming," Mariana said, pointing her finger toward the distant metallic sound, which was getting closer every second. Then, one by one, blue- and yellow-striped cars passed the spot where we were standing. They puffed and pounded on the metal tracks, their giant wheels slowing with a screech, and finally stopped.

"One last picture before my departure," David said, and then asked a man standing nearby to take a photo of us all with the train in the background.

"Okay, but quickly," I told David, waving the kids to come closer.

"Cheese," David said, and smiled. We all smiled one last time. David bent over to hug Lica, then Serghei. Then he straightened up to give Mariana a hug.

"I had a great time with you all. I'm going to miss you terribly," David said, wiping his tears.

"Come on, let's move!" I yelled. "Our tickets are for car number three—that's at the head of the train." I looked at David working his way to our car with his suitcases. I grabbed one from him and told Mariana, "Take the kids and go ahead. Tell them we're coming." I followed the kids ahead of David. He was trailing behind, trying to keep pace.

"Hello," David said, smiling to the conductor of our car when he finally got there.

The woman looked like she hadn't slept for three days and didn't care much for pleasantries, but the foreign "hello" made her crack a forced smile. She put her hand forward and said, "Tickets and passports," instead of hello. She flipped through my passport and gave it back to me. Then looked through David's with intense scrutiny. "American? Nice. I don't see Americans often. Go put your luggage in your compartment. We're leaving in ten minutes."

"My God, how do people get up there?" Holding his suitcase, David looked terrified at the four steep metal steps. The conductor shook her head impatiently while he lifted his suitcase onto the second step, then climbed onto the first step himself. Then he lifted his suitcase again and moved up to the next step—and to the next—until he got into the car.

"You should have gone up first to help him in," Mariana said, looking at two more passengers behind us, who were checking their watches.

"I know. Stay there," I told David when I saw him turning around to climb down for his second suitcase. "We'll bring it up." I jumped on the first stair, then turned around and grabbed the handle of the other case. Mariana lifted it up along with me and put it on the first step. I started moving up with my back still to David until the suitcase and I were in the car. "That's how you do it," I said. "Keep moving. We need to get inside. We're blocking other passengers from coming in."

"Where is our compartment?" David asked, moving down the hallway and looking at the numbers on the doors.

"There," I said, then slid a door to the right, and we looked into a tiny, dark-brown, outdated four-bed compartment, with two beds on top and two below, and a scratched-up table at the window.

"This is a sleeping car?" David asked, surprised.

"Yeah, I thought you understood. It's an international train. It has to have places where you can sleep."

"That's so cool. I've never been in a sleeping car before. Where do we put the luggage?"

"Lift the bottom beds. We put them underneath."

"Oh, that's even cooler." He looked intrigued and put his luggage on the bottom. "There are four beds here. Does that mean we'll have two more passengers with us? I was hoping it would just be us. It's our last night together."

"You didn't have the money to buy four tickets. Remember?"

"I'm sad." He dropped his head. "Where are the kids?" he asked all of a sudden.

I peeked out of the compartment and didn't see them. I spotted them bargaining with the conductor when I looked through the window.

"Looks like she didn't let them in," I said.

"Let's go outside then." He approached the door.

"We're about to depart," the conductor said, climbing on the step and blocking our exit.

"What did she say?" David asked impatiently. I translated what the conductor had said. "But I didn't say my last goodbye."

"Talk to them from here." I let him go to the window, but it wouldn't open. His face looked distraught.

"David, David." We heard Serghei's chirping voice, barely audible through the thick glass. He was waving from the platform, trying to get David's attention.

"Goodbye, Serghei! Goodbye, Lica! Goodbye, Mariana! I love you all," he yelled as loud as he could and sent them an air kiss.

"I love you, David!" Lica yelled, and sent him an air kiss back: "Mwah!"

"I love you too!" Serghei yelled.

Mariana waved goodbye in silence.

I went to the door, where the conductor was blocking the exit, and told Mariana over her shoulder: "You can go now."

"We'll stay until the train takes off."

"Go, you're just making him cry."

"We're not leaving until the train leaves," Mariana said stubbornly.

"All right, but when the train is gone, don't go over the tracks again." As I was finishing my sentence, the train whistle blew, signaling our departure, drowning my voice.

"What?" Mariana asked, and started following the moving train. I couldn't tell if she really didn't hear me or was pretending not to. Either way, I didn't have much confidence she'd listen.

Lica and Serghei were walking alongside her. But as the train picked up speed, only Serghei kept going, running beside our window, feet moving fast, like a little dog chasing a car—trying to keep up with the train so he could wave a little longer. Then he stopped too. David glued his face to the window to look at them one more time.

"It's over. Let's go inside," I said, and entered our compartment. I took the bottom-left bed. David dropped onto the lower bed on the right.

"I never thought I'd get so emotional," he said, then blew his nose. "Come here, sit next to me. Looks like no more passengers are coming, so it's our lucky night." He pulled me over and squeezed me with this left arm. I kept silent, listening to his heart, which was beating twice as hard. We sat there for thirty minutes, looking at the fast-moving imagery outside our window: white, yellow, and gray buildings zipping by, as if in a silent movie. Neither of us knew what else to say.

"Fun fact," I said to distract him. "In Europe, railroad tracks are narrower than in the former Soviet Union, so when we reach the Romanian border in a few hours, they'll have to change the wheels on the train."

"What? We'll have to get out?"

"No. They lift the train on a special platform, and you stay on the train while they're changing the whole bottom of it with the wheels."

"That's crazy." My trick seemed to work, because he quickly moved on to other thoughts. "Where is the bathroom in this compartment?"

"It's at the end of the car."

"One bathroom for all compartments?"

"Yes," I told him and watched for his reaction.

"Okay," he said, and left the compartment with a better attitude than I'd expected. I opened my bag to get a toothbrush and the pants and T-shirt I planned to sleep in, when I heard David behind me.

"My God, that's a tiny, tiny bathroom," he said. "I could barely fit. The smell is horrendous, by the way. I didn't find any toilet paper, and when I pressed the pedal of the toilet, a hole opened and my shit fell on tracks. I've never seen anything like that."

"That's Soviet train design. We dump the shit on the tracks. That's another good reason the kids shouldn't be walking over the tracks. Is that enough shock for you for one day?" I laughed, until a knock at the door made me stop.

"Tea, coffee, Coca-Cola, Fanta?" the conductor asked when I opened the door.

"Coca-Cola." David jumped up enthusiastically, finally learning to say "Coca-Cola" like a local.

"Tea with lemon," I said. She went back to her station and brought David an old-fashioned bottle of Coke. For me, she had a glass of tea in an ornate metal cupholder with a handle—the kind I was used to from my childhood.

"What's that?" David asked, intrigued by the unusual cupholder. "I want that."

"They're not for sale." I paused. "And you're not stealing it." I sat back down on the bed and sipped my tea. He laughed, lifted the bottle of Coke to his mouth, and swallowed almost all of it in one long gulp.

"Why are we stopping?" David asked, noticing that the train had slowed down.

"We've reached customs at the border with Romania. And it's the spot where they change the wheels."

"I need to see this to believe it." David tried to peek through the window but only hit his head on the bunk bed above him. "Goddamn, this train is for midgets." He sat back down in frustration.

"I don't think you'll be able to see much. The action is under the train, and we're not allowed to get out because it's an international border. Get out your passport. The customs officers will be in shortly."

David fumbled with his passport, preparing for whatever came next on this journey.

"Good evening," the Romanian customs officer said with a stern face, as if smiling would cost him money. "Your passports, please." He flipped through our passports, then turned to David. "Were you visiting somebody in Moldova?" he asked in English, unable to hide his curiosity.

"As a matter of fact, I was. I was visiting my fiancée and her family."

"Is that her?" He pointed at me, like I was in a police lineup waiting to be identified.

"Yes, that's her," David said.

"How did they treat you?" he asked David, keeping his eye on me. *What is he?* I wondered. *The American fiancée police?*

"Oh, man, they treated me like a king. I had the best time of my life." The customs officer finally let out a smile.

"Have a safe trip home. Hope you'll come visit our beautiful country again soon."

"Definitely," David said, taking his passport back from the officer, who opened the door to leave our compartment.

"This bed is so narrow and short." David examined the bed he was sitting on, then tried lying on his back. "Look, my feet are hanging off the end, and my hand is hanging off the edge," he said, and turned his big body onto his right side. "Also, I can't see you because of this hanging table between us." He tried to lift his head, but the train jerked, shaking David's body to the left, then the right, then the left again.

"Ouch! I just hit my head on the table twice." He rubbed his forehead.

"Actually, if not for the table, you'd probably fall out of bed." I laughed at his clumsiness. "Find a comfortable position. I'll go brush my teeth."

By the time I came back, David was already snoring, lying on his back with his mouth open. I went under the covers myself. In the darkness of the night, I finally had time to think of what David's departure meant for all of us. *Will he write me right away? Will he still call? When will he start our visa?* My mind was drifting after a while. I was falling into a deep, oh-so-needed sleep. *I'll think about it tomorrow,* was my last thought of the day.

It felt like I'd slept for just a minute, but the conductor was knocking on doors, a warning that we were approaching the Bucharest train station.

"David, wake up." I pushed him.

"Okay," he said, still semi drowsy.

After we arrived in Bucharest, everything moved quickly. Within minutes, we got our luggage and walked off the train onto the busy platform showered with bright sunlight. A bus with a sign saying "Airport" took us in, and off we went. Then we marched into the Bucharest airport's departure terminal and checked in David's luggage.

"Two hours before I leave," David said in a broken voice. He pulled me in, setting me on his lap and holding me in his arms. Then, as if remembering something, he put his hand in his pocket and said, "Here, I've got some dollars left. Take them with you for the bus tickets."

"When will I hear from you?" I asked, holding back tears.

"When I go back, I'll start the divorce proceedings with my wife right away."

"What do you mean? I thought you were already divorced." I pushed away from his arms.

"We're separated, but not officially divorced. I didn't have the money for that, because I had to buy tickets to come see you."

That would have been nice to know. "How long will that take?"

"If everything goes amicably, the courts take about ninety days to dissolve a marriage."

"What if it doesn't go amicably?"

"I'm confident it will because she wants a divorce as much as I do. Worst-case scenario? It will all be done by the end of the year."

"That means you can't even start our visa application until the end of the year." This was a lot to process just before he left the country. "And how long will it take?"

"I don't know, but I'll try to make it happen as soon as possible."

"You should probably go inside. It's getting late." I got up.

"But I've got an hour and a half."

"It's an international flight, so you should be there early."

"Okay," he said, looking at the long line at the checkpoint. At the end of the line, the airport agent let David cross behind the dividing tape, but he stopped me.

"You can't go inside if you don't have a ticket," the agent said.

David looked at him with begging eyes. "Can she at least walk with me until we get to the checkpoint?"

"No," the agent said. David turned to me and burst into tears.

"That's okay. You go," I said, and pushed him. "I'll stay here."

"You're not mad at me, are you?" he asked.

"I'm fine. Go."

He squeezed me one more time, tight, as if that was his last farewell, and said, "I love you."

"I love you too," I said automatically.

He walked away, turning back a few times, wiping his cheeks.

I took a few steps back, watching him walk farther and farther. Then I turned around and bolted to the exit.

I heard David's loud, desperate scream behind my back: "Irina!" But I didn't turn. I couldn't deal with moping David right then.

What the fuck does all this mean? He's going back to America, back to his normal life. And I'll be sitting and waiting here in uncertainty for months or years. What the fuck does it mean? I was shaking, almost convulsing, when I finally got out of the airport.

"A-a-a-ah!" I wept with the primal sound of a wounded animal, trying to keep my voice down so nobody around me could hear. I squatted in a corner, curled into a fetal position, and held on to my belly.

A woman approached me with a bottle of water. "Are you all right?"

"No, I'm not all right," I said, accepting her water to wash my face.

"Do you need help?"

"You can't help me." I smiled at her. "Nobody can. I just need to get back home, to Chişinău."

"There are microbuses that go from here to Chişinău every few hours."

"Thank you. I'll do that."

Chapter 31

Precious Cargo
Is Not a Burden

"I can't believe you didn't turn around," David said, almost sobbing, when he called me the next day. "I yelled your name three times."

"I didn't hear you." I took the easy way out. It was not a good day to talk about my emotions, since David was an emotional wreck himself.

"How was your flight? You went back to work already?" I bombarded him with questions, which seemed like a smart strategy.

"The flight was fine. But at work today, all I could talk about was you guys. I showed everybody our pictures. It was a tough day."

"Did you talk to the lawyer?" I thought it best to get to the point.

"Actually, I talked to two of them today, the divorce lawyer and the immigration attorney. The immigration attorney said he'll mail you a package with the list of documents you'll need to send him so he can start the process."

"Mail? It will take a month to get the package. Do you know what's on the list so I can start working on it?"

"Let me get the paper," he said, shuffling through something. "You'll need birth certificates for all three of you and your divorce certificate translated into English. Your ex-husband's permission to take the kids out of the country—"

"Wait. What?"

"Because your kids are minors, he said you'll have to have your ex-husband's permission to get the kids out of the country."

"What if he doesn't ... give ... permission?" I asked slowly, measuring every word, only now realizing how serious of an obstacle that could be.

"Will that be a problem?"

"I don't know. I didn't know I'd need such a paper, so I didn't talk to him about that."

"Can you call him and sort this out?"

Not an easy task...

"I don't think that's something I can solve over the phone. It's better if I go there in person."

"You're going to go all the way to Crimea? To see your ex-husband?"

"To make sure he signs the paper," I replied. "He doesn't even know I'm dating an American, let alone that we're leaving for America. I don't know how he's going to react, or how the kids' grandma is going to react." This one task could change the course of everything. "I need to go to Crimea to take care of this."

"You wouldn't try to get back with him, would you?"

"Why would I do that?" I shook my head in disbelief, surprised by his jealousy. Why would he even ask me that? As if such a foolish move could bring me anything but misery.

But the thought of going back to Crimea to face my ex-husband, who, unbeknown to him, just became my Fate Maker or my Dream Killer, depending on the day I found him, sent chills down my spine. *What if he doesn't give his permission for us to leave for America? Then what?*

* * *

"Hello, Papa!" Lica yelled at her father in English, when we called him the next day.

"Oho! You speak English, my daughter?" he asked her in broken English.

"I learned some new words," Lica said. "Do you like it?"

"I'm impressed." Igor laughed. "Are they teaching you English in school already? Where's Serghei?"

"He's playing with his friends somewhere outside," she said. "God knows where. We specifically told him to be home for lunch because we were going to call you, but he's missing in action, as usual."

"Is your mother bringing you to Crimea this summer?" I heard Igor ask her.

"Who else?" I answered for Lica, taking the receiver out of her hands. "Not like you can afford it."

"Good day to you, Irina Mihailovna!" Igor rumbled and gave the over-the-top laugh he used to show he wasn't bothered by something. "Hey, I'm not as useless as you might think. I was planning to go to Moscow for work this summer, but now, since you're bringing the kids," he stopped, as if thinking about it, "If I have to choose between money and the kids, it's an easy choice for me. I only get to see my kids once a year. Money can't buy valuable time with them."

Did he really have to say that? "We'll be there next week," I said. "After we send Mom off to Italy."

"She's leaving for work again? She just came back. How's Mariana feeling about this? She waited for her mother for so long."

"Some of us have to make the hard choices, Igor. We don't have the luxury of being sentimental when there's no food on the table."

"Yeah, yeah," Igor scoffed. "I forgot. You're the Iron Lady. I'm just an irrational, sentimental *nytik*."

"Well, I wouldn't call you a sissy. You are just, you are just … It doesn't matter," I cut myself off. My voice was trembling with emotions. There was no need to make Igor nervous that something was up, since he could always smell my mood from a mile away. "We'll be there next week," I said at last.

Two days later, Mariana, Mom, and I were in the bus station, standing beside a bus going to Milan. It was filled mostly with women who were leaving their kids or husbands on the platform. Mom had only one small, black duffle bag with her.

"I don't want to pack much," she said, "just in case I don't have anywhere to go. I don't want to carry heavy luggage around."

Mariana smiled and kissed Mom on the cheek, then let her board the bus. Mom climbed the steps in silence. We'd already said everything we could. There was nothing left to say. When Mom finally took her seat, Mariana looked at her face in the window and waved goodbye.

Mariana's lips were still stretched in a smile when, all of a sudden, she started sobbing. *Where did this come from?* I looked at her, and then it all made sense. She was just a kid. Seventeen was still a kid. I put my arm around her shoulder, but she turned away from me, with her back to the bus, wiping her tears quickly.

"I don't want Mom to see me like this," she said, switching to adult mode.

I elbowed her to cheer her up. "Tomorrow you get to send me off with the kids too. You'll have the house all to yourself for almost a week. Finally, some peace and quiet, huh?"

"Yippy!" She smiled unconvincingly.

* * *

The next morning, the kids and I were getting ready for the four-hour train ride to Odessa, where we'd catch a night train going to Simferopol at six p.m. We'd made this trip so many times before that the kids already knew the drill.

"Let's take two bottles of water," Lica said before we left. "It's hot on those trains."

"Can we buy a Fanta?" Serghei asked when we got to the train station. He'd spotted a woman carrying around a bucket of ice with bottles sticking out for sale.

"No!" Lica answered for me. "Sugary drinks make you thirsty. Then we'll need to buy more water. Then you'll need to pee every ten minutes, and we'll have to pay for the bathrooms, because the bathrooms at train stations aren't free, you know."

"Both of you, get on the train." I pulled Serghei's and Lica's hands. "You can pee for free on the train once it leaves the station."

"Yeah, but when the train is moving, the toilets are shaking in there. It's hard to aim. I always pee around it."

"So it's you who makes the toilets stinky?" I asked in a sarcastic tone, taking one of the wooden seats at the window.

"Nah-ah!" Serghei dropped on the seat next to me. "It's not only me. You watch, an hour from now, it'll be hard to breathe in there. You watch."

"Quiet!" I said, already feeling exhausted. *It's gonna be a long twenty-four hours.*

"I'm hungry," Serghei said suddenly, when we stopped at the border with Ukraine for our passports to be checked. "Mom, can you buy us some piroshkies?" He pointed to a country woman who walked on the train with a bag of hot snacks.

"Sereoja, we've already spent a ton of money on our tickets. We can't afford to buy everything you see on the road. Besides, that's the easiest way to get food poisoning—by buying piroshkies from street sellers. Here, I brought sandwiches and pastries from home that should last us until we get to Crimea."

Serghei pouted but took a sandwich.

The customs officer asked me for my passport. Then he looked at the kids' birth certificates and moved on to the next passenger.

Funny how nobody here cares if I take my kids back and forth across borders without my ex-husband's permission. Why do Americans care about our kids more than we do? What if Ukraine had such a law and I couldn't get permission to leave with my kids? Would I be stuck there for the rest of my life?

I looked out the window. We were approaching Odessa, The Pearl of the Black Sea, as residents called it. Though an outsider could argue that the "pearl" was still in its dirty shell, rather than polished and shining on a necklace. But everything was bigger in Odessa. It had a bigger and more rambunctious train station than ours in Chișinău. It looked busy, even obnoxious, with people running back and forth nonstop.

We looked so provincial in comparison. Even the train tracks here had so many lanes: long, endless, parallel, and intersecting. One wrong turn to the left and we could all end up in a ditch. How could we know if it was the wrong turn before it was too late?

"Get ready. We're changing trains here," I said to the kids, grabbing the luggage.

"Twelve more hours to go," Lica said like an expert.

"Well, the next one has sleeping cars. Without doors, but at least we can lie down and sleep in there."

"As long as it's not too hot at night," Lica said.

"Can I sleep on the top?" Serghei jumped when we got to our open compartment with four beds: two on top and two on the bottom.

"Last time you fell off the bottom bed onto the floor, so I don't think it's a good idea for you to sleep on the top."

"But I'm older this year, Mom," he whined. "Lica, come climb on top with me and look at other trains going by. It's so fun! We'll just go up for a little bit, Mom, before we go to sleep? All right?"

"All right, but only for a little bit." I put our package of food on the tiny built-in table and shoved our luggage under the bottom bed on the left, while I watched them climb to the top-right bunk.

"I can't see," Lica said, pushing her brother, trying to peek over his shoulder to look out the window.

"Stop pushing me," Serghei yelled back, "or I'll fall."

"Stop yelling, both of you!" I raised my head.

"Fine. I'm going down to my bed then." Lica put one foot on the table and stepped with the other onto her bed, then dropped down, pouting.

"Sereoja, you can watch passing trains from the bottom beds too," I said.

"That's so unfair." Serghei came down, also pouting. At least, they were equally upset.

I climbed onto a top bunk and stretched my tired legs. The train jerked, slowly moving away from the station. Soon the metallic noise of the rotating wheels changed into a soothing noise: *tuk, tuk; tuk, tuk.* I closed my eyes and unleashed my mind, which had been too busy all day thinking about mundane, insignificant things: how to get water, how to control my bladder. But now, in the falling darkness, my mind was free to wander. My body felt weightless, hanging in the air in between the three worlds. I smiled when a vision of Mariana popped into my head. "Come home on the shield!" she'd said the morning before we left.

"What?" I'd asked her.

"Isn't that what the Spartan mothers said to their sons before a battle: 'Come home on the shield'?"

"No, silly! 'Come home with the shield or on it,' which means with victory or bravery, at least. They had to drop their shields to run away. Only dead warriors were brought home on the shield. You don't want me dead, do you?"

"Oh, no. Come back with victory. Good luck!" she had said, and smacked me on my shoulder, as she always did. *Good luck, indeed.* My present, my past, and my future intersected like Odessa train tracks, going in all possible directions, or going nowhere at all. I couldn't tell.

"Mom, is Papa going to meet us at the train station in Simferopol?" Lica asked with a weak half-asleep voice.

"No. We'll take a bus to your dad's town from the station."

"Will he meet us at the bus stop in his town, at least?"

"Sure. Why not?"

"Mom, I'm serious."

"Who knows what your father will do, Lica? Half the time, he doesn't know himself. If he's there, you'll know he made it."

The bus stopped at a sign spelling out the city name, Staryi Krym, a health resort forgotten from the Stalin era. The white, three-story building was squeezed in between a strip of pine trees and a range of baby mountains, looking like a herd of lost camels in the distance. I peeked through the window at a row of small, white clay houses that I remembered from long ago. Their roofs, covered with red clay tiles, were chipped in a few places, and I couldn't remember if that was how they were before. It might have happened since I left, but it didn't look like much had changed around here.

The kids and I stepped out of the bus onto the dusty country road, pulling our two bags behind us. The air felt hot and sticky. *So Crimean!* I was waiting for relief, but the light summer breeze seemed to be entangled in a strip of tall, green grass growing in the nearby ditch, and it couldn't reach us.

"Papa isn't here," Lica said, disappointed, looking at the empty bus stop.

"We'll have to carry the bags ourselves then. You both take the smaller bag. I'll take the big one," I said, getting us ready for the twenty-minute walk on gravel and dust.

"Lica, look. That's Papa coming," Serghei yelled, dropping the handle of the bag that he and Lica were supposed to carry. He sprang to his father, who was jogging towards us in a pair of summer shorts and a tank top, with a cigarette in his mouth. He looked like a running, smoking chimney from a Russian cartoon. But a coughing fit interrupted Igor's marathon. He stopped to catch his breath and flicked the cigarette to the ground, then bent forward, spreading his arms like a net, right in time to catch Serghei.

"Papa, Papa!" Lica ran to her father, too, leaving me behind with the bags. Igor squatted and picked Angelica up with his free left arm.

"Look at you, my darlings, how big you are!" He smiled and kissed them both on their cheeks. "Let's go help Mom with the luggage," he said, and started walking toward me, bouncing the kids in his arms.

"Put them down before you break your back," I said. "They're much heavier this year."

"Precious cargo is not a burden," he said stubbornly. "Right, my daughter?" He turned to Angelica, who wrapped her hands around his neck.

"Right," she said, giggling like she used to when she was little. "Pop, that's fine, we can walk. Let's help Mom. The bags are heavy."

"Well, hello, Irina Mihailovna!" Igor said in a cheery voice, letting the kids down. "Welcome to our paradise!" He casually kissed me on the cheek, as if I'd just returned home from a short vacation.

"Pop, you're really tan," Lica said. When he bent over to grab bags from my hands, she touched his exposed shoulders. "Did you go to the beach already, to the Black Sea?"

"The only Black Sea I saw this summer was the bottom of a well," Igor answered. "For the last three weeks I've been digging a bottomless well for one old lady. Ten meters and no water yet."

"Is ten meters really deep?" Serghei asked curiously.

"That's like ten of you," Igor answered, marching ahead with our bags.

"Oho!" Serghei said, speeding up, trying to keep up with his father. "Are you going to work tomorrow? I want to see the bottomless well."

"We'll see, son. Maybe I'll stay home with you tomorrow. I don't know what your mom's plans are." He looked at me. I said nothing. "Babushka Toma made a big pot of soup for you," he continued.

"I love Babushka's soup," Serghei said.

"She knows. That's why she made it." Igor winked.

Igor pushed the wobbly, semi-rotten, wooden gate to my ex-mother-in-law's house with his foot, and it rubbed unpleasantly on its rusty, metal hinge. Then the gate swung wide open, letting us into the yard. I glanced toward the gray stucco house with a gray roof and barely recognized where I used to live while Igor and I were married. It looked older and sadder. The stucco on the left wall was missing, exposing yellowish clay underneath, half covered with a blue tarp.

"What happened to Tamara's house?" I asked in horror, looking at Igor and dropping our bags on the asphalt path right at the front door.

"Rain must have gotten in some cracks, so a piece fell off. We thought, since the stucco fell off anyway, maybe it's better if we extend this end of the house and make the rooms bigger. My stepfather and I dug a trench over here and laid the foundation." I gasped when I saw the ugly, uneven foundation sticking out of the ground. "But then I got called into digging the damn well. We thought it was a good opportunity because we needed the money for our construction. And now, for three weeks, our construction has been stalled because we haven't reached any water, and Dad can't do it alone."

"Eternal construction around here, as usual," I said sarcastically.

"Yes, goddamn it. Eternal construction, as usual." Igor laughed. "Mom, Dad," he yelled at his parents in the kitchen window. "Come outside. Meet your grandkids. What are you doing in there?"

"I'm coming. I'm coming," Tamara yelled back and emerged through the door with her hands up in the air, her plump body and gray hair on display. She'd aged, but her bright-blue eyes were sparkling. "The joy of my life came to visit Babushka." She kissed

Angelica, then Serghei, then me, then Angelica and Serghei again. "Look at you, Serghei, you are up to my chest now. One more summer and you'll be taller than me."

"That's because you're a shorty, Babushka." He giggled, and Tamara laughed, too, with her raspy, loud voice.

"Don't go in the house." Tamara stopped us before we even crossed the first step. "It's freaking hot in there from the stove. Hell, the whole house is like a stove. We'll eat outside in the *besedka*. Your *dedushka* finally built me one, after ten years of nagging."

"What a funny name, *besedka*," Lica said. "Isn't that a place where you talk with people?"

"You can talk there, but we can also eat in it. We have a round table with a bench around it. Did you see it?" Tamara said. "Over there under the apple trees? Go, sit down. I put the bread and the salad there. I'll bring out the soup from the kitchen. You're all hungry from the road?"

Serghei sprang toward the gazebo, making his way through the garden, without waiting for anyone.

"Sereoja!" Igor yelled. "Don't stomp on the potato sprouts! Don't you see them right in front of you?"

"I see them," Serghei responded and switched to hopping over the rows of potatoes like an obstacle jumper. Lica shook her head and went to inspect the field.

"Of course, he stomped on it." Lica sighed. "No regard for Grandma's hard work."

I took a seat in the gazebo next to my kids and looked around the garden, searching for the cherry tree. *Too early*, I thought, noticing tiny green cherries growing on branches that were covered in leaves. I should have waited and come two weeks later, after they were ripe. But, frankly, there was no time to waste on cherries. I noticed Tamara coming through with her pot of soup, followed by Igor and my ex-father-in-law, Mikhail.

"Here," Mikhail said, as he awkwardly set down a bottle of vodka with a cork made from a piece of newspaper. "The best homemade. For your arrival."

"The fifty percenter?" I frowned.

"Are you trying to offend us? It's a seventy percenter," Igor said, taking the seat next to me.

"How do you drink this firewater without burning your throat?" I grimaced.

"Lots of practice," Igor answered proudly. I looked at Tamara, who was standing on the other side of the table, pouring soup into our bowls without seeming to move a muscle. She, obviously, had lots of practice tuning out these types of conversations. I was the one who had been left to deal with her son's practice. "Don't worry." Igor smiled. "For you, we'll add some water."

"I'm not drinking that."

"Come on, just one shot," Mikhail insisted and started first. Igor poured until my shot glass was one-quarter full, added water, and pushed it to me.

Then he poured himself half a glass. "For you!" he said, and swallowed the pure venom down in one gulp. He breathed out deeply, like a dragon spitting out fire. I looked at the liquid in my glass, closed my eyes and, *what the hell,* went for it. The night was going to be long. I'd need all the courage I could get.

After downing his third shot, my ex-father-in-law, whose face was cherry-red already, slurped his soup with a theatrical air.

"I love you, children," he would say occasionally, caressing Lica's long hair.

"Oh, Dad's already gone." Igor smiled like he wasn't on the same path. "He only says, 'I love you' when—"

"When he's drunk," I finished his sentence.

Igor laughed and lit up a cigarette. "You still remember? So, how's your love life, my darling?" Igor asked me all of a sudden, blowing cigarette smoke upward, over my head. I turned my head away. It had been a while since I was in the company of a man smoking so close to me. "Don't be shy about it," he encouraged me. "We're divorced. You're a free woman. Life moves on."

"I'm dating someone," I answered, uneasily waiting for Igor's reaction. I felt like I was preparing to jump into a cold river.

"I hope he's a good man," Igor answered, unfazed. "You know, with kids and all, I want to make sure they're in good hands."

"I think he's a good man."

"What's his name?"

"David."

"David? Is he a foreigner?"

"Yes. He's American."

"American?" Now that jarred a reaction. "Like from the United States? What does it mean?"

"It means that the kids and I—if everything goes according to plan—we could potentially move to America."

Igor stopped blowing smoke, as if he'd run out of the power to breathe. The calmness in his face vanished like a veil going up in flames. His cigarette hung on for dear life in the corner of his half-open mouth, but finally fell and landed on his naked knee, right below his shorts. He jumped up to shake off the burning ash.

"What happened?" my mother-in-law yelled from the other side of the table.

"Nothing, Mom. Just eat your soup," Igor said, and walked away. I followed him, unsure what to say next. He suddenly turned around, almost bumping into me. "You're telling me that you could take my kids to America and I might never see them again?"

"It doesn't have to be that way." I lowered my voice. "We'll come to visit. You're seeing the kids only once a year now, anyway. It won't be much different."

"The difference is that they'll be across the world. It's not like I can hop on a train and go visit them whenever I have a chance. It could be years before you come back. Or never."

"Igor, what's waiting for them here? Look around us: decay and no hope. There, at least, they have a future."

"What do you want from me?" His face changed as the sadness and panic turned into irritation.

"Since you're their father, I need you to sign a notarized permission saying that you allow me to take them out of the country."

"Ah! That's why you came?" He walked away to light another cigarette, but his hands were shaking, and after a few tries, he gave up. "You're asking me to sign my kids away," he said in a somber, chilling voice that was a hundred times worse than if he'd yelled at me. My body was covered in goosebumps. I started shaking uncontrollably.

"Is everything all right?" Tamara came to check on us.

"Everything's wonderful, Mom. Isn't that how you say it: 'Life's wonderful'?"

"What's going on, you two?" Tamara wasn't buying it.

"Ira is taking the kids to America."

"When?" Tamara asked with worry in her voice, looking straight at me.

"I don't know. Right now, I need to gather the documents, and David's immigration lawyer will start the long process. It could take up to a year, or less, or more. I don't know!"

Tamara and Igor exchanged silent looks, like two accomplices disoriented by a bombshell, trying to come up with a plan. Igor dropped his hands and cursed. My heart yanked, as that could mean anything, from him giving up to him gearing up for a fight. I looked at Tamara for help. Her face softened.

"Is it for sure with this man David? One hundred percent?" Tamara needed confirmation.

"Nothing's for sure. David can abandon us at any time. He has no obligations, honestly," I answered, finally getting some control over my voice.

"So, this could be their last summer here?" she asked, turning around to see the kids, who were playing with their grandpa in the gazebo.

"If we're lucky, yes, this could be their last summer here."

It became silent suddenly. We all ran out of words at the same time.

"You all, go to bed," Igor said. "It's getting late. We'll see what we can do tomorrow."

"What are you going to do?" I asked him, worried.

"I'm not going to stand in the way of my kids' happiness. That's what I'm going to do."

What does that mean? I wanted to ask, but I was afraid.

"I'm sleeping at Tanya's tonight," he said, eyeing the gate. "I'll come back in the morning."

Tamara was right. The whole freaking house was like a stove. The windows were open, but the summer heat, trapped in the house from earlier in the day, was not about to give up. Sweat dripped off my forehead, down my face, and from my armpits down to my sides. I felt sick, feverish, but I knew I wasn't sick. Or was I? I couldn't tell. I looked at Lica sleeping next to me, a white bed sheet across her body, her legs sticking out. Serghei on the floor, sleeping in just his underwear. If I could just fall asleep and stop thinking, maybe I would feel better. I closed my eyes. My eyelids felt heavy, metallic. *If I could just fall asleep.*

"Lica, Lica," I heard Serghei whispering over me, pushing his sister.

"Leave me alone," she said, her voice drowsy.

Why is he waking her up in the middle of the night? I opened my eyes, annoyed, and sunlight hit me. "What time is it?" I asked.

"I don't know," Serghei answered. "But Babushka made breakfast."

I looked at the clock on the wall: eight a.m.

"All right, we're getting up. Is your dad here?" I sat up and rubbed the sleep from my eyes.

"No, he didn't come yet," Serghei said.

"It's kinda late for him not to be here." I didn't like this morning already.

Tamara set the breakfast outside in the besedka again. I sat down, keeping the gate in my view. I didn't have much of an appetite. But I knew I had to eat, so I poked the paper-thin pancake on my plate with my fork and shoved bits down, almost without chewing. My heart seized up when I heard the gate squeak in the distance, then it started beating rapidly when I saw Igor come through. I breathed out, uncertain of how to feel.

"Oh, son, you're here early," Tamara said to Igor. "Sit down, eat with us."

"Don't worry, Mom. I already ate at home with Tanya and the girls." *Right, he had two more daughters with Tanya.* This fact had escaped my mind yesterday. Besides, it was the first time I'd heard Igor refer to Tanya's place as "at home." It sounded strange, surreal, because he'd always called his mother's place "home," no matter where he'd been at a certain time. We'd truly become strangers. *What had stopped him from putting his foot down?*

"I'll bring Liza and Nika tonight so they can see their brother and sister," Igor said, looking at Serghei and Lica. *Brother and sister?* This notion shocked my ears.

"Igor, why don't you take Lica and Serghei to Tanya's instead?" Tamara interrupted her son diplomatically.

"If that's better, that's fine, but I don't see what the big deal is. I don't like keeping secrets from anybody. Tanya knows about Ira, and Ira knows about Tanya. Lica and Serghei know about Liza and Nika, and the other way around. Right?" Igor looked at me, then the kids.

"Yes," Serghei answered for everybody.

"Oh, look, I got the first 'yes.'" Igor laughed. "Anyway, I thought I'd come early so Ira and I can go to the city hall before they have long queues. Are you ready?" He looked at me.

"Yes!" I jumped up. "Let me get my purse." I ran into the house, frantically looking for it all over, as I couldn't, for the life of me, remember where I'd left it last night. The Houdini of purses was nowhere to be found! Almost in tears, I bolted for the front door to look for it outside, and then I saw it. My darn purse was right there where I left it yesterday: at the entrance, hanging from the coat hanger peacefully, like nothing had happened. I took a deep breath, wiped the cold sweat off my forehead, put my purse on my shoulder, and walked out of the house to where Igor was waiting for me.

"Let's go!" I said, as calmly as I could, though my entire body was shaking. I couldn't bear to be near Tamara's house for one more minute. Even the air around it was suffocating me, so I had to get out of her yard as soon as possible.

Igor and I walked in silence to the city hall for a long twenty minutes, while he was lighting one cigarette after another to fill up the time. There were no more words in the world that we could say to each other, and I didn't want to interrupt Igor's smoking ritual that seemed to calm him down with each new cigarette. At the door of the city hall, we looked at each other one last time, as if asking one another: "Are you ready to do this?" Igor opened the door and let me in first, still without a word.

"Is this really your ex-wife?" the city hall clerk, a young male in his early twenties, asked Igor.

"Yes," Igor said definitively.

"And you came here together to sign your parental release for your kids?" He smiled mischievously.

"Yes. My wife, I mean my ex-wife, found herself an American husband."

"An American husband?" The clerk smiled at me even more

mischievously, then turned to Igor. "And you're just signing it without any conditions? No payoff? Nothing?"

"What payoff?" Igor was confused.

"I've had a few cases where ex-wives with kids paid a little something for this paper, like a toll of passage. Or more precisely, their American fiancés made the payment."

"Really? How much?"

"One paid three thousand American dollars, another paid five thousand. One was asked for ten thousand, but he didn't pay. Everybody missed out in that case. The ex-husband got nothing, and the ex-wife is still in town because the American didn't want to deal with the situation. I recommend all parties be reasonable. That way everybody wins."

I could feel my face turning into an angry Zeus mask, throwing lightning bolts out of my eyes into the wannabe-anti-Christ.

Igor trilled his lips. "So if I were a smart and rational person, I could be a rich man." He looked at me, cracking a smile. "But I'm an irrational, sentimental sissy, so my kids are not for sale," he said with the stern voice of a poor man who was too proud for a handout. "Just fill in that document and let's get it over with." He pointed at the blank piece of paper on the clerk's table.

"As you wish." The clerk stopped smiling and started clicking on his keyboard, entering the information from our passports and the kids' birth certificates in his computer. A few minutes later, he printed out the shiny, yellow and blue paper with golden edges and handed it to me.

"One more thing. This document is valid for a year. If, for some reason, your visa situation is not resolved in twelve months, you'll have to get another copy next year."

"All right," I said, paid the fee, and hurried out to the exit, as if chased by a swarm of angry bees—afraid that the douchebag might come up with another ingenious scheme.

"Thank you," I said to Igor the minute we got outside, only then feeling truly free to do so.

Igor lit a cigarette, trying to keep his shaking hands together. "You go home, Ira," he said, detached. "I'll go to work from here. I stopped earlier to check the bottom of that well we're digging, and the water has started seeping through in some places. If we dig a little more, I'm sure we'll get to a vein of that water today." He took a deep breath, filling his mouth with smoke, then let it out slowly. "Symbolic, isn't it? We finally got to the water, the beginning of all life, today!" He took another puff on his cigarette. "You go, go, don't wait for me. You have a lot of things to take care of."

Chapter 32

Get in Line

As soon as I received a package from the American immigration attorney, I started reading down his list:

Passports. *Why is this plural?* I wondered, but the lawyer had an answer. "Passports for Irina, Angelica, and Serghei," he'd written. *They give them to children in America?* Our passport office issued me one passport and told me to bring the kids in for a photo. They would add the kids' pictures. All right. I'd deal with that when the kids came back from Crimea.

Birth Certificates. "Birth certificates for Irina, Angelica, and Serghei translated into English," the lawyer wrote. Why did we need birth certificates when we were going to have passports? *Wait a minute, the kids were born in Crimea, Ukraine.* Would their birth certificates even be accepted in Moldova? BIG FREAKING QUESTION! I needed to clarify this with the *Office of Civil Affairs.*

The Divorce Certificate. "The divorce certificate dissolving the marriage of Irina and Igor," the lawyer wrote. It felt weird that a random immigration lawyer in America knew my ex-husband's first name, as if he'd been watching over my shoulder all this time, taking notes on my previous life. "Also translated into English," the list said. *Shit, my divorce certificate was issued in Ukraine. Where do I find a Ukrainian translator in Moldova?*

Parental Consent Letter. "A notarized letter from Irina's parents stating that they have no objections to Irina leaving the country," the lawyer wrote. "If any parent is deceased, provide the death certificate of the deceased parent translated into English." *What?*

I read it again. Only God knew why the American government needed permission from an adult woman's parents before she could emigrate. What happened to people whose parents refused to sign such documents? Did they wait for their parents to die? Did they guilt them into signing the paper, or worse? Here was the plot of a Shakespearean tragedy just waiting to happen!

To top things off, Mom was in Italy. Where would she find a Romanian-speaking notary in Italy who could understand what she wanted? How was she going to send me that letter? And would I have to translate the damn letter from Italian?

Medical Records. "Medical records, including lifetime vaccination records for Irina, Angelica, and Serghei," the list said. *Fuck!* I rushed to the cupboard where I kept all our important papers. *Foo!* I breathed in relief when I found the kids' medical cards, which I'd brought with me from Crimea. At least I'd been smart enough to grab them before I left. But then I realized it would require insane detective work to find my own records. There was no computerized system in the medical facilities, and we'd moved so many times: from my father's village to the city, then I moved to Crimea, then back. How many times had I been to local clinics only to find out that my medical card had been misplaced and they had to start a new one? I couldn't even recall when I'd last seen my vaccination records. Maybe in high school.

What else was here? "Irina is required to undergo tests for sexually transmitted diseases and HIV. Note: If the HIV test is positive, entrance to the United States is not allowed." I sat down to read that once again. *When was the last time I'd taken a test like that? Three, four years ago?* I started frantically shuffling through my memory. Was there anyone who might have potentially infected me? *Why am I freaking out? Don't think about it right now,* I told myself.

Police Records. "Police records for Irina from local law enforcement authorities indicating there is no criminal record." A trip to the Ministry of Internal Affairs for this one. *Wait a minute.* Would I need a police record from Ukraine too?

Photographs. "Photographs of Irina, Angelica, and Serghei for immigration files. Please take the photos exactly as they are displayed in this brochure," the lawyer wrote. I looked at the paper attached. The photo samples had a weird angle, with one-quarter of the face turned to the left. *Strange, but whatever.* We'd do that when the kids came back.

Immigration Application Forms. "Fill out Form OF-230 I (Immigrant Visa Application, Biographic Data) and Form OF-156 (Nonimmigrant Fiancé Visa Application)." I skimmed through the forms, which were loaded with questions in bureaucratic English, which didn't resemble human English tongue. For God's sake, I'd need a dictionary for that, or David on the phone with me to get it done. Then I'd have to write my answers without any spelling errors, so I didn't end up looking like a moron. Who needed illiterate people in America?

Written Parental Permission for a Minor. "Written permission from Irina's ex-husband for Angelica and Serghei to leave the country." A hot flashback of my recent trip to Crimea came rushing in, and my face went numb. I took the pen and checked that one off. *Thank God, it was done.*

Bona Fide Statement from Irina on How Irina and David Met. I read through the first few lines of a letter to the United States Department of Justice and Immigration and Naturalization Service that I'd put together and sent to David for proofreading: "I placed a personal ad through a marriage bureau on the Internet on November 2000. I received a letter from Mr. David Draisey on December 2, 2000. I found Mr. Draisey's letter very interesting and responded in kind."

David mailed the letter back to me after correcting my spelling errors and adding entire paragraphs of "cheesy" details—things I wasn't thrilled to describe to any government official. I wondered how the immigration officer would react, reading David's version of our first meeting in the airport. "Our eyes met, and my heart sang with joy. We ran to each other and hugged. Then he looked deeply into my eyes and kissed me for the first time. It was like a fairy tale." Would he roll his eyes, thinking, *Oh, please, not another third-rate romance novel!*

David said I needed to sign the letter and get it notarized. *All right then. I'll just take this masterpiece to a notary.* Embarrassment was the least of my worries right then. I read the long list one more time, then packed all the documents, certificates, and papers I could think of, even ones that weren't on the list. *Just in case.* I had only one week of vacation left. I had to use my time wisely. I headed for the village clinic first, since it was the closest. Might as well start my detective work there.

There was only one woman in line at the doctor's office. Lucky for me that I had to do this in the summer. In the winter, the clinics had long queues of people with bronchitis, common colds, and even pneumonia. It could have taken me hours to get this one thing off my list.

"Good morning," I said, walking into the doctor's office.

"Good morning, Irina."

Out of all doctors, her? I looked at Dr. Lozovan, who was also a part-time doctor at the day care where I worked, and whose son lived in our apartment building.

"Are you sick?"

"No. You see, I need to have this document signed and stamped by the clinic. It's a record of all the vaccines my kids and I have received during our lives."

"Are you leaving the country?" Well, it hadn't taken her long to figure that out!

"Not yet, but I might," I answered vaguely. There was no reason to feed the village rumor mill yet. "I have my kids' cards with me. But I can't find mine. I wasn't born in this village, and I didn't go to school here. Do you know where I should even start looking for mine? I can't even ask my parents. My father is dead, and Mom is in Italy."

"She left for work again?"

"Yes, about a month ago."

"Your mother is a good soul. She helped me with food when we had all those shortages, and she was a cook at that cafeteria. I worked such long hours that, after I'd get off work, all the shelves in the stores were empty—and I had two small kids at home to feed. Do you remember those times?"

"Yes, I do. But is it better now, when the shelves are full but we have no money to buy things?"

She took the cards out of my hands and started flipping through the pages. "The kids weren't born here either, I see, and there aren't any vaccination records on these cards."

"What? Those are the only medical cards I have. Don't tell me I have to go back to Ukraine for them." My voice started trembling.

"Let me see what I can do." She took a blank form. "Soviet-style medicine was very standardized. Every kid was vaccinated on schedule or close to it. I'm going to write down a chart of when these vaccinations were supposed to be given."

"All right." I nodded. "How does this help?"

"If they were supposed to be done at a certain time, say three months after the child was born, or a year after the child was born, then they were done at that time," she said, raising her chin, as if trying to figure something out. "Do you remember taking your children to be vaccinated?"

"Actually, in Crimea, the pediatrician came to our house, so yes, I remember that."

"All right, then they were definitely vaccinated against TB and polio." The doctor started writing something on the form. "Have they ever had measles or chickenpox?"

"Measles first, then chickenpox."

"How old were they the first time?"

"Angelica was, maybe, six. Her brother caught it from her, so they both had it at the same time."

"All right, we've got a timeline. Add six years to her birthday, and four and a half years to Serghei's birthday for measles, and another year for chickenpox. Do you remember when you had measles?" Dr. Lozovan smiled.

We went through the same routine on my form until she filled up all the boxes. She stamped, signed the forms, and gave them to me. "Here, now you can go to wherever you're going."

"To America," I blurted out, forgetting that I wasn't supposed to say it. "Doctor, I don't know how to thank you. How much do I owe you?" I went for my wallet.

"For God's sake, put it away," she stopped me. "As I said, your mother is a good soul. It's the least I can do. Good luck to you in America. I always knew you'd go places." My eyes started watering. I shook her hand and left the clinic.

If the day continued like that, I might be able to take care of my birth certificate, and my father's death certificate too.

* * *

"Are you the last in line?" I asked a man I didn't know. He was standing at the end of a queue at the Office of Civil Affairs. We were outside an old, gray two-story building with stairs that spiraled along the outside wall from the scorching asphalt at ground level to the second floor, where there was a heavy, dark-green metal door resembling the hideous door from Hitler's bunker I once saw in a war movie.

From the bottom, the line looked like an endless anaconda tail. People were crowded on every step, holding folders of papers, which they occasionally used as hand fans to get relief from the blistering sun or to brush away flies. It was their feast day, as if the God of Flies had answered their prayers by bringing together so many sweaty human bodies in one place.

"Actually, there are four people after me," the unfamiliar man told me, saying more with his tired face than with his voice. "They went up there to that woman to put their names down on a list. You should do that too. This way nobody cuts in front of you. Besides, I hear that yesterday's line was so long that not everyone went through. Some had to come back this morning."

I snorted like an irritated horse and went up the stairs. But halfway up I hit congestion created by four men who were trying to come down.

"Where are you going?" one of them asked.

"I need to put my name on the list," I answered.

"You won't get through," he said. "What's your name? We'll pass it up the chain."

"Iancenco," I said, and the man turned around and tapped the person in front of him on the shoulder.

"Tell that chick with the paper to put Iancenco on the list." And my name went up the line, bouncing off the turning heads.

"What's her name? Yudenco?" the lady holding the list yelled from the top. The turning heads with the "what's her name?" question started coming down like a stack of dominos, catching up with me at the bottom of the stairs.

Fearing another broken-telephone situation, I ripped some paper from the notebook in my purse, wrote down my name, and sent the paper up the chain.

A few seconds after the List Lady wrote down my name, she yelled: "I'm going in. Who wants to be in charge of the list?"

"What? She's not working here?" I was surprised.

"No. She's been standing in line with us all morning. We self-organize," somebody from the middle of the line said.

"All morning? It's eleven o'clock. Have you been standing here for three hours?"

"Something like that."

In an hour, we'd moved up seven spots. I knew it was seven because I counted every time someone came down the stairs, as if moving a few steps up was a little celebration.

"What's happening?" I asked when the line stopped moving for ten minutes.

"They're closing for lunch for an hour," somebody said from the top, sending a shockwave down the line.

"They don't have anyone working during lunch? This line is already two days long." The crowd began to boil.

Somebody threw in an old Soviet joke. "Soviet service—the least obtrusive service in the world!"

True to the joke, two lady-officials with "don't even try to talk to me" faces locked the green door and went away without addressing any of our complaints. The crowd started dispersing in disappointment.

"Who has the list?" someone asked. "We should leave one person with the list here so new people don't start another line."

The crowd came back, and after a short discussion, a young man with glasses, quickly named "the Student," became the new commander-in-chief. I wondered if that was how citizens of ancient Rome voted on their people's business. *Vox Populi!* Isn't that what our history teacher would have said?

"It'll take a few hours before I get in," I said to no one in particular. "Do you know where I can find a translator around here?" I turned to the Student, trying to chase two hares at once.

"There are translators' offices in the center, a few blocks from here. But don't be gone for too long," he warned me. "We start crossing off names if people don't come back before it's time to go in."

"I should be back by then," I said, looking at the long list of names he held.

I entered the first office I found with a sign offering translation services, then handed a see-through plastic folder with my documents to the receptionist.

"I need to have these translated into English," I said. "My kids' birth certificates are in Russian, and my divorce certificate is in Ukrainian."

"Sure, we can do that. We don't really have a Ukrainian translator per se, though," she said. "But we have a girl on call who can figure it out."

"What do you mean 'figure it out'?"

"By the type of document. This is a divorce certificate, right? She has a template for that and just fills in the blanks, like names, places, and dates. It works out."

"The months in Ukrainian sound completely different from Russian," I objected.

"Don't worry. We have a list of months in a few languages that we can match up in Ukrainian, Belorussian, Romanian, Russian. You see what they did to all of us? Brainless rulers in high places broke up the country, and we, the poor people, have to deal with the wreckage. Give me your papers."

"These are the originals. I don't want to leave them here."

"You should have brought the notarized copies. All your documents have to be notarized anyway, no matter where you're submitting them."

"Where can I find a notary?"

"I don't know. People are leaving the country in droves nowadays. Notaries and translators are in very high demand, so you should find a few somewhere around here. Bring the documents back after they're notarized."

Well, that was useless. I exited the building in frustration. I'd wasted thirty minutes already, according to my watch. I rushed down three more blocks until a window with a notary sign popped up. There were three people in front of me, so I waited.

"Fifty leis for all documents that I notarize," said a woman in her early thirties when my turn came. She wore the thick makeup of an aged Hollywood movie star.

"Fifty? Are you sprinkling them with gold or something?" But I reached for my wallet. "I also have a letter to notarize, signed by me. Can you do that?"

"Is the letter already signed?"

"No. Do you want me to sign it?" I pulled the letter from the folder.

"Wait. It has to be done in front on me." She had me sit in the chair in front of her desk, where I laid the paper flat and signed. The "Hollywood star" took the letter out of my hands but returned it with a smirk.

"Is this in English? I can't notarize something I don't understand. You'll have to translate it into Romanian before I can notarize it."

"The letter needs to be submitted to the American embassy in English, not in Romanian. All you need to do is certify that I'm the one who signed it. Here is my ID card."

"To the American embassy?" The notary pushed my letter away, as if it was infected with plague. "How do I know what you wrote in there? Maybe you're calling them names, or threatening to blow up the embassy?"

"How stupid would I be to send that kind of certified letter?" I tried to reason with her. "Then they'd definitely know I wrote it. Look, if you really want to know what it says, give me a piece of paper and I'll translate it for you. I just graduated from the university as a translator." I pulled my diploma from my purse. It wasn't a document on David's list, and I hadn't imagined a scenario where I might need it. But lo and behold! *One should always be prepared when going to any agency in my homeland.*

"It can't be done by you. It has to be done by a different professional translator," the notary pouted stubbornly.

"You want me to pay for a translation of English text into Romanian, though I'll never use the Romanian text?"

The "Hollywood star" was in full paranoia mode. "How do I know you'll translate it correctly and not write some gibberish?"

There was no magic bullet for her logic. It kept fighting back like a werewolf, no matter how many times I shot it down. So, I picked up my documents and walked out, smacking the door after me. The lunch hour was over. I had accomplished nothing. I needed to head back. I went down a block and took a different route back to the Office of Civil Affairs. The street was busy with people walking up and down with their grocery bags, business briefcases, and other packages.

"Excuse me." I stopped a lady with a see-through package in her hands containing what looked like stamped documents. "Do you, by any chance, know where there's a notary around here?"

"Yes. It's right there, in that enclosed yard." The lady pointed. "It's a little off the beaten path, so not many people know about it. But Missis Nina will take care of you."

I rushed to Missis Nina's office for another try.

Slowly, so I didn't spook her, I started from afar: "I would like to notarize all these birth certificates and my dad's death certificate."

"No problem," Nina said, and fixed her fluffy hairdo, then proceeded with her job, making copies of my documents one by one. "Anything else?" She looked at my hand, halfway in my purse.

"I have this letter." I took it out carefully. "In English," I mumbled. "You just need to certify that I signed it." I said it fast, trying to get through before my heart jumped out of my chest.

"The letter is already signed," Nina pointed out.

"Oh, God! I totally forgot about that." I tried to keep myself together, looking at the paper, while a full confession started pouring out of me: "You see, I stopped at another notary before, and she told me to sign it, but then refused to notarize it because she didn't understand the English text. That's the only original I have, and it's already signed. What do I do?" My hands were trembling.

"Give that to me," Nina said, and put another piece of paper in front of me. "Sign this."

"But it's blank."

"I just need to see if your signature matches what's on your letter. You'll be surprised how many people signed their letters before they come to me. So that's my little trick to get around it." I smiled, relieved that the solution was so simple, and made a fast signature on the blank paper. "Oh, look, it does match." She smiled back. She took my ID card and started typing the data from my ID into her computer. Then she printed out the page and told me to make sure everything was correct.

"Is it all right that the letter is in English?" I asked. I didn't want to mislead her, now that we'd bonded over my signature.

"I don't care if it's in Chinese. That's why I have this disclosure." She pointed, and I read the paper in front of me:

"I, Nina Frecautanu, the notary public located in Chișinău municipality testify that Irina Iancenco has signed this document, which content is known to her."

"See," Nina said, "the last part is all I need to confirm, that the content of the letter is known to you." She stamped the document, signed it, and dated it July 4, 2001.

"That's exactly what I said to the other notary!" I exclaimed, as if I'd just found a long-lost kindred spirit. "Don't you all go to the same notary school?"

"I don't know what school she went to, but it looks like she needs to go to the Common Sense School." I burst out laughing. My God, did I need that laughter!

Fast, as if I'd just grown a pair of wings, I flew back to the translator's office to finish what I'd started earlier.

"Fifty leis," the receptionist said, taking the notarized documents out of my hand, bringing me back to reality. Jeez, this enterprise was gonna cost me everything I earned in a month. How did people with regular jobs manage this?

"Come pick them up tomorrow or, better, the day after."

"I was hoping to get it all resolved today. I have other places to be tomorrow."

"The on-call translator has to pick up your documents, do the translating, and bring them back after she's done. Tomorrow, at the earliest."

Well, you can't win them all. I let it go and moved on to the Ministry of Internal Affairs, where I had to obtain a police record. I pulled on the heavy, dark-oak door of the three-story building. It was imposing in a Stalinist-grotesque style, with an old Soviet coat of arms, made of gray cement, mounted on the rooftop, as if time had stood still here. A guard stopped me at the entrance and told me to go to the back door for police records.

The waiting room in the back was disappointing: small, run-down, dark, with no windows to the outside. Like something I'd expect to find inside a prison. Especially because an unsmiling woman in a police uniform was answering questions brusquely—speaking to people in our line as if she had to pay for each word out of her own pocket: "Yes. No. I said 'no.' Don't write on that line!" I looked at the next window, where a chatty young officer was so talkative that his line moved three times slower, so I stayed where I was. Fifteen minutes later, I was called in.

Unsure of the protocol for these things, I repeated what others in line had done before me. I squeezed my ID card through the window and said that I needed a police record for myself.

"How much?" I asked, getting money out of my wallet.

"When do you need it by?" the woman asked after she was done entering my information into her computer.

"I can choose?"

"If you want to pick it up next week, that will be twenty leis. If you need it urgently, like tomorrow, that will be one hundred twenty leis."

"Six times more?" I was shocked.

"If you want to save money, go with the regular price," the woman suggested, toning her voice down. "Check in three days from today. They sometimes finish it faster."

"All right," I said, toning my voice down as well. "Next week is fine."

"What language do you want on the document: Romanian or Russian?"

"Romanian is fine. I have to translate it into English anyway."

"There is an English version of the police record."

"I'd like the English one then. Thank you for telling me that. That's the greatest news I've heard all day," I said enthusiastically. The woman cracked a smile. She didn't seem to get compliments often.

Satisfied that I'd put one more document from my list in motion with the help of the least likely ally, I rushed back to the Office of Civil Affairs, three hours after I'd left, hoping I wasn't kicked off the list.

I looked for the Student the minute I got back. He was halfway up the stairs shouting at a man who was trying to get through. The crowd looked agitated. Two women on the lower stairs, one petite and one tall with wide shoulders, were pulling the man back by his arm and shouting, "We got a list here. Get in line!"

The man's companion, a woman with bright makeup melting down her face, shouted back at the two ladies—"*Curva! Curva!*"—and jumped at the bottom of the stairs like a yapping dog with a haystack of bleached hair.

"Who are you calling a whore?" Wide Shoulders stepped down to face her accuser, and the two women faced off, circling one another like gladiators in the ring, looking for a chance to strike. The only thing missing was the gladiators' knives.

Wide Shoulders swung first with one hand, pulling down hard on Yapping Lady's hair, and clung like a sneaky cobra until the woman's face stretched—as if she'd just become the victim of a botched plastic surgery.

"Ahhh!" Yapping Lady yelled, and made her own grab for her opponent's hair, then stuck the nails of her other hand into Wide Shoulders' arm, trying to force her to release her grip.

"Let me go!" They were screaming at each other, dragging each other's heads back and forth.

"All right, all right. Both of you let go!" Five of us intervened to pull the combatants apart, until they finally separated. The troubled couple conceded defeat and left.

"Everybody," I addressed the crowd. "Before you pull me down by my hair. I'm in line after that man." I pointed at the man who'd been in front of me this morning.

"What's your name?" feisty Wide Shoulders asked.

"That's fine, that's fine. She's on the list," the Student said. "But you might as well stay down there. There are at least ten people before you."

"Whoever applied in the morning, step closer," an official said when she opened the green door. She was holding a stack of papers. "We've got about twenty certificates here." She started reading the names of the lucky ones whose ordeals were finally over. The crowd started thinning out, giving the rest of us hope that our wait could be over soon too. But then she said, "We're not taking any more applications today. We still have a stack of certificates to issue, and digging through the older archives by hand is very time consuming. Those who have already applied can stay for another hour, until we close, but the rest of you, come back tomorrow."

The crowd sighed with a heavy, desperate "ah." I felt their indignation. This day was like a bumpy roller-coaster ride: up and down, twisted to the left, then jerked to the right. Why couldn't anything be orderly and consistent in my country? Why, depending on whom you talked to in an office, could you end up with a different answer, or no answer at all? Why was there always a front door, then a back door, then a side door to the same agency?

"Let's make a few copies of the list," the Student said after the office door closed. "Just in case I can't come in tomorrow. Because I'm sure there will be another line then." I suddenly felt exhausted and looked at my watch. It was four p.m., and I hadn't eaten anything all day. I decided that I should take food and water with me tomorrow. Tomorrow, it would start all over again.

Chapter 33

The Waiting Period

"Did you get the letter I sent with the care package?" Mom asked during her weekend call. "That letter, how do you call it?"

"The consent letter," I said. "Yes, I got it two days ago."

"I wrote it in Russian. Is that all right?"

"It's all right. I dropped it off at the translator's office. I'll pick it up tomorrow. Where did you find a notary in Italy who spoke Russian?"

"I asked someone here. Then she asked somebody else, and three people later, we found a girl from Moldova who helped me. When are you sending the documents to America?"

"I need to take the kids to the passport office and get their photos added to my passport. Then we need to get some immigration photos for our profiles. Then I'll get with David by phone to go through the list one more time to see what else might be missing, and then I can finally send it all."

"Then what?"

"David said that, after the lawyer receives my package and submits it to Immigration, there's a waiting period of about ninety days. If David's application is approved, I should receive notification from the American embassy about what to do next."

"My God! How long will that take?"

"I don't know, Mom."

"When are you going to Grandma's?"

"After school starts. We just have too much to do before then. I need to buy school supplies for the kids. We'll go to the bazar tomorrow and buy them new shoes and some clothes. They grew out of everything."

"Did you get those white summer pants with red flowers that I sent for Lica? They're not really for school, but I thought I'd send her something."

"Yes, we got them. Lica's been wearing them almost every day. That's like her new favorite thing, after the dress that David bought her." Mom laughed. She enjoyed compliments, which were few and far between.

"And the shirts I sent for Serghei? Those will be good for school."

"Yes, we got them all."

Loud TV sounds reached my ears from the other room.

"Turn that down!" I yelled.

"We're not doing anything," Lica answered. "The TV is just changing the sound on its own."

"Mom, let me see what's going on. I'll call you when I know more about our situation," I said.

"What's going on here?" I marched into the room. The noise coming from the TV was intense and unbearable, as if someone was scratching the glass with a metal claw.

"We turned it all the way down, but it just won't stop," Mariana said. I turned off the TV, then turned it back on. The sound was quiet for a while, then it got louder and louder, with no one touching the volume button, until it became unbearable again.

"What the hell is going on?"

"It's broken," Mariana finally concluded.

"We'll have to find someone to fix this." I sighed. I couldn't remember the last time we'd called a repair man for anything. We'd replaced the leaking hose in the bathroom ourselves, then unclogged the kitchen pipe with a plumber's snake, and patched up a broken shelf. But a TV screaming for no reason was one thing we couldn't fix.

"Who can we call?" I started thinking. "Nobody from the city is going to come out to the boonies. Where do we find someone locally? Do we look for flyers?"

"Let me go to Larisa downstairs," Mariana said. "She's like the village phone book."

I laughed, but fifteen minutes later, she came back with the name of a TV fixer.

"Larisa gave me a phone number for this guy, Slavic. He's her husband's classmate who does electronics repairs on the side. She called him for us. He'll be here tonight after he gets off work."

"Did you give him our address?"

"Larisa told him that we live above her apartment, so he knows where to come."

The bell rang at our door around seven p.m.

"Good evening to all of you, Irina," a man said cheerfully when I opened the door. He smiled and put his hand forward for a handshake. The light shining above his head showed his open, friendly, even charming face and his bright-blue eyes, and I recognized him. I'd seen him in the neighborhood before, drinking beer with Vlad, Larisa's husband, on the balcony on the first floor.

"I don't think we've been formally introduced. I'm Slavic, the repairman," he said.

"I know your face." I shook his hand. "Well, come in, Slavic. We have a problem with our TV." I led him to the bedroom, where the TV was.

"Let's see what's giving you trouble." He was in a good mood, evidently. "Oho! That's the same problem I repaired a week ago for a different client. This brand of TV *Spektr* has a weakness in the sound device. A sensor dies out after long use, so there's no control over the volume. It can jump from low to high for no apparent reason," he said like a doctor who'd diagnosed the same disease many times before. "Though this model was one of the last good

Soviet models, and it typically lasts for a long time. Look, the colors haven't even faded that much. How old is this TV?"

"Oh, God. I don't even know. We bought it after I graduated from high school, so it's at least fifteen years old."

"When Larisa told me about the issue, I suspected we might have to replace the sound device, so I brought the spare part with me." Slavic was not only knowledgeable but prepared.

"How long will it take?" Lica and Serghei asked almost simultaneously. "Our favorite cartoon should be on in five minutes," Lica said.

"I'll try to do it as fast as I can, but it might take a while. I have to take off the back of the TV to get to it," he answered and pulled his screwdriver out of his bag.

"Mom, we'll go to Larisa's to watch, if she lets us," Serghei said, speaking for himself and his sister. "If not, we'll just play outside until it's done."

"Don't stay out for long. It's getting dark."

"Aha," I heard Serghei on their way out.

"Your kids?" Slavic asked, removing the back cover of the TV and placing it on the floor. "Vlad told me you're divorced and you've lived alone for a few years now."

He sure knew a lot about me. "Is that relevant for the TV repair?"

"No," he said, unscrewing the device from the TV and putting it on the table. "But I talk to Vlad about you quite a bit."

"Why would you and Vlad talk about me?" I didn't know what to think of this.

"I've had my eyes on you for a while," Slavic said, putting the new device in the TV and glancing at my reaction from the corner of his eye. "I kept asking him about what kind of person you are and what you do. He told me a lot of good things about you, that you're going to college, learning English, and working at the same time. That's impressive." He replaced the back cover and paused to look at me. "But every time I wanted to make a move, he kept reminding me that I'm at least five years younger than you, and you have kids. So, I kept postponing and waiting. But when Larisa called me, I thought, here's a sign! It's now or never. Now is the moment."

"Now is definitely not the moment," I interrupted him.

He pushed hard on the screws with his screwdriver, until all four were secured, and continued. "I'm serious. I'd marry you. I don't care that you have kids. I'm a good, hardworking guy. Right now, I'm in the process of immigrating to Germany, so if you want, we can go to Germany together—you and the kids." He looked straight at me, dead serious. I believed him.

"Thank you for the offer, but I think you waited too long." I looked straight at him too.

"So not even the slightest chance?" Slavic was visibly disappointed.

"I'm afraid not. How much do I owe you?"

I reached for my wallet, and he was silent for the rest of the repair.

"You won't believe it," I told Mariana after Slavic left. "I just got the weirdest marriage proposal from the repairman."

"No way." Mariana laughed. "How? And why?"

"I probably exude some kind of immigration aroma that eligible bachelor-émigrés are sensitive to. Smell my armpits." I raised my hands. "Do I smell like freedom?"

Mariana turned her head away, bursting into laughter. "What's going on?"

"Who the fuck knows? I've been walking around this village a free woman for years, and nobody, not one single man, even once asked me on a date. They were apparently waiting for a divine sign. But, as soon as I'm ready to leave for America, the divine signs started falling from the skies onto their heads! You watch, I'll start getting whole stockpiles of wannabe boyfriends now."

Mariana started rolling on the bed, holding her belly. "You're killing me! You're killing me!" She wiped her tears. "Speaking of boyfriends"—she stopped laughing and sat down on the bed—"I need to talk to you about someone. I can't talk to Mom about him, because she's gone, and she has her own problems in Italy. I don't want her to worry about me. And I can't talk to Dad because he'll flip out. All he'd do is threaten to disown me if I ever get pregnant outside of wedlock. Very fatherly. Probably judging every man by his own actions. Anyway. There's this guy, Radu. He keeps asking me on dates, and I don't know how I feel about it."

"Where did you meet him? At the college?"

"No, he's not a student, but he's my age. Remember, I went to my friend Lena's village one weekend? He's her neighbor, and she introduced us. He works in the city not far from our college."

"Do you like him?" I asked cautiously.

"He's definitely different from other guys who've been drooling around me. Not book smart, but he's street smart. He can fix almost anything."

"But do you like him?" I insisted.

"He's the first boyfriend I've ever had, so I have no one to compare with."

"Boyfriend already?" I smiled.

"Kinda like a boyfriend. I don't know yet." She giggled.

"Is there something in particular that attracts you to him?" I continued with my sisterly interrogation.

"He's cute, but he's kinda short for me. If I'm on my heels, he's like half a head shorter."

"Does that bother you? Or are you thinking of what other people would say?"

"M-m-m ..." Mariana was thinking. "When you put it that way, maybe you're right. There's always this thought in the back of my mind, that people might be laughing behind my back: 'Look at her, walking with a shorty.'"

"Who cares what people think?" I switched my tone. "It's not like they're going to live your life for you. Besides, as Igor used to say, 'Everyone's equal height in bed.'"

"Yeah, that sounds like something Igor would say." Mariana started laughing. "I miss his jokes."

"Igor was good at giving life advice all day long. He's the book smart one, but unfortunately, not street smart." I sighed. "Why don't you invite Radu for dinner?"

"Oh! He'd freak out! I told him all about you, that you are like Iron Lady and shit. He's already scared."

"Even more reason to bring him for dinner. He needs to be Irina-approved. If he can't pass me, get him out of here! All he needs then is to get into your panties."

"Foo-oo-oo!" Mariana grimaced. "We haven't gotten that far."

"Wait until I buy you some condoms." I pointed my finger at her.

"I would definitely not get advice like that from Dad." Mariana shook her head.

"Or Mom," I added.

"Oh, not poor Mom. She'd probably die before she talked to me about condoms," Mariana said somberly.

"Where are those damn kids?" I asked, looking at the clock. "Go call them home. They don't get to stay outside past nine just because it's the last week of their summer break."

* * *

The next day, Mariana came home with a guest. "Everybody, meet Radu," she said, standing in the hallway with a young man who lingered one step behind her, as if trying to be invisible. I watched him shift from one foot to another, holding a grocery bag in one hand, but hiding the other hand behind his back. His dark hair was cut short. His tanned face looked tense. He was definitely a shorty compared to Mariana.

Angelica ran in from the other room. "Well, hello!" she said. "I'm Lica. And this is Sereoja." She pointed at her brother.

"*Privet!*" Serghei shouted his casual "hello" in Russian.

"Good evening, everybody. Good evening, Irina," Radu said, pulling a bouquet from behind his back.

"What is this for?" I was surprised, to say the least.

"Mariana said your birthday is on the sixth of September. I thought it wouldn't be a crime to start a week early," he said, and pulled a bottle of wine from the grocery bag.

"He's funny," I told Mariana. "Why didn't you call and let us know that you'd be coming home with a boyfriend? I could have cooked something festive. We only have basic stuff in the fridge."

"I told him, but he insisted on buying the produce. Radu, put it on the table in the kitchen," she said, and Radu did as he was told. The smell of salami, pastrami, feta, and smoked herring soon filled the small kitchen space.

"He's not only funny, but he's thoughtful." I winked at Mariana.

"Here, some candy for the kids," Radu said, getting out a bag with assorted chocolates.

The kids jumped up and ran to the living room, rummaging through the bag and shouting at each other to share.

"Thank you for all of this," I told him. "You didn't have to."

"My mom taught me never to show up at someone's house with my hands in my butt." He coughed, realizing that might be a little vulgar, and corrected himself. "I mean, without anything in my hands. Especially if I'm coming to someone's house for the first time." He coughed again.

"Especially if you're trying to impress someone," I joked. Radu's cheeks turned red, but he didn't respond. "So, what are you both up to?" I asked.

Radu looked at Mariana, but she just shrugged. "I thought I would come introduce myself," he said, "since Mariana told me that her mom is in Italy. My mom works there too. She's been there since my brother and I were teenagers." He started mumbling, "So I know how it is to grow up at home without your mom. Siblings rely on each other a lot, and you're her only sister here, and you're responsible for her …"

"Are you asking me for permission to date my sister?" I interrupted him. "That's so old-fashioned, but cute." I smiled.

He cleared his throat. "I just don't want you to think that I'm some Alfonse who has nefarious intentions towards Mariana. I'm taking this courtship very seriously, and I just want to let you know that she's in good hands." He coughed again.

"I can see that." I looked at Mariana, who was quieter than I'd ever seen her, then I looked at Radu's serious, concentrated face. Though they were still standing next to each other, I could no longer tell that he was shorter than her.

"And when you leave for America, I'll take care of her too," he said.

"I don't need to be taken care of. I'm not a child," Mariana objected.

"You told him about America?" I looked at my sister accusatorily. "I thought we talked about keeping it in the family until the waiting period is over, so we don't jinx it.

"He's not a stranger. He's Radu," my sister said dismissively.

"I didn't mean to cause any trouble." Radu didn't know where to put his hands—at least he didn't put them in his butt.

"Well, since the cat is out of the bag, let it roam free," I said peacefully. "Why don't we just sit down and have some dinner?" I showed Radu to his seat at the table and told Mariana to get out wine glasses and plates. "We have a lot to talk about," I continued. "Tell me about your parents and about your brother. What do you do? What are your plans? Can you pay a dowry?"

"A dowry?" Radu looked at me spooked.

"I'm just messing with you!" I laughed.

He breathed in relief. "I always thought that in Moldavian culture, the bride has to provide the dowry," he said to get back at me.

"Well, you're not getting that either, my dear friend."

"I'm definitely not here for her dowry." He laughed.

"I'm glad we established that. Now, Mariana, pour us some wine! I have something to celebrate. I got the HIV test results today, and they look fine, so the damn immigration package is all done. I'm going to send it to America tomorrow."

"*Noroc!*" Mariana clinked her glass with mine.

"Also, can you call your father and ask him when I can ride on his bus to Grandma's?"

Chapter 34

Twin Towers in the Village

Looking through the bus window, I watched the country, autumn scenery flying by, which was no different than any other time I'd gone to Babushka Veta's village. On the left, I saw a field of tall yellow corn with cobs jutting out of their cocoons. On the right, a field of sunflowers with bright-yellow petals and big, black seeds at their center, all turned toward the road. It was harvest season, as many times before, but today was different. I was saying goodbye to those fields. I might never see them again. During the long two-hour ride, I had time to think about what I was going to tell my grandma.

I would tell her I would be leaving soon to a far away and foreign country, but to not worry about us. It would be hard, no doubt, starting our lives over with a new language, new customs, and new people, but it would be better for me and the kids in the end. It would be life changing, an adventure even. After all, Babushka Veta was a runaway bride herself, who took off with Grandpa in the middle of the night against her father's wishes, risking it all with just the clothes on her back. "I hoped he would marry me," Babushka would say when she retold her and Grandpa's story. "But I didn't know for sure. As my mother put it: 'There are not enough men after the war, and too many women who need husbands.'" We were not exactly in my grandma's postwar era, but we were looping around in a sort of post, postwar time warp, as if we were stuck somewhere in the fifties. Just being alive was no longer enough. I needed more.

I would tell Babushka not to worry, because Mariana would come to visit her often. Besides, Mom wouldn't stay in Italy forever. She would be back home in a few years and look after her.

I opened the old wooden gate with the chipped white paint at her country house. Its rusted hinges squeaked melodically. The chickens, who were pecking at some grass nearby, raised their heads, looking worried, then ran away from me, making clucking noises. My grandma peeked out to see who was coming, reacting to the running chickens as if they were an alarm. But the branches of a green vine with juicy, ripe red grapes hung over the entrance door and front porch, blocking her view. She squinted, not recognizing me at first, but her familiar wrinkly face changed slowly as I approached her. She smiled broadly by the time I reached her.

"Hello! Hello!" she greeted me, giving me a hug. She kissed me on the left cheek, then on the right, as always. Since she didn't have a telephone, I couldn't let her know I was coming, so every time I appeared at her doorstep, it was a pleasant surprise.

"Look at those grapes!" I said, picking a few and eating them off the vine.

"Well, it's September. This is when they always ripen." She hurried to the summer kitchen. "Go call Dusya," she told me, meaning her daughter-in-law, my aunt, who lived next door. "Let's have lunch together."

"You're talking to each other again?" I asked, surprised. The last time I was here, they weren't on speaking terms. Babushka and my aunt were like oil and water. You never knew when Dusya could get offended by something Grandma said or did—or didn't do for her. So, she'd stop talking to Grandma for weeks at a time until she needed something. This push and shove between the two had been going on since I was a kid. Which put me and my cousins—Dusya's kids—in an awkward position. All we wanted to do was play with each other in peace, but instead we were used as communications middlemen. It was especially tough when Grandma wouldn't let me go to Dusya's to watch TV, since she was TV-less.

"Yeah, Dusya ran out of oil the other day, so she got over it," Grandma said, giving me the short version of how the standoff ended. I went to Dusya's house to call her for lunch.

It was a nice, warm day, so we set the table outside under the grapevines. They hung over us like the scene in a Renaissance Italian painting.

"Eat, eat," Babushka kept saying. "You came a long way."

"She *is* eating," my aunt answered for me with an attitude, moving her short, plump body on the chair. I looked at her, slurping soup, missing one tooth on the left side of her mouth, like a pirate's wife. Her short, dirty-blond hair looked uncombed and messy, like it had been neglected for a few days.

I let the food settle in, then said, "I'm leaving for America."

I'd found that being straight forward was the best approach.

"America?" both of them asked in unison. "That's so far away," my aunt stated the obvious.

"Our Baptist minister is from America," Grandma reminded me, perhaps because that was the only thing she knew about it.

"How come you're going there?" my curious aunt probed carefully. She suspected there was going to be a story.

"I met an American online."

"What's 'online'?" My grandma was confused.

"It's like a computer thingy," my aunt tried to explain.

"What's a com … thingy?" My grandma tried very hard to say the word "computer."

How could I explain that to her when she didn't have a single gadget of modern civilization in her house? Besides, if Mom couldn't wrap her brain around this, good luck explaining it to Babushka.

"So, what happened after you met online?" My aunt was pressing on.

"He came to Moldova to meet me. We're getting married, and the kids and I are moving to America," I said.

"Ah, you met him in Chişinău." Grandma finally got it.

"Yes," I said. "I met him in the city." That was much easier to explain.

"What's his name?"

"David."

"Ah, Dah-vid, like in the Bible," Grandma said, stressing the "ah" sound.

"I guess he's like something from the Bible. He's our savior, that's for sure." I sighed, thinking this title fit well enough. "We're going to have a new and better life in America." I was looking for words to explain my reasons. But here, in Grandma's village, where the only memorable sight was a twin water tower, not much needed to be explained.

"Is he a Christian?" Grandma continued when I stopped talking.

"I believe so." I shrugged. She knew it wouldn't make a big difference to me if he wasn't. I'd been far removed from all things religious, but my grandma always said she prayed for us every night, so I cherished that.

"Will I ever see you and the kids again?" Babushka struggled to get these words out.

"We aren't leaving yet," I tried to calm her down. "David just started our visa process. It will take a couple of months before we can go."

"Who's going to take care of me when I'm too old?" she asked in a broken voice, which broke me a little too.

"You have your son next door and his wife." I pointed at my aunt across the table. Grandma got quiet, which was her way of getting emotional. The gravity of what I'd just said was sinking in, so she switched the conversation to small talk.

She asked me how the kids were doing in school, whether

Mom had learned Italian yet, if my brother was still working at the bread factory, and when Mariana would finish college. She wanted to know it all, as if trying to absorb all the information she could get for the last time. *It's never enough air, when it's your last breath,* I recalled—a dark quote from a movie about rebels before their execution.

After a while, my aunt left us alone to hash things out. But just a few minutes later, I saw her running back, her belly jiggling. *What the hell?* I'd never seen her run before.

"Ira, Ira! You need to see this!" she yelled at me and gestured for me to follow. I went after her, not quite understanding what she was doing or why she couldn't just tell me what was wrong. She dragged me inside her house and pointed with a crooked finger to her old-fashioned black-and-white TV screen.

"Look!" she yelled at me again.

"What is it?" I asked her, looking at something burning on TV.

"That's in America! I don't know where, but it's in America."

I was listening to the announcer with my eyes open wide in disbelief. They said it was New York. I could hear my blood pumping through my arteries. *Thump-thump, thump-thump.* The Twin Towers were engulfed in flames, and one was going down slowly and unrealistically, like in a bizarre horror movie. Terrified people coated in dust ran away from burning buildings. It felt surreal to be watching this scene while standing in the middle of nowhere, in a remote Moldavian village where my aunt couldn't even remember the name of the American city. The day just split into two parallel realities. Here was the black-and-white image of the burning Twin Towers, and there was the serene Renaissance painting with chickens running between our feet.

"Is this war?" I whispered. I fell onto my aunt's chair and grabbed my head with both hands. I couldn't stop shaking. I was rocking myself, trying to brush off the physical pain that clung to my body like a hawk with sharp claws. I only realized I was crying when I couldn't breathe.

As soon as the first shock wave had passed, another wave of worries hit me. Would America close its doors to immigrants until they figured out what the hell had happened? I felt angry, and hopeless, and scared for America and our future.

My aunt's old beat-up rotary phone rang all of a sudden. Dusya picked up the receiver and repeated in Russian several times: "Alyo! Alyo!" Then she turned to me. "I don't understand what this man is saying. I think he's speaking English. Maybe it's David."

How could he possibly know my aunt's number? Then I remembered I'd given it to him for emergencies, right before I left the city. This was an emergency, all right.

I ran to the phone. "David?"

"Yes," he said, his voice flat.

"What's going on in New York?"

"It was a terrorist attack."

"What's going to happen to our visa?"

"I don't know."

"Will everything stop now?"

"I don't know. The lawyer doesn't know either. In a bizarre coincidence, I just finalized my divorce today, and I dropped my divorce decree at the lawyer's office."

"Today?" I yelled. "Of all days, today?" I put the receiver down and went back to Grandma's house. *We'd need all the Babushka Veta prayers we could get.*

The evening was ruined. The night was restless. I felt trapped in Babushka's village like a wild beast in a cage. I couldn't wait for the next day to come so I could catch Valera's bus at two p.m. and leave for the city—as if getting to the city could give me some relief.

Valera met me at the bus stop with his usual routine greeting. "Hello. Get in the back."

I did as he asked, moving past the passengers with their casual, everyday expressions, as if nothing had happened. As if there'd been no terrorist attack in New York. Everything was going on as usual in this part of the world. The sunflower and corn fields looked the same as yesterday, but today they seemed out of place. *How can anything be so peaceful here*, I wondered, *when there is so much grief in America? Does anyone but me care about what happened yesterday?*

An old lady sitting next to me was petting a live white goose in the net at her feet, trying to calm the bird down. I imagined how this goose would become dinner at someone's house tonight, *as if nothing had happened.*

* * *

"Ira, Ira! Did you hear what happened in America?" Mariana yelled when I stepped in the hallway, bringing back memories of the burning buildings, as if the fire was now in my house.

"Yes, I saw it at Dusya's."

"Is David all right?" Angelica ran to ask me.

"New York is a long way from Seattle, so he's all right."

"Is it like really, really far?" Serghei wanted to be sure. I nodded.

"What are you going to do now?" Mariana asked.

"There's nothing we can do but wait." I went into the living room and sat down, exhausted. Everybody followed me, looking lost. I was waiting for some relief, but it wasn't coming. "As they say, there's nothing worse than waiting or trying to catch a leaving train."

"What if David gets scared or something and abandons your visa?" Mariana asked, looking at all of us.

"I don't want to think about it right now," I said, though I knew it would be at the forefront of my mind. "We'll continue as normal, until we hear otherwise from David, or until we don't hear from him anymore. Then we'll know one way or another."

Chapter 35

Continue as Normal

The words "continue as normal" were on my mind when Vasily Gramovich called out of the blue a month later. It was his usual way of checking on me. After his "How's your mom" and "How are your children," he would ask, "Are you still looking for a translator job?"

"Yes," I would say and ask, out of politeness, "Are you still trying to open your business?"

"Yes," he would answer and give me another reason why the business wasn't open yet. "The Romanians are dragging their feet" or "Victor is just too greedy." But today he said, "Actually, we're opening on Monday. I'm calling to see if you're still available. Tatiana said she is."

"Are you really opening?" I asked, still skeptical.

"I swear on Shura." He laughed.

"Why on Shura?" I needed that laughter. "Shouldn't you swear on your mother like a good Russian?"

"Hell, no. I love my mother. If Shura goes kaput, who cares?" He rumbled in laughter again. His raspy smoker's voice on full display.

"What are you telling me? You don't believe in your business?"

"You can only believe in God. Everything else is relative."

"Vasily, I'm serious. I can't abandon my crappy but stable job at the day care for your fantasy business. Are you one hundred percent sure that you'll make it?"

"Only God or an idiot is one hundred percent sure of anything. I'm neither, so I would say I'm seventy-five percent sure."

"I'll have to talk to …" I almost said "David" but switched at the last minute. "Let me talk to my day care before I give you an answer." I needed a backup plan, so I could function as normal.

"Sure," Vasily agreed. "Let me know no later than a week from today. Or just stop by the same office you visited last winter. I rented it out officially this time," he said, and hung up.

Nervously, I dialed David and asked for his opinion. With so much up in the air, we needed some sort of plan.

"What should I do?" I asked David about Vasily's offer.

"I don't know if it's a good idea to switch jobs now. You'll be leaving soon."

"Your own lawyer doesn't even know when it will happen. What if everything drags on for six months or a year? The firm will pay me twice as much." I was trying to convince myself more than David.

"Honey, if you need money, I can send you a hundred here and there."

"No, I want to make my own money and not depend on you," I insisted.

"Are you worried about something else, maybe?" David asked.

"Wouldn't you? They bombed the shit out of America. At what point are you going to say, 'This international marriage thing is just too much for me.'"

"I will *not* abandon you!" David said sternly but passionately, as if pledging allegiance to both America and me. "I will not abandon you!" David repeated, softer this time.

"Then I'm going to take this office job," I said. "At least we'll have some spending money for the trip."

David finally gave in.

When I arrived at Vasily's office on Monday, Tatiana was sitting at one of the office desks, looking bored.

"How's it going?" I asked her. She'd been on the job for an entire week already, so she had the inside scoop.

She pointed at the closed door of Victor and Vasily's office. "I'm supposed to answer their phone calls, but nobody's calling, so I'm making them coffee all day. That's all I've done so far. Yesterday, Vasily gave me this contract to practice typing, like I can't type."

"Irina, you've arrived." Vasily rolled in from the other room with a cigarette in his mouth. A thick cloud of smoke followed him, almost choking Tatiana, who was sensitive to smoke, apparently. "Here," Vasily said, giving me two pieces of paper. "Can you translate this sales contract into English?"

"We have a sale already?" I asked anxiously, unsure whether my regular English dictionary would work for this task, since I hadn't bought a technical dictionary yet.

"No, this is an old contract. I just need you to practice," he said, and left the room. I looked at Tatiana, who gave me an "I told you" look, and we both smiled.

"How do I turn this computer on?" I asked Tatiana, looking at the device on my desk as if I'd never seen one before. When I'd used the computer at Leonid's Agency, he was the one who turned it on and switched it off, so I was trying frantically to recall how he'd done that. Tatiana got up to help me.

"You'll need to open a Word document that has English as a default and type your translated text in there. That way you have the English spellcheck," she said, but then she saw my scared face. "Do you know how to do that?"

"I know how to write e-mails in English, but I don't recall opening Word documents." To her credit, Tatiana didn't show any shock or disappointment, but I could have bet my life on the fact that she hadn't anticipated being my trainer that day, at least not by choice. Yet, there I was, needing help, so she stepped in. Hey, it would break up the monotony, I decided. What would she do otherwise? Type all day?

"Go here."—she used the mouse to point at the word Programs—"and look for the 'W' symbol. When you double-click on it, a page will open." She seemed amused by my expressions every time she moved her hand up and down the computer screen, as if showing me magic tricks. "You know what?" she said. "Let me choose the language for you now, and I'll show you the easy stuff later. Like how to add a page number and change fonts. Okay?"

"Okay," I said, afraid to ask what a font was.

"I think it will be easier that way."

Oh, no argument there. I was in way over my head! But I'd figure things out. I had to.

On the following day—as I struggled to translate a few stubborn oil-industry terms that I couldn't recall from my studies and couldn't find in my dictionary—I really started panicking. There was no way I could return the translation to Vasily in that unfinished form. Then it dawned on me that Violeta worked for an oil company. I wrote down the stubborn words on paper. I could call her and ask for help. It seemed like a brilliant idea.

"What are you doing? Slacking?" Victor appeared out of nowhere, catching me with a pen and paper instead of typing on the computer.

"You scared me." I jumped. It was the first time I'd met Victor, so I looked him over carefully. His head of graying hair was nicely combed, his mustache neatly cut. He seemed like any average grandpa. But his appearance and his manner were contradictory. You could see he was enjoying my spooked reaction to him, especially when he smiled with the mysterious long grin of a man who had too many skeletons in his closet.

Vasily, on the other hand, giggled at my reaction, like a mischievous cartoon sailor, moving his free-spirited mustache up and down. His tall figure towered above Victor. They were an odd pair, the Lilliputian and the Telegraph Pole.

"Keep working," Victor said, "everybody should contribute to this firm's success." Tatiana and I exchanged looks: *Could he be any more condescending?*

"Don't be scared, ladies," Vasily said in a consoling tone. "He's just in a bad mood. Gabi, the Romanian owner, said our Romanian investor fell through. He's looking for alternatives and asked us to find a bank in Moldova that can finance our expansion here. We've been calling local banks all morning, but no luck. Do you have any acquaintances who can help us?"

"Shouldn't this have been resolved before you opened the office here?" the wise Tatiana asked.

"We'll find a solution. Don't worry," Vasily dismissed her question. "Irina, didn't you have a friend or a relative working at a bank?" I'd never thought he was listening as I talked about college. But apparently, he did.

"I have a college friend, Tanya, who works for a bank," I said. "But I've never talked to her about business, so I don't know if she can help."

"Can you call her?"

"All right," I agreed halfheartedly.

I waited to call Tanya until that night, and she was rightfully concerned about my request.

"How much do you know about this Vasily Gramovich and his business?" Tanya asked me when I called her. It startled me when she put it this way.

"I work for him, but … but I haven't seen his account books or anything like that, so I can't say that I know much." I thought about it a few more seconds and continued, "Tanya, you really don't have to take this on, if you don't want to."

"I get commissions if I bring in new clients, so if I can make a few bucks on this, I'll take them. But they'll go through the same process as any other client. I can't cut corners. We're now also in charge of collections, and I don't want another client I have to track down to collect payments."

"I understand. How do you want them to contact you?"

"Bring them to the bank at nine tomorrow morning. I'll meet them at the entrance."

Waiting again, I thought when three days went by, and there was no news from the bank. A week later, Victor walked into the office, expression darker than a rain cloud, and looked at me like I was the reason for his troubles. He picked up a folder from the drawer and left without saying a word.

"What's wrong with him?" Tatiana asked.

Vasily tried to laugh it off. "He just needs to blow off some steam," he said. "There's a minor setback, but we'll find another bank." He lit a cigarette, and I sneaked out at lunch to call Tanya from a pay phone.

"Ira, I'm sorry. I can't do anything for them," Tanya apologized. "They have no collateral to back up the loan. They don't have a bank account here. Only the Romanian owner has a bank account in Bucharest. They brought some documents for oil rig equipment, but when we started asking more questions, it appears this equipment isn't in use. It's just sitting on some train tracks in Romania, still in boxes. We don't even know if the equipment is functional or it's just a useless pile of metal. It's too big a risk for our bank. My aunt flatly refused to fund their loan."

"I'm sorry, Tanya. I had no idea."

"Honestly, Ira, I think you should be careful with these two. I don't see a valid business model there, definitely nothing resembling an oil-extraction business, as they claim. I don't know how they can stay afloat when the business is just on paper. Can you go back to your day care job?"

"No," I said. I couldn't imagine going back to my day care principal to beg for my job.

I rushed back to discuss our situation with Tatiana. *She needs to know too*, I thought. But Tatiana was no dummy. She must have figured something out on her own, because she was grilling Vasily with questions when I entered the office.

"When are we getting paid?" she was asking him. "It's been almost a month. I have to pay my rent and my utilities."

Vasily mumbled something, chewing on his cigarette butt. He pulled his wallet out of his pocket.

"I'll give you fifty dollars each. That's all I have on me. Victor hasn't paid me yet."

"Vasily, the deal was a hundred dollars a month—each," Tatiana said sternly. "If you're not going to pay us, I'm not coming in tomorrow."

"I'll straighten things out with him, and we'll pay you the rest."

"You do that," Tatiana said. "But until then, I'm staying home. I live on my own; my parents can't help me; I have no one to borrow money from. If I don't get paid, I don't eat. It costs me money to come to work, so I see no point in wasting my money on bus fares instead of food." She left the office with her head held high. Tatiana's courage helped me speak up too.

"Vasily, why did you promise us all these things if you just have a paper business?"

"Victor says everything is going to be okay, so I'll call him tonight and sort things out."

His faith in this man confused me. "Don't you see? He's just fooling you? He has no business plan. He has no money or connections. He probably promised Gabi a bunch of stuff he can't deliver, and Gabi cut him off. He's just a wannabe businessman who doesn't know what the hell he's doing. I can't believe I listened to you, and now I have no job."

"Everything is going to be all right. Everything is going to be all right," Vasily kept repeating. You could see that he truly believed it, like a man who couldn't let go of his last hope.

"No, it won't," I said, finally coming to terms with the fact that it was over. "It won't."

Chapter 36

In-Between Time

Going up the stairs to my apartment, I dragged my feet, my winter boots seemingly made of lead. The terrorist attack in New York was going to slow things down. It was inevitable, and I was going to be stuck here, jobless, for months in the meantime. I felt sick. *Now what? Chemotherapy or lobotomy?*

"Oh, my God! Finally, you're home!" Mariana yelled when I opened the door.

"Please don't tell me we have more bad news." I sighed.

"I think it's good news."

"You think?" I perked up. "Can you be more specific?"

"Lica, bring it, bring it." She pushed my daughter into the other room. "Look! A package for you!" She shoved a thick, heavy, yellow envelope into my hands. It looked very, very foreign.

"From America?" I was about to faint.

"No, from Bucharest." Mariana pointed at the sender's address. I looked at it, surprised.

"Oh, my God, it's from the American embassy in Bucharest!" I exclaimed.

"What does it mean?" Everybody asked me at the same time.

"I don't know." I ripped the edge of the envelope and pulled out the first page.

"Dear Irina Iancenco, this letter is a confirmation that the Consulate of the United States in Bucharest received your application for a K-1 Fiancé Visa," I started reading. I could hear my heart beating, not where it was supposed to, in my throat. My knees went soft. "Let's sit down." I took the envelope into the kitchen and dumped everything out on the table. The stacks of papers, organized in groups, looked mysterious, like four unicorns arrived from a faraway land. But I recognized the certificates that I'd translated in the summer.

"That's almost the same package I sent to David," I said.

"Why are they sending them back?" Lica asked. "Is something wrong with them?"

"I don't know, but it looks like these are the documents that our immigration lawyer collected for our visa." I turned back to the letter, looking for an answer.

"Please fill in the following forms," it said, "along with the list of documents that are required (see list attached)." *More forms, seriously?* "When completed, mail them to this address. Allow time for your package to be received by the consulate, then call the following phone numbers to schedule your appointment for an interview with the U.S. consulate in Bucharest."

"Translate! Translate!" Mariana yelled.

"I think this is it!" I turned to her, almost out of breath. "It's finally happening! I need to call this number and schedule an appointment with the American consulate."

"Aaaaah!" Mariana smacked me on my shoulder, like she always did when she was super excited. "You're going to America!"

"When are we leaving?" Lica asked cautiously. "I thought we were going to be here for New Year's."

"And I have plans to go caroling with my friends for Christmas," Serghei said, also disappointed. "That's the only time of the year when the *haitori* get paid for wishing happy New Year!"

"I'll call the embassy tomorrow and we'll find out, but if they give us a visa, we're leaving for America as soon as possible. Haitori or not." I put the letter on the table and shuffled through the rest of the papers for additional information.

"All persons listed in the K-1 Visa application must attend the interview," I read. "So, we'll have to buy three train tickets to Bucharest for all of us? What else is here?" Another document said, "All persons in the visa application are required to take a medical exam and vaccinations for entry into the U.S. at any approved-by U.S. consulate hospitals in Bucharest."

"Didn't you already get the vaccinations taken care of?" Mariana asked.

"I don't understand. Why do we need to go through this again?" I was confused, and frustrated because I thought the hardest part form-wise had been finished. "The hospital hours are in the morning, but the medical exam results are given only in the afternoon," I noticed. "So, we'll have to spend at least two days in Bucharest. That means we'll need a hotel room for two nights." I looked at the list with hotels names and their rates. "Oh, my God, how much will this trip cost us?" I felt a cold, unpleasant sweat creeping down my back. I moved to the price list for everything else attached. "Give me a piece of paper and a pen, I need to write this down," I said, trying and failing to add up the prices.

- 3 train tickets: $50 (plus/minus)
- Medical exam: $100 x 1 adult, $50 x 2 kids = $200
- Visa issuance: $95
- Hotel: $60 for 2 nights (plus/minus)
- Food and emergencies: $50

I drew a line at the bottom of the list. "So, the total comes to four hundred and fifty-five dollars," I said, "or five hundred to be safe. Where am I going to find this money? It's like ten times more than I have on me right now. Besides, I just lost my job today."

"How did that happen?" Mariana asked.

"I should have seen this coming, honestly. But it might be for the best, because I'm going to be very busy now. Let's hope David calls me tonight."

I was in luck, because David did call.

"Happy Christmas to you!" David sang to me when I picked up the receiver. It reminded me of his call last year, but his voice sounded different. Everything was different then—a call before his heart attack, and before the terrorist attack. "I wished so much to have you here for Christmas," David said. "Instead, I'm spending the holidays alone."

"You're not alone. You have your family there," I tried to encourage him.

"It's not the same," he said in a somber, cracking voice.

"Well, actually, I have very good news."

"Yeah?" David said with anticipation in his voice. "Did you get the immigration package?" His voice spiked.

"Yes." I smiled.

"God finally answered my prayers! You made my day, honey. Does it mean that you could be in America before New Year's?"

"I don't know. I'll have to call the embassy tomorrow to see when I can schedule an appointment. But there's a lot we need to do before then, and it's expensive."

"How much?"

"I wrote it down. Let me read it to you, but don't get mad, okay?"

"How much?"

"Five hundred dollars," I said, waiting for his reaction.

"Ooh!" He sighed. "It's going to be very tough, but I'll figure something out."

"Then, if we get the visa, we'll need money for the airplane tickets too."

"Honey, I don't think I can pay for all of this. It was a very slow month at the dealership. Can you contribute too?"

Contribute? With what? My pee-pee? I was about to scream into his ear. "I'll talk to Mom," I said, trying to juggle my options. If we had to wait for Mom to help us with airplane tickets, this could drag on for a couple of months. What if our visa expired before then?

I dialed the consulate phone number first thing in the morning. After the third ring went unanswered, a voicemail recording kicked in: "The U.S. consulate in Bucharest is closed for Christmas holidays from December fifteenth to January first, so we can spend time with our families. We will resume our work on January second." I put the phone down.

I would have to wait three more weeks just to schedule an appointment. *What was this? A competition to see what killed me first? The Broken Dream Syndrome or the Disappointment Freight Train?*

* * *

"What are we going to do now?" I was talking to Mariana, who stood next to me while I stirred boiling potatoes. "My fifty dollars won't last long." I turned, pointing at her with the steaming spoon in my hand, as if I was holding the money.

"We'll be fine. Mom said she'll send us some euros for New Year's." She opened the fridge and looked inside. "After the holidays, you'll know for sure." She slammed the door shut without taking anything out. She'd just completed this exercise for the third time, as if something different would appear in our fridge if she kept looking inside. "This is your last New Year's at home, so let's celebrate properly."

Celebrate what, exactly? I wasn't feeling the magic of the season, honestly. The potatoes were ready, so I turned off the burner and was about to dump the hot, boiling potato water into the sink. But a long doorbell ring disrupted me halfway.

"Did Sereoja forget we don't lock the doors during the day?" Lica shouted, and ran to open the front door.

"Good evening." We heard a deep male voice from the hallway. Mariana and I looked at each other. *Who was that?*

"Good evening," Lica answered and ran to the kitchen. She waited until the guest caught up with her and, theatrically raising her hands, announced him. "It's the other Sereoja, your cousin from the village!"

"Whoa! What a great surprise." Mariana clapped.

What a great surprise indeed. My aunt told me he'd been working in Moscow for several years now, so we hadn't seen him in God knows how long. Sereoja smiled, exposing the dimple on his left cheek. It looked just the same as when he was a kid.

"Happy pre-Christmas to you," he said, taking off his hat. "I don't know if you celebrate Christmas in the new style, on the twenty-fifth of December, or stick with the old style, on January seventh. Since the new date caused a lot of confusion, we now celebrate them both." He placed his large country bag on the table, and I recognized its sunflower pattern from an old photo of his mother. It had obviously been made from her dress. "Mom sent you some village produce for Christmas," he said, and pulled a plucked chicken out of his bag, sticking its yellow feet out of a newspaper wrap. I smiled. Christmas Day might have changed in the country, but wrapping everything in newspaper was still old school.

"Oho!" Mariana took the package from his hand and put it on the table, giggling. Then she turned around to pinch his shoulders. "What's up with these?" His shoulders had grown larger and more muscular since the last time we saw him, though he hadn't gotten any taller. "Have you been working out?"

"On a construction site, everyone's a Schwarzenegger," he joked.

"I'm more interested in what happened here." I pointed at the balding spot on his once thick head of black hair. "You're too young for this."

He caressed his head intensely, as if that could make his missing hair grow back.

"My Uzbekistani blood is finally taking over," he said, squinting his blue eyes. In that moment he reminded me of my father, who also had the rare combination of black hair with blue eyes.

"What do you mean 'your Uzbekistani blood is taking over'? Since when are you an Uzbek?" Mariana asked.

"It's a long story."

Oh, I had totally forgotten about that. Sereoja's mother, Anastasia, or simply Tasya, had created quite a scandal, when at sixteen she got entangled with an exotic student from Uzbekistan Mahmud, and got pregnant. Afraid of being thrown out of her parents' house, she ran and cried to her older brother: my father. He went to talk to Mahmud, man to man. Nobody knew what my father told Mahmud, but after that talk, he married Tasya and took her home to Tashkent. But on the eighth month of her pregnancy with my cousin Sereoja, Tasya called my father and begged him to bring her home, so he did.

From that point on, my father was Tasya's personal hero, and by extension, so was my mother and his children. So, every time she had a chance to remind us of her gratitude, she did.

"I got something else," Sereoja said. "Before I left, I stopped at Uncle Vasya's on the hill. He gave me this." He put a two-liter Coca-Cola bottle on the table. Rough around the edges, the bottle had obviously been reused a few times. And now, it was half filled with a light brown liquid.

"What is it?" I asked, excluding the possibility this could actually be a half-empty bottle of Coca-Cola. Though it was amusing that the iconic American drink had made it to his village in the first place.

"It's homemade cognac," he said.

"Cognac?" my sister and I asked.

"I didn't know you could make cognac at home," I said.

"Well, it's not exactly like the one from the stores. It's a little sweeter and much smoother. It goes down like a balsam for your throat. Uncle Vasya calls it 'home medicine.'"

"You peasants are always coming up with some affectionate nickname for alcohol." I laughed. I sipped a drop directly from the bottle. The liquid pinched my tongue. "It tastes like Coca-Cola, but it's definitely alcoholic-y," I said, wrinkling my nose.

"Oh, this stuff will knock you down if you're not very careful, so don't be fooled."

"You want some?" I asked him, trying to reach for the shot glasses.

"Oh, no!" he flatly refused. "I've been drinking almost nonstop since I got home last week. I actually came here to take a break from it. It's getting to my liver."

"From cognac to poison, it's only one step," I paraphrased Napoleon. "Mariana, put this in the back of the fridge. We'll have some of this 'medicine' on New Year's." Mariana took the bottle from my hands and opened the fridge again, this time with a valid purpose.

"We'll save your mother's chicken for New Year's too," I said. "But I'm cooking these gizzards now." I put our frying pan on the stove top. "You arrived at the perfect time. Your gizzards will go perfectly with my plain mashed potatoes." I poured oil in the pan. "Here, peel some onions and garlic," I told him. "Do you know how to do that?"

"Of course," he huffed. "There are no soft hands in the country, as our uncle Vasya says."

"By the way, how's our uncle? Still alone?"

"Yeah, still alone, living in Grandpa's old house since Grandpa died."

"How old is he now?"

"He celebrated his fiftieth birthday last weekend, and he invited over seven of his classmates for homemade wine and cognac. Funny thing, all seven are in their fifties, and none of them has been married even once."

"That's unusual, a small village like yours with so many bachelors that age."

"We normally have widowers in their fifties, but not bachelors. A few of them came close to getting married but didn't make it over the finish line. You know, no one at the celebration remembered Uncle Vasya dating anyone. Maybe once, when he was eighteen."

"Did they tease him about it?"

"Oh, yeah! The more they drank, the rowdier they got. At the end of the evening, they started some theories that they all might be gay and they should date each other."

"How much cognac did they have?"

"A lot."

"Who's this?" I heard my son's accusatory voice behind me in the doorway. He always tried to sneak in the house unnoticed when he had to pee. Then he'd run back outside to play with his friends before anyone could stop him.

"That's your namesake, my cousin Sereoja," I said. I didn't know why, exactly, he was up in arms. Was he thinking I might have a secret lover? It was cute, if he was trying to be protective of David.

"I didn't know about your cousin with the same name," he said conciliatorily.

"Come on!" Lica stomped her foot. "How come I remember all Mama's cousins but you don't? We stayed at their house when we were little."

"I was obviously too little to remember. What are we having?" he said, following his nose like a food detective, deciding whether it was worth staying.

"We're having dinner, that what we're having," I said.

"My friends are still outside." He was making a last plea, but the smell seemed to persuade him more than my words, and he finally gave in.

"Don't just stand there, be useful," I told him. "Get out the jar with the salted dill from the fridge. I need to add some to these gizzards."

"What's this? Coca-Cola?" Sereoja Junior asked when he opened the fridge.

"Put it back. It's not cola, it's cognac," I told him.

"What's cognac?"

"None of your business," Mariana interfered. "Put it back. Your mother told you to get the dill, so get it."

I dropped the cut dill in the sauce and told Mariana to get the plates and forks. We all sat down around the table for the last hurrah before Christmas. It had finally started feeling holiday-ish. After all, we had the letter from the American consulate in our hands, so that counted for something.

"When Mom sends us the money," I said, "we'll buy some mandarins, so it can smell like a real holiday in the house."

Chapter 37

Bring Your Own Medicine

"Man, it's getting dark out there so fast," I said, entering the house with bags of groceries from the bazar, including mandarins and one lemon for the tea. Too bad my cousin had left already. It would have been fun for him to spice up his country taste buds with city citrus delicatessens.

Lica and Mariana followed me to the kitchen. They were almost dancing behind my back, arguing about who would get her hands on the bag first. I didn't say anything, after all, they'd been waiting for me at home all this time. I'd decided it would be faster to go to the bazar by myself and avoid arguing with kids about what we should buy.

"Why is Serghei sleeping here?" I asked Mariana when I saw my son at the kitchen table, head dropped on his hands, with a half-empty plate of food next to him.

"He's been there for the last fifteen minutes. But he always does that," she complained, "plays until it's dark, then falls asleep while eating dinner. Sereoja, wake up!" Mariana pushed him.

"M-m-m-m." Serghei lifted his head. "Leave me alone."

"If you're done, go take a bath. I'm not sleeping with your dirty ass on the same bed!" Mariana yelled at him. "I poured a bucket of hot water in the bathtub for him. Tell him to go," she said to me.

"Sereoja, you heard her. Go, take a bath," I told him.

Serghei got up, murmuring, dragging his feet, with one hand against the wall.

"Quit being so dramatic." Mariana rolled her eyes.

"Are we saving the mandarins for New Year's?" Lica asked, and I nodded. "Well, can I at least smell them today?"

I was about to say "sure," but a loud crash came from the bathroom before I could speak. Something big and heavy had fallen to the floor, and it sounded like it was still rolling.

"Goddamn it, Sereoja!" Mariana yelled. "Did you break something?"

The three of us ran into the bathroom to find out, but the room was too small for all of us and we got stuck in the doorway. Serghei was on the floor, hanging onto the bathtub, trying to push himself up, kicking the empty metal bucket at his feet.

But I ignored that when I noticed Serghei's pants covered in mud. "Did you just sit with this dirty butt on our kitchen bench?" I asked.

"Mom, I … Mom …" he struggled to explain, but he finally stood up straight.

"Take everything off!" I snapped. He dropped on the floor, trying to pull his pants off, moving slowly, like he was about to fall asleep.

"What are you doing?" Mariana yelled. "You've smudged the mud everywhere on the floor now."

"I'm tired," he protested.

"Look at this!" I yanked the leg of his pants, which had gotten stuck on his foot. "Your clothes are as dirty as a drunken Vitalic. Go, bring your changing clothes," I said, pulling him up off the floor. He wobbled on long, skinny legs out of the bathroom, and I grabbed a rag to clean the floor.

"Mom!" Lica yelled from the other room. "Tell Serghei to stop! Look what he's doing. He got the rug all twisted."

I flew out of the bathroom like a hawk. Serghei leaned on the bed and pushed himself off the floor. But his knees kept bending, and the rug under his feet slid farther and farther away from him—like a scene in a Charlie Chaplin movie—until he fell, belly-down, hitting his head on the mattress.

"What are you doing?" I yelled angrily. But Serghei didn't respond. In fact, he didn't even move. His body lay on the floor, half folded in an awkward position, hands twisted inward. *He couldn't have hit his head that hard.* I lifted him up, more confused than shocked. His head swung backwards, and he drooled from his open mouth, his face looking pale as a corpse.

"Serghei!" I shook his head, trying for a reasonable explanation of why he'd behave like that when, just a few minutes ago, he'd seemed fine. "Sereoja!" I yelled louder this time, feeling that as more time kept passing, the fewer reasonable explanations there could be for why he wasn't responding.

"What's wrong with him?" Mariana asked in a shaken voice.

"I don't know. He just dropped for absolutely no reason. I don't understand." I put my ear to his mouth. "I can't hear him breathing." I started hyperventilating. I had to set my son down on the bed. His body had become heavy all of a sudden.

"Bring me a mirror from the bathroom," I commanded.

"Why?" Mariana asked, but she hurried to get the mirror, and I brought it close to Serghei's mouth.

"I read about nurses during the war. They carried a small mirror with them and placed it near a wounded soldier's mouth to see if the mirror would fog. If it did, he was still alive."

"Are you nuts? Don't talk like that right now." Mariana trembled.

"You think I want to?" I was about to lose it myself.

"Is it fogging?" Mariana asked with hope in her voice.

"I can't tell." I wiped the mirror clean and put it to his mouth once more, unsure whether I should trust the mirror trick when my hands were shaking, and my mind was in full-blown panic mode. *What mysterious disease could strike my son like this out of nowhere?*

"Is this happening because he drank from that bottle?" Angelica burst into tears.

"What bottle?" I was perplexed.

"That Coca-Cola bottle your cousin brought from the village. I told him to leave it alone because it's for New Year's, but he wouldn't listen. I caught him taking a few big gulps a couple of times."

Mariana ran to the kitchen and pulled the bottle out of the fridge.

"Look." She brought it to me, and I gasped. The two-liter bottle of homemade cognac, which had been half full, was only a quarter full now.

"Did you take any of this to your college friends today?" I asked Mariana.

"No!" Mariana looked insulted.

"I wouldn't be angry. I just need to know." Internally, I was desperately hoping her answer would change.

"No, I didn't!" she said, shaking her head.

"Are you telling me that Serghei drank a half liter of cognac by himself?" I looked at his still body on the bed. "Oh, my God, call the ambulance."

"Do they even send ambulances to our boonies at this time of night?" Mariana asked, her voice soft.

"I don't know, just call."

I lifted Serghei up and carried him to the bathroom to wash his face with cold water, hoping that would wake him up. He moved his head a few times, but he looked as good as dead.

"All right," Mariana popped her head through the bathroom

door, "they said they'll send the ambulance, but since it's so far from the city, it won't be arriving soon."

I breathed in relief anyway. *What would I have done if they'd refused to send an ambulance?*

"Help me dress him," I said, taking Serghei out of the bathroom. I laid him down on the bed while Mariana frantically pulled clean clothes from his drawers.

"Hold his legs," I barked at Mariana after two unsuccessful attempts to put a pair of clean pants on Serghei. "Lift his head up," I told her, calmer this time, and pulled my son's sweater over his head, then moved on to the sleeves. His hands were soft and lifeless like the rag doll that David and I bought last summer. *Oh, my God, what would I tell David? That I let my nine-year-old son get drunk? What kind of mother am I?*

"Watch him," I told Lica and Mariana and rushed to prepare a hospital bag with spare clothes. Then I went looking for my wallet, needing to count how much money was left after my trip to the bazar. It wasn't much. Just two hundred leis, enough for one more grocery trip, but would that be enough for a hospital stay? My broken foot fiasco had taught me that I'd need some money to grease the doctors at the hospital, for sure.

"What's taking them so long?" I asked Mariana, looking at the clock. "We called them thirty minutes ago. Can you go to the road and keep an eye out for the damn ambulance? I don't want them to get lost then leave for the city without us."

"It's freaking dark out there," she said.

"It's seven o'clock. There are plenty of people outside. I need you to go."

"I'll go with you, Mariana," Lica said, reaching for her coat and her boots. They both left in a hurry.

I sat down next to Serghei and touched his neck to check his temperature, the way my mom did when we were kids. It was burning hot, a sign he was still alive. The calm that I'd tried to maintain disappeared suddenly, and hot, salty tears flowed from my eyes and down my cheeks. *What if this is the end?*

"Ira, Ira, the ambulance is here," Mariana yelled from the corridor, bringing in two paramedics with her, a man and a woman in white hospital gowns.

"What happened, Mommy?" the man asked with a stern, unemotional face.

"You see, we had this bottle of homemade cognac in the fridge." I was stumbling over my words, embarrassed and disappointed at the same time.

"Ah, alcohol poisoning."

"You think it's poisoning?" This word sounded so terrible, and so absurd.

"Yeah," the woman confirmed. "It's very common around the holidays."

"With small kids like this?"

"You'd be surprised," the woman continued, lifting my son's shirt up to listen with her stethoscope. "His breathing is a little slow. Are you ready for the ride? Who's going to carry him downstairs? You don't have a lift here."

"I will." I picked up my son from the bed and dropped him over my shoulder. "Mariana, can you bring our coats and the bag downstairs?" I asked her on my way out, following the two paramedics who were on the stairs in front of me.

The ambulance roared out of the village with a wild siren shaking its old, rundown body. The wheels were rumbling so loudly on their axle that I was afraid we'd lose them at our first pothole. I crossed my fingers as I used to do in childhood, praying that we wouldn't break down. *Thump!* The ambulance shook and threw me from one side to the other. Serghei's body bounced on the stretcher, falling to the very edge. *They hadn't even tied him to the stretcher?*

I was in awe and groped in the dark until I detected two pieces of ripped fabric, instead of belts, on each side. There was nothing they could strap him with, I realized. But couldn't they have warned me? I pressed down on my son's body, trying to keep him in. At least we were riding toward help. I tried to keep myself calm. *We'll be in the hospital soon*, I told myself.

"What do we have here?" a female doctor on duty asked when they rolled in my son.

"Alcohol poisoning," the paramedic said unceremoniously.

"They never learn to hide their wine. Do they?" the doctor said sarcastically.

"It was cognac this time," the paramedic answered for me on his way out.

"Was it even a good, expensive one?" The doctor felt compelled to joke with me.

"It was homemade," I cut her off. "Does it really matter?"

"Homemade is the worst when it comes to alcohol poisoning."

"Can you please help my son as soon as possible?" My voice started trembling.

"Here's the deal," the doctor said methodically, like she was dissecting an insect one leg at a time, "your son will need his stomach pumped. Then he'll need an IV with saline solution for recovery, but the hospital is out of IVs. We don't even have single-use syringes right now."

"What do you mean? You don't even have syringes in the hospital? How do you treat your patients?"

"Everybody knows to bring their own medicine to the hospital," she said, like I had personally drained the hospital's supply. "We haven't been funded for months. All we can do is provide a bed for your son and a nurse to check on him. I'll write you a prescription for all of these."

"A prescription? Are you insane? Where am going to find a pharmacy still open at eight p.m.?" I looked at my watch.

"There's a pharmacy in the center that works all night." She sounded bored.

"In the center? It will take me an hour, at least, to get there and back by bus, and my son has had this poison in him for more than an hour. He can't wait all night while I buy an IV and syringes. I don't even know how much all this will cost. What if I don't have enough money? You're going to kill my son!"

The doctor and nurse looked at each other—two con artists dealing with a sucker—but then realized they needed more bait. The nurse stepped in first: "We can pump his stomach with a potassium permanganate solution mixed with warm water instead of medicine from the pharmacy. It's some nasty, cheap stuff I have in the back, but it will work. That will give you time to go buy an IV from the pharmacy, and when you come back, we'll hook him up with it."

"You're serous? You expect me to leave my son here alone with you?" I said, not trusting these two for one second.

"He'll be under our supervision," the doctor said.

"In a hospital that has no medication whatsoever? That's really reassuring."

"Look, we can stay here and talk about it all night, but your son still needs the IV. Of course, we can try to wake him up and see if he'll drink on his own, but there's no guarantee that, with his irritated stomach, he'll keep liquids in."

"All right, all right," I said, defeated. Making a decision to stay or go was like playing Russian roulette with my son's life. "I'll go," I said.

I was walking fast, almost running from the bus stop to the bright green light illuminating the name of the pharmacy: Felicia. *How ironic*, I thought, *because "Felicia" is derived from "happiness."* I pushed the door open and walked inside, where the bright light blinded me for a few seconds as my eyes adjusted after the darkness. I looked around. Though it was late, there was a handful of people there buying medicine.

"My son is in the hospital," I said loudly, speaking over the heads of the people to the pharmacist in white scrubs and cap. "The hospital sent me here with his prescription. Where can I fill it?" But the young pharmacist on duty was too busy running back and forth getting medications from shelves.

"You can stay right here." An older lady, wrapped in a gray shawl, pointed behind herself. "There are three of us in this line from the hospital."

My lips started trembling. I was not expecting to waste more time in line. I instinctively pulled up the sleeve of my coat to look at my watch, but felt afraid to discover how long I'd been gone, so I put it down again. By my rough calculations, I'd left the hospital about thirty minutes ago.

"Don't worry," the old lady said, and touched my hand. "This youngster is very nimble." She pointed at the pharmacist who, indeed, didn't stop even for a minute. Her concentration gave me the feeling that she understood us, the poor people, stuck in her pharmacy in the middle of the night. Then I noticed that her name tag said Felicia, a coincidence that pushed my worries to the back of my mind. My brain had needed some "divine" sign that everything would be all right, and this was it. *Felicia will save us*, I caught myself thinking.

A few minutes later, Felicia grabbed Serghei's prescription and swirled around the pharmacy like a mini-tornado with a halo, filling up a plastic bag with medications, IV wires, syringes, and God knows what else from the shelves. She rang up the totals and said in an angelic voice: "One hundred eighty leis."

She was definitely sent from Heaven. I breathed, relieved. That left me with twenty leis, which I would need to get back to the hospital, and it was even enough for the trip home.

I arrived at the hospital after ten p.m.

"How's my son?" I gave the nurse the bag from the pharmacy.

"We pumped his stomach, so he's asleep now. Come, I'll show you to his room," the nurse said.

"Did he wake up when you did it?" I asked, following her.

"Yes, when we pushed the tube down his throat, he threw up really good."

"Did he cry?" I cringed, imagining what this had been like.

"For a little bit," she said empathetically. "Mostly because we were holding his hands. He's strong, he was fighting us very hard." She giggled. "But now he's clean, like a freshly washed glass."

I followed the nurse into the semi dark hospital room and looked around. The room was almost bare. Serghei was on the left, lying on his right side in a short bed with rails, one designed for five-year-olds. His long, naked legs were bent at the knees and stuck out of a tiny, thin blanket that might cover an infant but not a schoolboy. I could hear him breathing unevenly in a high pitch, then a low one, as if the sounds were coming from two different raspy musical instruments. But then I noticed he had company. A little girl on the other side of the room was breathing like a trumpet. She and Serghei were a snoring duo.

The nurse turned on the light without warning. *Did she have to be so unceremonious? She could wake them both up.* "I'll hook him up to the IV," she said, getting right to business, looking for a vein on Serghei's arm. "It will take about an hour for the liquid to drip through."

"He's hot," I said, feeling the sweat on his forehead. "Is that normal?"

"We gave him some aspirin to help with it, but once the saline flushes the rest of the alcohol out of his system, his temperature will stabilize." I couldn't look at her poking him with a needle, so I walked toward the girl's bed.

"Where is her mother?" I asked the nurse.

"Her mother lives in the village. She can't stay with her because she has other kids at home to take care of. But the girl's been here for five days, so her mother will pick her up tomorrow."

"Alone for five days? She's so little. Doesn't her mother have a husband to look after her other kids?" I pulled on the tiny blanket, which had worked its way under the girl's feet, and covered her up. The motion disturbed her, so she purred like an annoyed kitten and rolled to her right side, folding her tiny hand under her cheek.

"Her mother didn't look like she had a husband," the nurse finally responded.

I wondered what a husbandless woman looked like in her eyes, since she was such an "expert." Did she look like an intense go-getter, or like a scared country woman hiding her eyes? *Do I reek of husbandless, too?* I wondered. What if the girl's mother really had no one else to help her with the kids? I knew Angelica would have been home alone tonight, if not for Mariana. Would that mean I was a horrible mother? Twice in one night?

"You don't have anywhere to sit in here," I said. "Where can I get a bench?"

"Normally we don't allow parents with kids over seven to stay with them in the hospital," the nurse said.

"I'm not leaving my son here alone!" I glanced at the little girl on the other bed. They'd have to drag me out of this room feet first. "Besides, it's too late. Buses have stopped running to where I live."

"I'll bring you a chair," the nurse said, finally giving in. "But just so you know, since you're not a patient, you won't get any food."

Right. Food. My stomach growled, and I realized I hadn't eaten dinner.

"Here, I found a baby stool in the other room," the nurse said, holding it out to me. "All the chairs are taken."

"Fine." I was too tired to complain. The bottoms of my feet were burning and stinging. I pulled the stool closer to Serghei's bed and sat down. His forehead was sweaty, and his chest was moving up and down unevenly, as if he was forgetting to breathe from time to time. Other than that, he looked peaceful. If not for the IV sticking out of his arm, you could hardly tell he'd had a rough night.

I put my hands on the rails of his bed, leaning my body forward, trying to find a comfortable position for resting. I lay my head on my hands and closed my eyes, needing to take a break for just a bit. My dreamy veil hadn't yet taken hold of me, when I sensed Serghei moving. *No, just let me sleep.* My body was rebelling. I tried to lift my head up, but it felt heavy as cast iron.

"Sh-sh, sh-sh, sh-sh," I cooed as I rocked Serghei with my hand, trying to put him back to sleep as I had when he was little. The soothing sound of a chirping waterfall reached my ear. Was I dreaming? I hadn't noticed any fountains in the building. But my hand felt a sudden warmth, as if dipped in a hot spring flowing from under the blanket. Was the IV dripping? I jumped and rushed to turn the lights on.

Serghei squinted and moaned grumpily, then stretched and kicked the blanket off—and I saw it! The endless waterfall was squirting from underneath his underwear. He was peeing! Like a baby! I ran to wake him up, but what good would that do with him having a needle in his arm? I looked under the bed where a bedpan would normally be, but there wasn't one. I ran to the corridor and called for the nurse, but no one responded. Even if they had, it was too late! Serghei was lying in a puddle of yellow, smelly, disgusting urine, squirming uncomfortably.

Defeated, I went for the bag of clothes I'd brought from home. At least I'd put his spare pants and shirts in there. Where did I put his underwear? I started frantically looking through the bag over and over again. Irritated, I dumped everything on the floor, but the elusive undergarments were still at home, forgotten in the rush. I'd have to work with what I'd brought. I pulled my son's wet and sticky underwear off him—and his shirt, which was also soaked with the urine that had spread under his back, all the way to his head. His hair stank. His entire body smelled like potent tear gas. I turned him on his side to take off his shirt. But his arm, still hooked to the IV, was not cooperating.

"Mom?" I heard Serghei asking for me in a tired, raspy voice. "Where am I?"

"You're in the hospital," I said, still trying to wrestle his shirt off without tangling the IV.

"Why?"

"You got alcohol poisoning."

"Poison? From what?" He tried to lift his head but dropped it back on the pillow.

"Don't you remember? You drank the cognac from the Coca-Cola bottle in the fridge." I shook away tears as I remembered what it was like to not know if he was breathing. "You scared me. You could have died, Sereoja." He looked at me with blurry eyes. Of course! He couldn't remember a thing!

"Oh, look who woke up," the nurse said when she finally arrived.

"Can you please bring us some clean sheets?" I rushed to cover up my son's privates with his blanket. "He had an accident."

"No, I didn't!" Serghei slid his hand to verify but turned his head away, embarrassed.

"Ai, ai, ai, such a big boy and an accident," the nurse shamed him. "That's what happens when the saline solution goes through you too fast."

"If you knew this happens, why didn't you leave a bedpan or something? You don't even have a plastic cover on the mattress. He's literally in a pool of pee," I said. Not only did this hospital not have syringes, but apparently a bedpan was too much to ask for.

"Let me take his IV off"—the nurse didn't answer my question—"then he can go to the bathroom by himself." *Great advice.*

"Why's the room spinning?" Serghei asked, trying to sit up for the second time. "I'm thirsty, and my head hurts." He grabbed his head with both hands.

"You have a hangover." The nurse laughed. "I'll bring you some water, and I'll see if I can find some clean sheets. Usually, we get only one set of sheets for the shift."

"What happens if someone needs two?" I was perplexed. "Also, where can I wash him?"

"There's a shower at the end of the hallway, but the water comes out rusty and icy cold. Honestly, our patients don't like taking showers in there, because the window's busted, and the room is like an icebox. Did you bring soap?"

"No! I didn't think I'd have to bring soap to a hospital."

"We've got some bleach solution for disinfection in there, but that's about it," she said on her way out. *What the actual fuck?* I was about to curse.

"Get out of that wet bed, at least." I pulled my son out. "Step into your boots," I said, when I saw him shivering, his skin turning blue from standing on the bare floor. I looked for a towel to dry him off but couldn't find one, so I ripped my scarf off my neck and used it as a towel instead. "Here, put your pants on."

"No underwear?"

"No underwear. You're Tarzan today. We'll also use our fingers instead of a toothbrush. Like in a jungle." I was trying to recall what other essentials I'd left behind. I'd have to call Mariana with a list of stuff to bring us. I looked at Serghei struggling to put his sweater on, so I pushed it down hard to get it over his head. His normally big head now seemed enormous because of his swollen, red cheeks. As Igor liked to joke: "Big head, big brains." *Yeah, not tonight, buddy, not tonight.*

The nurse came back with a plastic cover and one bed sheet.

Without saying anything, she swiftly flipped the mattress over, dropping its wet side on the rusty, metal frame. *She isn't going to change the mattress?* Unabashed, the nurse put the plastic cover and the bed sheet on the dry side, and left. I guessed not. Why was I even surprised? But before I had time to object, Serghei climbed over the rails, dropped his head on the pillow, and fell asleep within seconds.

New Year's Eve morning in the hospital was a drag. After three hours of sleep, everything was slow and tiresome, and gray. Even leaving the room to ask when they were going to bring Serghei's breakfast seemed like a major accomplishment.

"Later. After we know who's staying and who's leaving," one of the nurses said. "We'll feed the ones who'll remain here for the rest of the day."

Two male patients with waxy faces were standing in the hallway, dressed in washed-out, ripped hospital gowns. They'd been waiting to hear about breakfast too and got agitated.

"If you're not going to feed us, can we go home for the holidays?" the older one asked, hand pressing the wall for support. His feet scuffed the fallen cement that had chipped away from the wall, leaving a deep gap behind. Daylight shining on the wall exposed a dark crack, rising to the ceiling, which I hadn't noticed last night.

The night-shift doctors, however, were already in "ignore" mode, rushing to get out of the hospital, so they were punting all questions to the next crew. But the doctors on the day shift hadn't switched to work mode yet, leaving an hour-long power vacuum, when no one in the hospital knew who the hell was in charge. Patients soon began serving themselves, taking out their own bedpans, and bringing their own water.

The little girl in our room woke up too.

"What's your name?" I asked, but she kept quiet, pretending not to hear me. Then she used the rails to climb off her bed, showing the skills of a kid who often did things on her own. I rushed to help her only when her foot got stuck. She let me, without making any fuss.

"You wanna pee?" I asked the nameless girl. She nodded, so Serghei and I took her hands and walked her to the bathroom at the end of the hall.

"Do you know how long my son has to stay here?" I asked our night nurse when I saw her leaving on our way to the bathroom.

"Don't worry," she said. "The doctors stuck on duty during New Year's don't like to have many patients here. They'd rather celebrate in peace with a glass of champagne, so they'll release as many of you as possible today." She smiled, like it wasn't a big deal.

Thirty minutes later, the new doctor looked at Sergei's chart with absent eyes and asked me only one question: "Do you want to go home today?"

"If you think my son's well enough to go," I answered.

"There's nothing more that we can do for him here. Just keep him hydrated," he said. "Liquids are the best cure for a hangover. Right?" He winked at Serghei, who dropped his head. He'd probably prefer to give away his pinky if it meant there were no more questions from doctors.

"Mom, what's a hangover?" Serghei asked, walking next to me with a limp when we finally left the gray, unpleasant hospital building behind. The bus stop was just around the corner, but it felt like it was a kilometer away.

"That's how you felt yesterday," I answered.

"Hangovers suck!" he said with the seriousness of a boy who'd become an adult overnight. I glanced at his tired, pale face. His lips were almost white, as if a vampire had sucked all the blood out of them.

I was sure I didn't look like a beauty queen either. I could almost feel the black circles growing under my eyes. "Yes, hangovers suck."

Could we just get through this New Year's Eve and make it to the American embassy in one piece? *Was that too much to ask for a New Year's wish?*

Chapter 38

Avral

"Oh, my God! You're home!" Mariana yelled as I opened the door to our apartment. I instinctively raised my hand as a shield. Her scream hurt my ears and was bringing back visions of last night's chaos. Now I felt like I had a hangover.

"He's walking on his own?" She pointed at Serghei as if she'd just seen Jesus walk on water, then shrieked, "You stupid little piece of shit! You scared me."

"You scared all of us!" Lica joined in. "We thought you were dead!"

"I didn't mean to," Serghei mumbled. He concentrated on removing his boots, which stubbornly wouldn't come off, no matter how hard he tried.

"Stop, both of you," I cut in. "He already got his punishment at the hospital."

"Why didn't you call?" Mariana turned to me again. "We were worried sick!"

"There was nowhere to call from," I said, hanging up my coat. "And I didn't have coins to call from a telephone booth. Besides, we were waiting all morning to be released. They just took their time, like they always do." I sat down to take off my winter boots covered in the mud that had collected on my way from the bus stop.

"You still should have called," Mariana said more calmly this time.

"I would have if we'd stayed another night." I dropped my boots next to Serghei's.

"Good thing you didn't have to stay at the hospital on New Year's Eve." Lica sounded relieved. I was relieved, too, that we'd finally dropped all the exclamation marks from our conversation. "Are we still having the New Year's get-together with your college friends?"

"Oh, shit! I totally forgot about that!" Exclamation marks were back.

"Do you want to cancel?" Mariana asked.

"No," I said. "Only four of them are coming for a last hurrah before we leave. We have time to put it all together if we start cooking right now." I rushed to the kitchen and started frantically taking out all I could find in the fridge. "Besides, we need to have some fun tonight. You have no idea how depressing that hospital was."

"When are we going to roll the grape leaves?" Lica asked prudently.

"We'll have to skip that. We'll make a rice pilaf with Tasya's country chicken instead. It's less time consuming."

"How about the *Olivier* salad? That one takes forever," Mariana objected.

"Not if we start boiling the ingredients right now." I filled pans with potatoes, carrots, and eggs, poured water on top of them, and turned on the oven.

"I'm talking about chopping all of these," Mariana objected again. "That takes hours."

"I announce a New Year's *avral*." I looked at everyone in kitchen.

"What's '*avral*'?" Sergei had finally found the courage to say something.

"That's what they say in the navy, when they need all hands on deck."

"Serghei too?" Lica looked at her brother with pity.

"He's the reason we need an *avral* in the first place," Mariana reproached.

"Don't worry." Serghei seemed offended. "I can chop the potatoes."

"Oh, please." Mariana couldn't help it. "We could all choke on the potato cubes the way you cut them."

"Are you from the Culinary School of Perfect Potato Cubes all of a sudden?" I interjected. "We're gonna eat whatever potato shape he cuts. All right?"

"Is that okay with you, Mariana?" Serghei puffed up his chest.

"Mama wouldn't like that," Mariana mumbled, displeased.

"Mama isn't here, is she?" I reminded her sternly. I was the captain of this ship now. "Besides, I've got other tasks for you. Get that chicken ready for pilaf. I'll get the dough started for the bread. We need to bake some. We're getting low."

I brought the flour from the pantry and mixed it with water, yeast, and salt, then kneaded the dough in a deep plastic bucket until it was so firm that it stopped sticking to my hands. After that, I put the bucket on top of a bowl filled with warm water, so it would rise faster. That little trick, which Babushka taught me, would come in handy right now. Our small kitchen looked crowded and busy, like a well-choreographed anthill. A soundless ballet of movements interrupted by short commands:

"Give me that towel." I stretched out my hand to Mariana, who was cutting chicken on the other side of the table, and she threw it to me without even looking. The towel floated in midair for a few seconds like a small parachute. I jumped, caught it with one hand, and twisted it like a rope, so it was easier to lift the pot with hot boiled potatoes and carrots. Steam rushed up as I poured off the water into the sink—and kept billowing when I put the pot in front of Serghei.

"Peel and cut," I said.

"I'll peel the boiled eggs." Lica took charge of this operation, as she had many times before.

"Good," I told her. "Then I'll peel some onions for pilaf."

Serghei was chopping potatoes on his cutting board with an intense expression on his face, moving his knife so fast that it made a cicada sound.

"Hey, don't cut too close to your fingers." I stopped him. "We don't need another trip to the hospital today." He huffed but didn't say anything. "Make some room on the table," I told everybody. "I need to roll the bread dough. It's risen enough." I looked at the clock. It was already five p.m., and there was still so much to do. I rolled six pieces of dough into six spheres and dumped them in the oiled bread forms that my brother had brought from his bread factory. The two sets of three forms fit perfectly in the oven. Now, we just had to wait about forty minutes for the bread to bake.

"Mom, I'm sleepy," Serghei said, chewing slowly on a piece of steaming bread that had just come out of the oven.

"Go, lie down," I said, "since you've already paid your dues." He left for the bedroom without much resistance.

"I feel like taking a nap too," Mariana said, tasting the rice pilaf for the third time.

Lica slapped her hand. "Don't stuff yourself before the guests come!"

"When are your friends coming?" Mariana stomped her foot. "I'm hungry. Or am I supposed to sew my mouth shut until midnight?"

"You know what, let me call them, because with all this craziness I don't remember confirming the time." I left the kitchen and called Tanya, the banker, first.

"Happy New Year's Eve, Taniusha!" I said into the phone receiver.

"Happy holidays to you too." Tanya laughed in response. "May the Old Hag of the Old Year leave us in peace."

"Amen." I cheered at her raspy voice, which brought pleasant memories of fun times in the past. I needed a good distraction from how exhausted I was. Like my son, I could have used a nap too. "So, when are you guys coming tonight?"

"Coming where?"

"To my house," I answered, hoping that she was joking. "Remember, we talked about it? It could be my last year at home."

"Are you leaving for America already?"

"Not yet, but I thought we talked about celebrating this new year together."

"You're more than welcome to come to my house. Bring your kids, too, so my daughter has more children to play with."

"I can't." I couldn't believe that Tanya had no recollection of my invitation. I felt like a little girl who'd been cheated on her Christmas presents. "I'm the host. You, Violeta, Alex, and Nora were supposed to come to my house. I still have to be here for the other three."

"Sorry, I totally forgot about that. Why don't you come to my house tomorrow then? We'll have plenty of leftovers."

"We'd rather stay home and rest. I had a rough night last night." I cut it short, without much explanation.

"Sorry for my mistake, but it's too late for me to change. I'll see you next year?"

"See you next year." I let her go, dropping the phone receiver back into its hook, finally accepting my fate. But the receiver vibrated under my hand the minute I put it down. It was Violeta.

"Sorry, Ira. I can't make it tonight." At least Violeta remembered that we'd made plans. "My parents got all emotional on me, wanting to see me on New Year's as usual. It sounded like a good idea when we talked about it. But it turned into a big logistical nightmare."

"That's fine. Don't feel bad about it," I consoled her, feeling disappointed but somehow relieved. I called Nora, who didn't answer. So, I left her a message and looked for Alex's phone number in my notebook but couldn't find it. I hoped he'd call me before showing up.

"Go ahead and eat some," I told Mariana when I came back to the kitchen. "Two of my guests already canceled."

"What? The guests aren't coming?" Lica was utterly distraught, as if her personal friends had bailed on her. "And Sereoja's sleeping. Mariana, do you want to be haitori with me tonight?"

"No-o-o! That's for you kids," she protested. "I'm too old for that."

"Such a lame New Year!" Lica pouted, full of sorrow. I felt like crying too. The exhaustion of last night in the hospital started to kick in. Maybe it had been crazy to believe I could handle having guests and a celebration. Maybe it was better that no one would come. We could go to bed earlier, New Year's and all.

A long doorbell ring startled me. Lica jumped off her chair to open the door, losing the inconsolable pout she had just a minute ago.

"A little early for haitori, don't you think?" I asked Mariana, looking at the clock: eight p.m. "Aren't they supposed to come right before midnight?"

"Mom, Nora and Alex are here!" Lica ran back to tell me the news.

"Well, well!" I went to meet them at the door, wrestling with a weird feeling in between happiness and disappointment. I'd just made peace with cutting the New Year's celebration short. But now I had to put on a brave face to entertain the guests that I thought were not coming.

"Happy New Year to your house, Irina!" Alex trumpeted solemnly from the doorway and handed me the bouquet of flowers he'd been holding awkwardly. I looked at it, amused. In these hard times, a stick of kolbasa would have been more appropriate than a bouquet. But "don't look a gift horse in the mouth" my grandpa (may his soul rest in peace) would say.

"Thank you," I said with a forced smile.

"Here, there's more." Alex handed me a brown bag with a bottle of vodka sticking out. Of course. Alex without vodka was like a fish without water.

"Happy New Year to all of you!" Nora said from behind him. "I brought a cake. I hope that's all right."

"Nora, you are a savior!" I clapped in excitement. Perhaps I could come back around to the celebratory attitude—if there was cake. "I didn't even think about it today. You see, last night I had to take Serghei to the hospital with alcohol poisoning."

"What?" Nora was in shock.

"Long story short, it was an accident. But he's better now. Sleeping in the next room."

"How are you holding up? You should have called and canceled."

"Honestly, that idea came to me about half an hour ago. I actually left you a message, but I might have been a little late."

"Oh, you must have called my home number. I left my house over an hour ago," Nora said, taking her boots off. "I was waiting for Violeta at the bus stop. We were supposed to come here together. I almost went back home because I didn't have your address or your phone number. But then Alex showed up, and luckily he had your address, so we came here together."

"Good thing you met Alex then, because Violeta just called me. She's not coming, and neither is Tanya. So it's only going to be you two."

"Really?" I could see the disappointment on Nora's face. I felt for her. Without Violeta and Tanya, I'd have to work twice as hard to keep these two entertained. And though I was clearly not up to par, the train was out of the station, as Igor would say. Jeez, what was up with all these sayings that I suddenly recalled, as if having flashbacks of my entire life before I dropped dead?

"Let's set up the table." I pushed Mariana with my elbow.

"Sereoja, what happened to you?" Nora asked when he poked his uncombed head out of the bedroom, awoken by all the commotion in the hallway.

"Nothing," he said, hiding eyes with dark circles. "Happy New Year's!" he deflected and walked toward the kitchen.

"Be useful while you're there," I yelled after him. "Bring the salad from the fridge. Nora, Lesha, you can go take a seat."

"Let me help." Nora jumped up to take the plates out of my

hand, happy to have something to do. She set them neatly around the table. Mariana brought the basket of bread with thick, unevenly cut slices, as if she'd just learned how to use a knife. *Yet she'd complained about Serghei's potato cubes...*

"Oh, homemade bread," Nora noticed. "Still warm. When did you have time to bake today?"

"It somehow worked out." I shrugged.

"Here's the Olivier." Serghei put the bowl of potato salad in the middle and sat down. He looked exhausted, as if he'd just run a marathon instead of walking.

"Since everyone is here, can we start eating?" Mariana asked.

"Sure. Why not?" I looked at my guests who were sitting quietly in their chairs. "Bring the pilaf and the wine. Let's get this party started," I said, trying to lighten up the mood.

"I brought some CDs." Nora reached for her purse. "We can let them play in the background."

"Unfortunately, we don't have a CD player," I replied and saw the question "What are we going to do without music?" in Nora's expression. The New Year's Eve that had started on the wrong foot was going deeper into the maze. "I'll turn on the TV," I deflected. "The Eve concert should be on soon."

Alex went for the vodka bottle. "Anyone?"

"No," both Nora and I shook our heads simultaneously. I slammed one empty shot glass in front of Alex. He would have to drink his vodka alone. I wasn't ready for prime-time hard liquor yet. Even the thought of my uncle's cognac in the fridge was making me cringe.

I poured village-made red wine for Nora and myself, using the tall wine glasses left from Mom's birthday.

"Who's ready for a toast?" I asked.

"Not me," Serghei said, dropping his head into his hands, which were resting on the table. I couldn't tell if he meant it as a joke, but Mariana jumped on it.

"Yeah, that's really funny, Sereoja!" She swung one hand above his head, pretending to hit him. He made a face, as if he'd been hit.

"So, what happened?" Nora asked for the second time. Serghei shoved two spoons of pilaf into his mouth in response and started chewing loudly, pointing at his full mouth to show that he couldn't speak.

"Bring the pickles!" I pushed Serghei when I saw Alex's twisted face. He'd just emptied his shot glass in one swoop. What kind of host was I without pickles on the table when vodka was present? He obeyed, but a ring at the door sidetracked him.

"Mom," he yelled from the hallway. "My friend wants me to go caroling with him."

"You can't go anywhere. You're still recovering." I arrived at the scene.

"But, Mom!" he whined.

"There is no 'but.' You should have thought about it yesterday." My patience had a short fuse at that point.

"I want to go," Lica said, showing up from the other room. "Mariana," she yelled. "Natasha is here for you. She wants you to go with us."

"Oh, for God's sake!" Mariana stormed in. The future haitori, half inside the door and half outside, kept trying to convince Mariana to go with them until she reluctantly gave in. Serghei saw his sister and Mariana go off with such sad eyes, as if saying goodbye to them forever.

"You'll be fine." I touched his shoulder.

"No, I won't. You said this is our last New Year's at home. I'll never get a chance like this again." He went to pout in the living room.

I went back to Alex and Nora with a jar of the promised pickles, leaving Serghei in the other room to cool off. "So, where were we?"

Alex was standing up, holding a half-empty bottle of vodka over Nora's head. She leaned backward so he wouldn't hit her by accident.

"*No-roc!* And hap-py New Year's!" he yelled, slurring his words. *Had he downed a shot glass per minute while I was gone?*

"So, when is the next bus from here?" Nora asked, looking at her watch.

"It's ten minutes be-fore mid-night. We're not go-ing any-where," Alex said adamantly.

"If you wait until after midnight, you won't get out of here until morning," I let Nora know.

"Maybe we should leave now." She tugged Alex's sleeve.

"We ne-e-ed to clink the bell with Ira at mid-night," Alex insisted and dropped back on his chair.

"Do you mean clink glasses?" Nora was getting ticked off. I couldn't blame her. She was stuck here with me and Alex, who was always a cheap drunk, but tonight he'd beaten his own re-cord. He was resembling Igor in the way he flapped his arms and spoke loudly.

"I can walk you to the bus stop if you want," I told Nora, of-fering to put her out of the misery I'd created with my insistence on having this party, on a day when I had no business hosting anything.

"But then you'd have to come back alone in the dark." Nora looked at me, worried.

"There are plenty of people outside. And haitori are out there knocking at people's doors for a few more hours. I'll be fine."

The front door swung open suddenly, hitting the wall with a loud bang.

"*Aho, aho!*" Mariana and Lica were chanting as they walked into the room, bringing Natasha and everyone else with them for a traditional Christmas carol.

"Haitori are here!" Alex met them with an enthusiastic clap. That encouraged the kids to chant their Christmas wishes even more enthusiastically. Serghei snuck up from behind and started throwing rice at us, screaming the last words in unison with every-one else: *"La anul! Și la mulți ani!"*

"I've always wondered, what does that mean?" Alex, born in Russia, didn't speak Romanian.

"It means 'many years to you,'" Nora translated. I smiled. Nora, Russian-born herself, kept up with our changing times.

"How much money did you make caroling?" Serghei pulled Mariana's hand, impatient for an answer.

"This year was bad," she said. "Everyone's strapped for money. People mostly paid us with sweets." She pulled a few candies out of her bag.

"Sadly, I'll have to pay you with sweets too," I said. "Anybody want some cake?"

"Yeah!" they answered almost simultaneously.

"Nora?" I implored.

"Sure, let's have some cake," she agreed. We both knew it was too late to catch the last bus to the city, even if we dropped every-thing instantly and ran like it was an avral.

Chapter 39

Is This the Last Time I'll See You?

I opened my eyes on January second like I was in a new era. Everything seemed different, and everything should have felt different, because on that day I could call the American embassy in Bucharest. I dragged the house phone with its long cord into the kitchen and settled it in front of me on the table. I put a notebook and a pen next to it to be ready to take notes. It was eight a.m. *Too early. I don't want to seem desperate,* I thought, like I was trying to call an ex-lover or something. I had no idea if you could be deemed desperate if you were the first caller of the year at the American embassy, but I didn't want to take any chances.

I poured myself a hot cup of tea, dropped a spoon of strawberry jam in it, and stirred it slowly, trying not to make noise. As if my soft *cling, cling* of the tea spoon could wake the kids up in the other room. They were sleeping just fine. I was counting down the minutes to nine o'clock.

"Good morning," I said in English with trepidation in my voice, when an official in Bucharest finally picked up the phone. "My name is Irina Iancenco, and I call in regards to my fiancé visa."

"Is it easier for you if we speak in Romanian?" the woman on the other end asked me. That almost threw me into a nervous coma: *Am I so hard to understand?* She took my silence as a "yes" and switched to Romanian. "Did you mail the finished *pachet* to us already?" She was rolling her Romanian "R" with such a thick English accent that now I had a hard time understanding her. *Pachet, pachet? What does it mean?*

"Your package with additional documents. Did you mail it to us already?" the woman said, like she could see the confusion on my face over the phone. *She must have worked for the CIA before. Or maybe she's still working for the CIA.*

"I thought I was supposed to bring the package with me," I finally said.

"You are supposed to mail it to us. Then allow us a few days to receive it, then you can call us to set up an appointment."

I puffed the air out of my lungs. *How did I miss that? Good thing I called instead of just showing up at the consulate like a bimbo.*

"Since I've got you on the phone," the woman continued, "I'll look through your original package that came from the U.S. really quick, just to make sure that everything is up to date. Have you gotten a recent police report?"

"Yes, I sent one in the summer."

"The police reports are only valid for ninety days. You'll have to get a more recent one."

What is she thinking? That all this time I was going around on a Bonnie-and-Clyde spree (but without Clyde), robbing banks and shooting people, while waiting for my immigration papers to arrive?

"Also, I don't see a police report in your maiden name. We need them in both of your names."

"Okay," I said defeated. By now I was accustomed to there always being another paper to submit. It would have shocked me more if she'd said that everything was finally complete.

"I'll get them both, and I will mail the package to you shortly," I said.

Another trip to the Ministry of Internal Affairs was in order. At least this time I knew where to go, what exactly to ask for, and how long that would take. A few more trips like that and I could be a professional document-collector. That knowledge gave me the peace of mind and the strength to deal with another three-week delay.

Waiting for the Ministry of Internal Affairs to pump out another police report for me, waiting for Mom to send us the care package from Italy—that was delayed because of the holidays—waiting for David to get paid so he could send us the money for the trip to Bucharest. Waiting, waiting, and more waiting.

First came Mom's package with Italian chocolate and other sweets for the kids, and a hundred euros for groceries and utility bills. "I can't send you more," she said. "I just finished paying back the money I borrowed for my trip."

Then David came through: "I wired you five hundred dollars. I know it's barely enough for the three of you for your trip to Bucharest, but I can't send you more. My rent is due on the first."

"That should be enough," I said, looking through my expenses list one more time. Money had been tight since I lost my job at Vasily's and didn't get my old job back at the day care. But Babushka Veta's food supplies and Mom's occasional money transfers were getting us through while I was dealing with endless paperwork collection for our visa.

Then three weeks later the Ministry of Internal Affairs came through with two freshly printed police reports in both my names. It was time for me to pack my envelope and go to DHL. The first private mail courier in the country was quite a ways from my home, though. One bus, one trolleybus, and one long walk.

"Write the American embassy's address here," the man at the DHL counter said casually, like he shipped priceless packages like that every day. "Two hundred leis," he said. *Damn, that's almost twenty dollars out of David's money gone.* But I knew the price was right. *How much does a dream cost?* Or how much would it cost to restore all these documents if the Moldova Postal Service lost my package? The heartbreaking scenario sent goosebumps down my arms, so I gave him the money quickly. He wrote me a receipt and dropped my envelope into a big box with other parcels. It irked me, as if he had thrown my baby in there.

I raised my hand. "Hey, I wanted to send it certified so I can get the receipt back when the embassy receives my package."

"They don't sign for mail at the embassy. But don't worry, it will be there it two days, tops."

"So soon?" I was surprised. I was expecting it to be a week, for some reason.

"That's DHL for you."

I walked away, smiling, holding my receipt in my hand with a feeling that I'd just made a great purchase. That's how I'd felt in the past when I bought a new dress, or had a new hairdo, except today, I had nothing to show for it. I walked down to the trolleybus stop, murmuring the words to "Hotel California," barely noticing people around me. I rushed to the back on the half-empty trolleybus when it stopped in front of me. I put the purse on my lap, with my hands still holding the receipt that I was not yet ready to put away, and looked through the window at the people bundled up in winter coats, as if they were from a different planet.

"Well hello, Irina." A man took a seat next to me. "I haven't seen you in a long time."

"Gicu?" I could not believe my eyes. "What are you doing here?"

"You don't remember that my architect studio is two stops away? You used to take this route to come see me on the weekends." He smiled at me mischievously.

Oh, jeez!

"Of course, I remember this route! But that was like two years ago." I tapped nervously with my foot. "I'm here for a completely different reason today."

"Where are you going?" he asked curiously. I looked at him

with a long, doubting look, calculating whether I should tell him the reason for my happiness today that he'd just ruined.

"Actually, I already went...to DHL," I started probing carefully how far I should go with my confession, but he read right through me.

"International package?"

"Yes, to the American embassy," I finally blurted it out. His facial expression changed in an instant.

"Ah, oh, ay," he mumbled incoherently. "You are going to America?" He couldn't hide his shock.

"Yeah. I was studying English—you know that. And now I'm going to America."

"For work?"

"No. To live there. Forever," I said slowly and methodically, like I was stabbing him with a knife.

"How?" He looked at me intrigued.

"I'm marrying an American, so the kids and I are leaving for America, hopefully soon." He blinked a few times in disbelief. "You're missing your stop." I pointed at the door, when I saw that the trolleybus stopped near Gicu's studio, but he didn't move a muscle.

"That's all right." He glanced at the window. "I'll go with you to the next stop, to where you change to your bus, and I'll come back," he said, finally breathing evenly. "You see, I remember a lot about you." He turned to me.

"Whoa, I'm honored!" I laughed.

"Seriously, I remember a *lot* about you." He whipped out his smile. "I'm actually glad that we met today, because I was thinking about you the other day. You see, the way we ended things..."

"*You* ended things."

"Yes, the way I ended things between us was not the most graceful."

"My stop!" I yelled, and rushed to the exit. He followed me out of the trolleybus. As I was coming out, I saw the tail of the bus that was going to my village, and for a split second I was debating if I should run for it. *I'll get the next one,* I told myself, unwilling to interrupt the movie at the most interesting part.

"Especially," Gicu continued his speech like nothing had happened. We both dropped on the bench at the bus stop like two robots. "Especially if this could be the last time I see you. I just wanted you to know that I'm sorry."

"Apology accepted. How's your wife?" I looked straight into his eyes.

"A wife is a wife." Gicu tilted his head. "She's actually a perfect wife for me. We have a little daughter. I called her Romanitza."

"Like a daisy flower?"

He giggled. "Isn't it a great name?" It was hilarious to hear him be tickled by this, so I giggled too.

"Well, if you ask me, that's a very unusual, radical name for around here. I would honestly say it's weird to name your child after a random wild flower."

"I know. That's exactly what's great about it." He giggled even more. "She's gonna be so unique."

"You sound so fatherly," I said, realizing that my anger that I'd held against him for two years had suddenly disappeared. "I never thought I'd see this side of you. Like n-e-v-e-r! You were so, what's the right word for it? Eccentric. Not the fatherly type."

"Well, that's what a marriage to the right woman does to a man." He smiled. We both looked at the ground for a moment, staying still for this strange point in time. "Is this really the last time I'll see you?" he asked me.

"I believe so," I confirmed. "But I'm glad we met today. I might have never known that you were sorry. You could have called me, you know. An apology, even over the phone, is still an apology."

"I didn't want to intrude. I didn't know if you had someone already. Apparently, you did. Are you happy?"

"So far, so good."

"I just hope he treats you right. You were always good to me. You deserve to be happy. I don't want you to get hurt so far away from your motherland with no one to help."

I jumped. "Here comes my bus," I said. Gicu jumped too. "Thank you. That was very nice of you." I touched his hand. He looked a little lost, as if deciding to take the bus with me or not. Not dwelling on if he decided to follow, I headed for the bus. "Goodbye," I said as I waved from the steps of the bus, making the decision for him.

"Goodbye," he said back, and sent me an air kiss. "Safe travels!"

I took the first empty seat on the bus. My mind started wandering places, shuffling through my memory lane. The long-forgotten things that Gicu and I had done together: fun and not-so-fun dates, long conversations and infuriating arguments he would get into with someone else in the middle of our date just to prove a point. He was prone to do and say things that were not mainstream. But honestly, so was Igor, and so was David.

Three men, so different, but somehow so similar in their eccentric ways. A poor guitar player who refused to sell me off; an artsy architect who named his only daughter after a flower and was damn proud of it; and finally, a car salesman who traveled across the world to find himself a bride.

I appear to have a type: the rebels and the crazies!

* * *

When I called the American embassy in Bucharest on the third day after sending my packet, I got a short answer from a lady speaking perfect Romanian: "We received your package." I let out a breath, not knowing what I would have done if she had said otherwise. "We can schedule you for an appointment on February twelfth. Will that be okay?"

"That will be perfect." My palms started sweating.

"Did you already choose the local hospital for your medical exam?"

"Yes." I pulled the list with hospitals in front of me, then read her the name of the hospital I circled earlier, the one closer to the embassy.

"All right," she said. "We will send your package there. Call them and make an appointment. You shouldn't come to the consulate appointment without the medical exam first."

"All right," I said. *Is this really happening?* "See you on the twelfth." I put the phone down and screamed from the top of my lungs: "We are going to Bucharest!"

Chapter 40

To Bucharest, Again

Mom wired us the money for the train tickets, so we could take the five hundred with us that David sent us for trip. *Just in case*, she said. The kids and I took the night train with sleeping cars to Bucharest, the same route that David and I went nine months ago on his way back to America. *Nine months, really? Enough time to give birth to a child, it took so long.* The train was quite an upgrade for the kids, who were usually travelling to their father's in open cars without doors. They weren't even bothered by the usual smell of urine, coming from the toilet area, and were looking in fascination through the window, as if we were going to a far and magical land.

I was antsy. *Will it all go smoothly? Will they need more documents? Will they deny us the visa?* All different scenarios of how this trip might end were running through my head. It seemed impossible to close my eyes for just a few minutes, but as soon as the train took off, the calming *tuk-tuk* of the train's wheels put me and the kids at ease until we finally fell asleep.

We arrived at Bucharest in the morning. It was chilly but sunny, and even smelled like flowers, as if spring had claimed this February day for itself.

"Are we taking a bus from here?" Lica asked, ahead of her brother, as usual.

"Violeta said in Bucharest a bus fare for three costs almost the same as a taxi for five dollars. So we're taking a taxi," I explained and waved at a cab driver standing nearby waiting for a signal.

Lica and Serghei giggled and rushed to the cab, probably afraid I might change my mind.

"We need to get to this hotel," I said as I showed the driver the paper with the address. He nodded and pulled out of the train station into a wide plaza.

"Wow," Lica said. "It's so pretty."

Bucharest was, by far, the biggest city they had ever seen, so they both stuck their faces to the taxi window, looking around, absorbing every new thing that was popping up in front of their eyes: tall, gray and beige buildings with sophisticated ornaments of the past era, large streets full of nimble cars.

"Mercedes, BMW," Serghei said, naming the brands of the cars that were passing us. "Mom, what's that?" Serghei asked, pointing at a car with a funny humpback in the rear.

"That's Dacia," the driver answered for me. "It's an old Romanian car. I'm detecting by your accent that you're from Moldova. They don't have cars like that where you're from?"

"We have our own old and ugly Soviet cars. We don't need competition," I joked. He laughed. Good thing he didn't get offended.

The hotel lobby was surprisingly narrow and dark, though it had three perky golden stars bolted to the side wall. That must have been a Romanian star rating system, because, in the real world, this hotel would have been rated with two stars at best.

A bored concierge in a black suit with a juicy stain on his sleeve met us at the front desk. "You have a reservation? How many people? Identification card or passport?" he asked me in perfect Bucharest Romanian.

"Mom, what's he saying?" Lica asked while I was reaching for my purse. "You told me that our dialect is different, but I didn't think it would be *so* different."

"All I understood was 'passport,'" Serghei said.

The concierge looked at them as if they were second-class citizens. I cringed. If they were getting a "superiority" treatment for their accents from a person who spoke the same language as them, I could only image how people in America would react to their foreign accents until they mastered their English.

"One room with two beds on the second floor. Here is the room number." The concierge wrote on a piece of paper.

"Two beds? But there are three of us," Lica objected.

"We can exchange it for two rooms with three beds," the concierge said with a smile. "That will cost an additional…" He poked his keyboard.

"No need," I interrupted him. *So, he's all right with our accents when we talk money?* "Let's go," I told the kids. "We'll figure something out." I paid sixty dollars for two nights and grabbed the plastic key from his desk.

Our small, semi dark room with two twin beds only confirmed my first impression. The three stars rating was definitely off, but I was happy to finally put down the heavy duffel bag I was carrying on my shoulder. I tried to pack as little as possible for the trip, but somehow we still managed to fill it.

"Let's take a shower," I said, taking my winter boots off. "We all stink from that train."

Serghei ran to the bathroom first. "Mom, they have hot water here," I heard him yelling as soon as the water started running.

"In normal countries, they always do." I went to check on him. "Make sure you turn both the red and the blue faucet handles, and regulate the temperature; otherwise, you'll burn your skin."

"That's what the red one is for? For hot water?" He bulged his big brown eyes.

"Since they have a lot of hot water here, can I take a bath instead?" Lica came with her spare clothes. "We never take real, long baths at home. Only showers with lukewarm water from the bucket."

Serghei came up with an idea: "Let's take a bath together, with real bubbles, like on TV."

"Foo, Sereoja," Lica cut him off. "We're not babies anymore."

"Whoever takes the bath last can stay in the bathtub longer," was my solution.

"Okay then, I'll go last," Lica finally agreed, but she kept nagging her brother to get out of the tub already, because, in her opinion, he was taking too long.

By the time I came out of the shower, bundled in a rough, white bathrobe, the kids were asleep in one of the beds. This time they didn't argue, or perhaps Lica didn't have the heart to kick her brother out to sleep on the floor. I dropped on the other bed to stretch my legs too. We had an entire day to kill until our medical exam the next morning, so we'd find something to do later once we had a chance to rest. As I lay my head down, the anxieties of what was to come pushed themselves to the forefront of my mind, but exhaustion pushed them back. There was still so much to do, but being in Bucharest made me feel like we were one step closer.

* * *

"I'm hungry," I heard Serghei's voice over me. I looked at my watch.

"Four p.m.?" I jumped off the bed. "We took a good nap. Didn't we? Let's go out to the market and buy some groceries." I pulled my pants and my sweater on. "Are you ready for an excursion?" Their faces lit up.

We exited the hotel and took to the right.

"Let's walk this way," I said, hoping to find something similar to the little markets that we had at almost every corner back home.

"How much longer?" Serghei asked after four blocks.

I stopped a local woman with a blue headscarf wrapped around her head. "Excuse me, do you know where can we find a market or a store that's open? I tried two doors on this street that looked like stores, but they are closed."

The lady looked at me like I had dropped from an unknown planet. "The stores are always closed on Sundays."

"That's different," I said. "Our stores in Chişinău are always open on the weekend."

"You, the heretics from over the Prut," she mumbled. "Don't you people go to church on Sundays?"

I almost swallowed my tongue in indignation. Never thought that having open stores on Sundays somehow made us heretics.

"If you're hungry, stop at that buffet," she said, pointing her finger to a flashing light in the window that was turning on and off its name "*Paradis*," as if the old lady tried to redeem us from our godless sins and send us straight to Paradise. "Their prices are very affordable," she said, and moved on.

"You hear that, Mom?" Serghei pulled my sleeve.

Affordable for whom? I heard my mother's voice in my head.

"Let's check out the prices first," I said. "But if it's too expressive, we are going back. We still have some snacks left at the hotel."

"Nah-ah," Serghei objected. "Maybe half a bag of chips, some cookies, and raisins."

"And two bananas and two apples," Lica added, pleading my case.

I pushed the door of the café that jingled with a soft bell sound. The bright light almost blinded me, like the sun itself had struck my eyes. It was sparkling clean inside. The tables, neatly arranged at the window, had a white cloth underneath, covered with an orange table cloth on the top. It smelled of baked goods and savory sauces. I could see why the owners called it Paradise.

"We don't really have a menu," the young cashier at the register said when I asked her for one. "The names of the dishes are on the display." She directed me to a long table with a glass cover. There were slices of pizza with red peperoni circles and sausages, but also some with toppings I hadn't seen before were lying there in several rows. *Pineapple pizza?* I was in shock to discover one of them here, of all places. *So this is how it looks?* I moved quickly to the salad and the fruit bar, still convinced that pineapple on pizza was just wrong.

"I want that. No, that." Serghei pointed something out to his sister, wiping the saliva from the corner of his mouth.

"I don't see any prices here." I turned to the cashier, feeling I was about to lose the hunger battle and give in, no matter how much the cost.

"It's an all-you-can-eat buffet. You pay a flat price per person," the cashier said.

"What do you mean by all-you-can-eat buffet?" I had never heard that concept before.

The cashier was trying hard to contain her laughter. "You pay once but you can come back for seconds after you're done with the first round," she explained in the simplest way possible.

"Mom, did you hear that? We can go back for seconds," Serghei translated for me. For some odd reason, he understood every word the girl at the counter said, though she had the same accent as the concierge at the hotel.

"Are you sure?" I asked the cashier. "Are you absolutely sure that we can do that?" I asked her once again because that definitely didn't sound like any buffets my mother used to work.

She gave me a "are you really that stupid" look and responded with all the sarcasm she had in her bones: "I'm one hundred per-cent sure. Otherwise, I would have been fired a long time ago for giving away free food."

Be that way, I responded to the young chick in my head, but I wasn't at the slightest ashamed to push back. I didn't feel like getting arrested for stealing food right before my interview at the American consulate. "How much?"

"For the three of you, considering the two are kids, it will be…" She showed me the totals in Romanian leis on her calculator.

"Do you accept dollars? We exchanged very little in Romanian currency before our trip, because we didn't know how much we would need."

"We sure do. Eight dollars," she summed it up, taking ten dollars out of my hands and giving me back the change in Romanian leis. "Sorry, we don't have small dollar bills here."

"That's okay. We're here for two more days. I'm sure we'll need the local currency for something." I smiled and turned to the kids to give them the trays: "Go, get loaded."

They both ran to the display, walking back and forth like busy chipmunks, stuffing their plates with pizza with colorful toppings, macaroni salad, chicken wings—lots and lots of chicken wings.

Serghei was beaming. "This trip is so cool."

"Good thing that grumpy old lady sent us here," Lica agreed.

I watched them eat their food, a second and third time too. It was a growing concern that Serghei might explode, but he managed to stay put for a few more chicken wings. We had a lot to do the next day, so being well fed was a plus.

The next morning, I was up at least two hours before it was necessary. I brushed my teeth, put my clothes on, combed my hair, combed my hair again, put lipstick on, wiped the lipstick off. *Not like I'm going on a date or something.*

"Wake up." I shook the kids.

Lica lifted her head, looking at the clock showing seven a.m. "Didn't you say the appointment at the clinic is at nine?"

"We are not taking any chances," I responded, pulling the blanket off Serghei, who sneakily went back under the covers. "Sereoja, if you do it again, I'll squirt you with cold water."

He knew I wasn't joking, so he dropped out of the bed and went to the bathroom to wash his face, dragging one foot in front of another, with his hands flopping on his sides. The kids cheered up only when they saw that we were taking a taxi again.

"Mom, can I pay the driver?" Sereoja whispered into my ear, when we sat in the backseat.

"Are you playing a millionaire?" I pushed back. "Wait until we get there, so we know how much to pay." I looked at the taximeter that was already at five dollars equivalent in Romanian currency, but I couldn't see any building that would look like a clinic yet.

"Where are you going?" I asked the driver, when I saw him making a loop around the area.

"I took a wrong turn," he said. "We'll have to go back a little bit."

I tapped my fingers on the handle of the door impatiently, about to go on a cursing tirade. I didn't know if that was an innocent mistake or if the taxi driver intentionally took a wrong turn, trying to make an extra buck. I only calmed down when I looked at my watch. *Still plenty of time.* So, I held my marbles. When we finally stopped, Serghei grabbed the money that I had prepared for the taxi driver out of my hands and handed it to him with such an indulgent expression on his face, as if he were a rich American kid paying for his ride.

The clinic's lobby was clean and spacious, with a soft light coming from above the high ceiling.

"Good morning," a middle-age lady at the registration desk said, with sunshine and rainbows coming out of her ears.

"Good morning." I involuntarily smiled back at her, as if I had stepped into a futuristic world. *I want to live in a country like that, where I am treated like a human being.* I got emotional all of a sudden, as if I had discovered Romania all over again with fresh eyes. "We have a medical appointment at nine for the American embassy," I said softly, holding back my anxieties.

"Let me check you in." The receptionist took the paper from my hands. "Are you ready to pay the two hundred dollars for your exam today?" she asked me, as if she was giving me a choice. I put the two one-hundred-dollar bills on her counter without any hesitation. She could have asked me anything today, and I wouldn't object. "Wait here," she said, giving me the receipt. "It will not be long." Her voice was so silky that my heart, which was about to jump out of my chest half an hour ago, had calmed down in an instant.

A doctor in white scrubs approached us a couple minutes later and asked me for our paperwork. He looked at all our medical records, and said, "You came prepared." I smiled, giving myself an imaginary pat on the back, but then he said, "The dates of some of these vaccines are old, so we will have to administer them again for all three of you." *Interesting. Our clinics never mentioned that.* "Then, unfortunately, we'll have to retake your blood samples for HIV and STD testing here."

"But why?" I couldn't understand. "I just went through all of these tests back home. I thought we only had to take the physical exam here."

"We have to certify that the test results are accurate. We've had cases with inaccurate medical certifications issued in Moldova," he said very diplomatically.

"I have to retake my tests, which I honestly took at home, because my country has a reputation of a crook?" I was appalled. The doctor went silent. "All right." I felt like a lab rat that had no choice but to comply. "How long will it take to get the results?" I asked him in a trembling voice, afraid that he would tell me to come for them next week. That would trigger an avalanche of unexpected delays.

Will I have to cancel my interview at the consulate for tomorrow? When will I be able get my next appointment? A month from now? Where will I get the money for the second trip?

"Don't worry," the doctor, reading the desperation on my face, said in the calmest and most cheery voice possible. "The test results will be ready at two p.m. today."

Your words are magic! Your words are God-sent! I wanted to yell, but I choked on my own emotions. I could swear I saw a halo surrounding the doctor's head when "two p.m. today" came out of his mouth.

"This way," the doctor said, and we followed him into a room where a nurse was ready for us with the single-use syringes organized neatly on the table. *It sure looks like a torture chamber.* Though I would have taken a chamber with needles over an uncertainty any day.

"Who wants to get vaccinated first?" The nurse smiled. Serghei looked at his sister with his eyes about to pop out of their sockets, but when he saw her hesitating, he stuck his arm out first.

"It didn't hurt at all," Serghei said joyfully after it was over.

"It pinched a little," Lica said after she was done.

I turned my head away when the nurse poked me with a needle to draw blood out of my arm. "I'm glad the clinics nowadays no longer have the old multi-use needles that we grew up with," I said to distract myself.

"I remember those from when we grew up too." The nurse smiled. "They were thick and damaged, and needed to be sterilized after each use. Some of them were so old they ripped your skin and left a huge hole behind that took days to heal."

I nodded, bonding with her over our childhood needle story, certainly grateful that a pinch was all my kids had to worry about.

"Come for results in the afternoon," the nurse said, and let us go.

The afternoon couldn't come soon enough, though. I jumped when the doctor entered the waiting room at two p.m. with a yellow package in his hands. My head was spinning from the anxiety that was building up all day.

What if I don't pass this medical exam? What if I have AIDS?

What if this Romanian clinic finds some mysterious disease that could kill my American dream forever? I felt like all my blood had left my face when I saw the doctor moving towards me. I most certainly looked like a corpse.

The doctor smiled at me. "Everything is fine," he said, while I was trying not to faint. "The results are good," he hurried to assure me. "Take this package to the consulate tomorrow. Don't try to open it. It has to have the original seal," he said sternly, trying to prevent any funny business.

"Absolutely," I said, taking the yellow package from the doctor's hands and hugging it, as if it were my baby. *The torture was finally over!* After this, the interview at the consulate tomorrow should be a piece of cake, unless something dramatic happened, but it couldn't possibly be worse than today.

Chapter 41

The Finish Line

The appointment at the American consulate was at two p.m. I looked at my watch, with a sensation of a "pin in my butt," like Babushka would say, that was burning me to get us moving. I was already dolled up in a long black skirt with a fancy cut on the left side, and my new peach sweater that I bought for the interview. I even wore my high-heeled winter boots for the dramatic effect. I didn't wear them often because they were uncomfortable, but my other boots were so worn out that they didn't deserve to go with me to such a high-level event.

"Are we coming back here after the appointment?" Lica asked.

"I don't want to pay for an extra day, so let's pack everything up. We have to get out of the hotel room at eleven. Besides, it's faster for us to get to the train station from there. This way we won't miss our seven o'clock train back home tonight."

"Can we go to Paradis for lunch?" Lica asked.

I went for my purse to count our money. There were two one-hundred-dollar bills and one ten-dollar bill left in my wallet.

"Ninety-five dollars for the visa," I said. "That would take care of the first hundred. Then ten dollars for the taxi to the consulate, then from the consulate to the train station."

Serghei did the quick math. "There is still one hundred left."

"I want to keep this one for when we go home." I wasn't ready to let go of it. "We'll have a lot of expenses before our departure."

"So, no Paradis?" Lica wrinkled her lips.

"Let's just finish up our snacks so it's easy to carry our duffle bag, because this damn thing is heavy," I deflected. "But if everything goes fine, I'll buy you some piroshkies at the train station before we leave."

"M-m-m, piroshkies." Serghei smiled.

We got to the consulate two hours early, but there was already a small line of ten people there. I dropped my heavy bag on the ground at the end of the line.

"Sit down on the bag," I told the kids. "It will take a while before we get in."

"Just like we do on our way to Crimea," both of them said.

"Papa calls us 'his camping kids,'" Lica said nostalgically.

If there were a lazy-watch contest, my watch would've won the prize. Its silver hands were moving at such a leisurely pace that I had to put it to my ear twice to make sure it was still running. Then, standing on my high heels for two hours made my old, ugly boots seem so appealing. Too bad they were at home, and I was in Bucharest with the bottoms of my feet burning.

"The guards are coming." I giggled like a little kid on Christmas day. "Get up," I yelled at the kids. "They're letting people in." I picked up the duffle bag and moved closer to the gate.

One of the security guards stopped me and said, "You can't go inside with this bag," and waved to the next person to go around me.

"Why?" I was panicking.

"Because of security concerns."

"What security concerns do you have with me?" I tried to reason. "I'm a mother with two kids, for God's sake. I came a long way from Chişinău for this appointment. I can't miss it. I'm just going to leave this bag here at the gate. I don't care," I shouted, determined to get in.

"Ma'am, you can't leave this bag at the gate," the guard insisted. Out of the corner of my eye, I saw two other guards approaching, reacting to the quarrel that I'd started. I imagined getting myself arrested for disturbing the peace, or even worse. They could detain me as a suspected terrorist. I was about to cry.

The second security guard came up with a better solution than putting me in handcuffs. "Ma'am, take your bag across the street." He pointed with his finger to a small kiosk with some knick-knacks in the window. "Maybe you can persuade the owner to store it for you."

I picked up my "monster" and ran across the street.

"Can you please store my bag for me?" I begged the woman working in the kiosk. She looked at me strangely. Perhaps no one had asked her anything like that before. "They wouldn't let me in the consulate with this," I explained and pointed at the structure behind me. The line at the gate dissolved. Even the people who came to the consulate after me were already inside. My kids and I were the three lonely figures left on this side of the gate. I came up with a quick solution and said, "I'll pay for it," afraid that they would close the gate if I took too long.

"Don't worry about paying me," the woman finally said with an unexpected compassion. "Get it inside." She opened the door and let me bring my bag in. Her tiny under-the-counter space was cluttered with merchandise in boxes. It was a miracle the woman had enough space for her legs.

"You have no idea what this means to me," I mumbled on my way out. I grabbed the kids by their hands and ran back to the gate.

"Come this way," the guard said, letting us into a spacious courtyard with a long staircase going up to the entrance of a yellow building where the consulate was.

"Run, run," I said, dragging the kids up the stairs and pushing the heavy, oak double door, only then allowing myself to take a deep breath and wipe the sweat that was pouring down my face. I ripped my scarf off my head to let some air in and looked around.

The large lobby with several rows of chairs was full of people. I counted about forty of them.

"Can we go back to our spot in line?" Lica asked with hope in her voice.

I looked at my watch: two-fifteen. "I don't think so." The lazy bastard of a watch that dragged its arms all afternoon was in a hurry all of a sudden. "Looks like they called somebody else to the window instead of us. Let's sit down and wait. They'll call our names eventually." I dropped in the first chair, still pissed that I came so close to missing my appointment because of a silly duffle bag. "At least we got inside," I said, half relieved.

My breathing went back to normal and my watch went back to crawling. It was hard to stay still, though. Every time a person got away from the window, my ears would perk up for a few seconds, listening to the next name the clerk called.

"Not us." I sighed, disappointed when I heard them call someone else. "Still not us," I said when the next one went through. "We've been waiting here for two hours already." I looked at my watch. The crowd in the lobby thinned out. There were now more empty chairs left than there were taken. *Are they going to call me last?* I wondered.

"Iancenco," I heard finally. I jumped. A sharp throbbing pain grabbed the bottom of my feet.

"God damn," I whispered. Apparently, all this time, my feet, trapped in my tight boots, were planning their revenge by quietly swelling inside. A small river of blood deployed down to my toes as soon as I was up. It felt like standing on needles. "It shouldn't take long." I put on a brave face and made my way to the window, limping like a duck.

"Are you okay?" the tall, slim lady officer who called me over asked, looking at me with her tired eyes that had seen better days.

"I'm fine," I lied, watching how she pulled my thick and heavy file from her drawer, then glanced over my medical records that I brought from the clinic with boredom. I didn't know if I should be content or concerned that she wasn't showing any emotions.

"Where are the kids?" she asked me with concern this time. "They have to be present since they are also in the visa application."

"They're right there." I turned my head to their seats. "Come here," I called them closer. The officer compared their faces with their photos in my passport, like an art appraiser trying to deduce if they were the originals or replicas, then asked me suddenly:

"How did David and you meet?"

"Online," I answered. "It's in the file." I pointed at the folder.

"How long have you and David known each other?" she continued, as if she hadn't heard me. My brain buzzed like a mini power-er station, doing rapid calculations in my mind, but it seemed to short circuit, so I answered quickly, like I did on my English exam, trying to hide my nerves:

"Since November 2000."

"So, for fifteen months?" She helped me out.

"Yes," I agreed immediately, hoping that she had better things to do than trick me with a mathematical technicality.

"How do you keep in touch?" Her face remained unchanged.

"Via e-mails and phone calls. I printed all his e-mails." I pulled from my purse a notebook with David's correspondence.

"Why are they glued together?" she asked, pulling the first page.

"These are my personal items. I didn't know I wasn't supposed to. The good copies are in the file." I pointed at the documents on her desk with my shaking hand. She flipped through the pages, reading a few of them.

"Have you met him in person?" *Did she even read my file? Or is she quizzing me on it?*

"He came to visit us in Moldova last May," Angelica answered for me.

The lady officer finally cracked a smile. "All right, then. Everything seems to be in order."

I breathed out cautiously, and sneakily looked at the watch. *Fifteen minutes? Shit, it seemed like she drilled me for at least half an hour.*

"Please, go to that window across the lobby and pay the visa fee for all three of you," she said casually. "When you're done, come back with the receipt and I will stamp your visa."

"Sorry? Did you say I have to pay three fees for one visa?" I asked her in a shaking voice, hoping I misunderstood. I could not remember anyone at any point (not the lawyer, not any consulate officials that I previously talked to, not even David) notifying me that I had to pay three separate fees for one fiancé visa, when only I was the bride. "How much?" I asked, trying to do the math in my head. I had only two hundred five dollars on me (after I paid for the cab today), and my panicky math was suggesting that I was approximatively a hundred dollars short.

Could I have spent less money on the hotel, and on taxis, and going to the buffet with the kids? I couldn't imagine telling the clerk that I didn't have enough money for the visa. I was frantically looking for a solution. *Should I stay an extra day in Bucharest and ask David to wire me a hundred dollars? Would the consulate even consider letting me come back tomorrow instead of rescheduling the appointment?* If I did that, I would have to kiss our train tickets goodbye. Where were we going to stay tonight if we remained in the city? *Should I ask to pay for my part of the visa fee to secure the visa itself, and pay for the kids' visas later?* I was afraid the officer would say, "It's all or nothing." *Should I ask somebody in the lobby to lend me one hundred dollars?* But who was going to lend money to strangers?

"One hundred eighty-five," I finally heard the clerk's voice through the pounding boombox of competing thoughts in my head.

"One hundred eighty-five each?" I asked in even more horror.

"No, one hundred eighty-five total. You pay only half the fee for the kids."

I backed away from the window, catching my breath, feeling incredibly exhausted, as if I had just finished a marathon. *I have enough money! I have enough money!* I wanted to yell.

I felt weightless walking to the cashier's window across the lobby, as if I had propeller-wings behind my back. Another crisis of the day was averted. Imagine if I had taken the kids to Paradis that morning, I would've been three dollars short. After thirteen hurdles, the finish line was finally right in front of me. *Pay the damn fee and be done with it.*

"I need a receipt for one hundred eighty-five dollars," I told the cashier with a smile, shoving my last two hundred dollars through her narrow window. She ran my bills for authenticity through a scanner. *Who's gonna be so dumb to bring counterfeit money to a consulate?* I rolled my eyes.

"What's wrong?" I asked her with trepidation when she casually returned my bills to me. My palms were getting sweaty.

"I don't have change for a hundred. It's the end of the day. I gave all my small bills away."

"But I need to pay for my visa," I said, trying to talk as calmly as I could. I went all in. "Just keep the change." *If I have to sell my engagement ring to get us to the train station, I will.*

"We are not allowed to do that," the cashier answered politely, but stern. *Now is the time to play Operation Clean Hands?*

"What am I supposed to do? I can't go back home without a visa only because you don't have change!" I raised my voice, on the verge of a nervous breakdown.

"Try to break one hundred at any currency exchange. There are a few of them in the area," she said, finally coming up with a smart thing to say.

I looked at my watch: four-thirty p.m. I rushed to the guard who helped me earlier with my duffle bag disaster.

"When does the consulate close?" I asked him.

"In thirty minutes." He looked at me, confused.

"I need to run to the exchange to break down my hundred," I explained as fast as I could. "Is it okay if I leave my kids here? It will take me twice as long if they come with me." I pointed at the chairs where they were sitting.

"That will be all right. Just make sure you're here by five. You can't leave them in here after the consulate closes."

I nodded and ran back to the kids to tell them what happened. "Stay put, and don't go anywhere. I'll be back."

I barely had a chance to register their confusion before sprinting out.

"Mother fucking, fuck, motherfucker!" I cursed as I ran to the first currency exchange I saw a block away from the consulate.

"Can you break one hundred dollars into smaller bills?" I spit out my words to the cashier so fast as if the entire world was on fire.

"We're only allowed to exchange dollars for Romanian leis," the man at the exchange said in a monotone voice.

"Can you, then, exchange five dollars into Romanian leis and give me back ninety-five dollars?" He shook his head. "Or fifteen dollars in Romanian leis and give me back eighty-five dollars? I can't exchange more. The American consulate only takes dollars for the visa fee, so I need the rest in American currency," I pleaded.

"We can't give you any change in dollars," he refused again.

I had no more time to waste on the bastard, so I ran to the next exchange two blocks away, but I got the same result there. I scanned the area, looking for the next one. I was getting farther and farther away from the consulate as I rushed through the middle of the busy street with people zipping by, but it felt like I was alone in the Sahara. As if I was walking on quicksand instead of asphalt. I was afraid to look at my watch. I didn't want to know what time it was, but I could hear the sound of its silver arms speeding up like a runner approaching the finish line.

I'll look at it when I find the exchange. I'm not going home without my God damn visa! Third time's the charm? I finally spotted the third exchange. I repeated the same request to a young, cute cashier, who looked like she just got out of high school.

"All right," she said in her teenage falsetto, and exchanged five dollars out of my troubled one hundred into Romanian leis, giving me my desired ninety-five dollars back without any questions.

Oh, I'd kiss your rosy cheeks right now, if you wouldn't think I was a weirdo. I was singing inside. Now, I could finally look at my watch. I wasted twenty minutes on this "expedition." It would take the same time to get back, unless…

Here it goes, the final, final finish line. I breathed out, like a bull before the fight, and gathering my last bit of strength, I bolted back to the consulate, with my feet most certainly covered in blisters by now. The security guard was glad to see me.

"Mom, finally!" My kids, the last ones left in the building, jumped from their seats. "What took you so long?" They were interrupting each other. I waved at them to sit back and wait. I marched directly to the cashier and squeezed through the window with my bloody one hundred eighty-five dollars without change. Everything around me started moving incredibly slowly as I was getting my receipt.

Here was me, returning to the officer's window, who was waiting for me to finalize my visa, walking on my flamingo-like feet, putting one foot in front of another slowly, unpretentiously. There was the clerk giving me back my passport, seeming like she was captured by a camera, filming her hands one frame at a time. Here was me again, taking my passport with our United States of America visas out of her hands with the date on the stamp: February 12, 2002.

The images of everything that I went through for the last couple of months were coming at me in small pieces like in a fast rotating kaleidoscope: angry faces in long lines, dirty trains, vines with juicy grapes, burning Twin Towers, roaming chickens, the nurses with syringes in their hands, grumpy hotel concierges, security guards at the consulate gate, the cashier who made my day miserable.

I spread my arms like I was about to fly. *The worst is finally behind me.* I heard the evil spirit whispering into my ear, "It's not over yet." I would think about it tomorrow. Today I wanted to celebrate. We were finally free to go to America!

Chapter 42

The Long Farewell

"Mom, what now?" Angelica asked me on our way to the train station, sitting in the back of the Bucharest taxi one last time. "Now that we have the visa, are we leaving for America next week?"

"I don't know," I answered honestly, chilling my brain after the consulate *salto mortale*, flipping through the images of the city that brought me so much grief but also so much joy. "We should probably call David from the train station to let him know that we got it."

"And buy us piroshkies," Serghei reminded me.

I smiled. "And buy us piroshkies because we did good." I ruffled his hair.

At the station, I spotted a calling area with a rusted red telephone booth so old-fashioned that it threw me back to my youth, when I worked as a telegraph operator in the Chișinău airport, right at the time I met Igor. *Full circle?*

"Can I make an international call to America?" I asked the man on duty, as rusty and old as his telephone booth.

"It's somewhat spendy." He showed me the price list.

"I'll be brief. I don't have much to say." He took my payment and showed me in.

"David?" I said in the receiver when I heard him picking up the phone. I could tell it was long past midnight in America by his drowsy, robotic voice. "Sorry I called you so late, but I didn't want you to wait."

"Are you kidding me? I couldn't close my eyes all night expecting your call," he said, life returning to his voice.

"Well, the wait is over. We got our visa!" I smiled, anticipating his reaction.

A heavy sigh of relief came out of David's mouth. "Tell me, tell me everything."

"I'd rather talk more when we get home. This call from Bucharest costs me a dollar per minute."

"Shoot. Okay, then. How long is the visa for?"

"Ninety days, so we need to plan our trip soon."

"Yeah, about that. I'll need about a month to come up with money for your airplane tickets and to rent a new apartment for us."

"A month?" I screamed in disbelief. *What the hell was he doing for the last three months while I was running around like a vampire slayer getting shit done?* "All right. We have to go to our train now. I'll talk to you from home." I dropped the receiver.

* * *

Mariana must have been listening to every noise outside our apartment door, because she almost ripped the door off its hinges when she heard the noise of our feet coming up the stairs.

"How was it? How was it? Did you get the visa?" she blurted out all the questions at once.

"Yes," I answered after finally getting ourselves into the house.

"Oh, my God. Oh, my God!" She was screaming and jumping. "I'm so excited for you." She squeezed my neck with both her arms.

"Get away. You're strangling me." I pushed her.

"So, what's the plan? When are you leaving?" She couldn't contain herself.

"First, we need to buy the tickets. But I need to find out how much the tickets cost. For some reason, it's always cheaper when I search for tickets here than when David searches for them in

America. Then we'll have to make a trip to Babushka's. We can't leave without saying goodbye. Then, we'll have to plan for Serghei's birthday."

"You're staying home for a month? I thought you had to leave right away." Mariana seemed disappointed for both of us.

"I thought that too, but David is not ready, so we'll be here for Serghei's birthday in March."

"His last birthday at home." Mariana looked at Serghei.

"Our last celebration at home," I corrected her. "Just think about it like a long farewell."

The next morning, I went to the travel agency to get an estimate for our airplane tickets. A tall blonde in high heels with a tight white shirt and a navy-blue mini skirt met me in the lobby with a simple "Hello." She was good-looking and she knew it. Her expensive French perfume was teasing my nostrils from afar.

"I'd like to get an estimate for three tickets to Seattle: one for me and two for my kids," I said.

"Estimate, huh?" Her smile-less face was unimpressed, as if I was there just to annoy her with my question with no intention to pay up. Her name tag—Svetlana—jiggled on her firm breasts as she sighed.

Nevertheless, "her highness" started the search on her computer, and after several minutes of intense clicking, she said, "That will be four thousand five hundred dollars for three two-way tickets."

"Four thousand five hundred dollars?" I whispered in horror. "Are these tickets to the moon?" Svetlana rolled her eyes. "How much for three one-way tickets?" I asked.

"At customs they always want you to have two-way tickets, or they may not let you in the country."

"I'm getting married there, so we don't need return tickets because we're not coming back," I said more to myself than to her. Svetlana planted some seeds of doubts, though. What if American customs indeed turned me back because I didn't have return tickets? *Besides, what if this marriage thing doesn't work out?* The return tickets could be my guarantee that I could come back home safely.

Svetlana trilled her lips. "If you insist." She did the search again. "It will be three thousand five hundred to Sydney."

"Why are you sending me to Seattle through Sydney?" I tried to deduce a logical explanation, but none was coming to mind.

"You're going to Australia, right?"

"I'm going to America. I told you I need tickets for Seattle."

"I've never heard of a city like that in America." Like somehow her lack of knowledge was my fault.

"Sorry, but the city doesn't disappear because you don't know about it. Please, check your computer one more time, but this time for Seattle in America." My irony was coming even from between my teeth.

Svetlana hit her keyboard hard, perhaps punishing it for her failed geography class.

"It will be one thousand fifty dollars. Are you paying for them today?" she asked me impatiently.

"I would like to reserve them for now, but I'll need the invoice."

"Thank you for wasting my time," was what Svetlana wanted to say considering her face, but she printed the invoice so she could get me out of her hair faster.

I hurried home and called David.

"It's not cheap, but one thousand is a hell of a lot cheaper than four thousand," I said, laughing when I recounted what happened at the travel agency to David. He laughed too. He'd been in a cheerful mood since we got our visa.

"Good news," he said. "My childhood friend Tom has offered to help us with the plane tickets." For a groom who was in constant financial constraint, David sure was resourceful.

"That's so nice of him!" I cheered up.

"He said to fax him the invoice and he would lend me the money to send them to you."

"Does it mean that you'll be sending us exactly what's on the invoice? Not even a little extra for the trip?"

"Honey, I need to rent us an apartment, and that's expensive. In America, you have to pay the first month's and the last month's rent, and the deposit before you sign the lease."

"I'll figure something out," I agreed. "Let me find out how to fax an invoice to America, because I don't have a fax machine at home."

The search for someone willing to fax an invoice to the United States quickly turned into a half-day saga. Svetlana told me they didn't fax invoices internationally. Another agency wanted to charge me five dollars, which I refused to pay. The third stop at Air Moldova airline turned into an interrogation of epic proportions, as if me asking them to fax an invoice before buying the tickets was evidence that I was trying to rip them off. The airline agent was quizzing me relentlessly on why I needed to fax my invoice to America. Why couldn't I just tell Tom how much the tickets were worth? I started wondering that myself.

"Perhaps Tom needs proof that I am not a lying, scheming bitch!" I blurted out my true thoughts. She smirked but nodded, as if she could finally relate, and faxed my troubled invoice free of charge without any further questions. *That's it? That's all it took? Just me being blunt?*

A few days passed as I waited in agony, unsure if Tom got my invoice or if I had to repeat the unpleasant faxing ritual once again, but on day three, David called to tell me he sent us the money.

At least we'll get the airplane tickets out of the way. I was strolling cheerfully on my way to pick up the money from the Western Union.

"One thousand," the cashier at the Western Union office said as she counted the money David sent me. "Twenty, forty, fifty," she said, putting the last fifty dollars on the counter. *Does she have to say it so loudly?* I looked over my shoulder twice, and then took the money off the counter with my shaking hands. I quickly shoved it to the bottom of my purse and moved the purse in front of me so I could see it at all times while I walked up to the Air Moldova airline building. I avoided eye contact with the man who opened the door for me, as if he could see written on my face how much money I had and rip the purse out of my hands. I imagined how I would tell David that I was robbed, and how his friend Tom would say: "You're such a sucker. She's probably lying to you so you'll send her more money."

"I reserved three airplane tickets to Seattle," I said to the ticket agent, and put in front of her the invoice that Svetlana printed for me. "May I pay for them here instead of the travel agency?" I sounded upbeat.

"You absolutely may," the ticket agent said, sounding upbeat too. *Svetlana will be so pissed.*

The bulky, outdated ticketing machine printed the first, then the second, then the third ticket with squeaky, pitching noises as if it was giving birth to kittens. I parted gladly with the money that I had in my possession for ten minutes, and took the warm tickets out of the cashier's hand with the same feeling of exhalation that hit me in Bucharest at the American consulate. The visa was a huge accomplishment, but it was theoretical. The tickets in my hands were something practical, as if I was already holding America in my hands.

Once I returned home, I wasn't the only one captivated by the tickets.

Mariana almost ripped them out of my hands. "Let me hold those American tickets," She massaged them with her fingers, parting them like a hand fan, then put them to her nose. "Is this what a thousand dollars smells like?"

"This is what paper and ink smells like."

"You're going to Paris? Then to New York?" Mariana screamed.

"Those are connecting flights. We won't even leave the airport." I laughed.

"Still. I've never been to Paris, even in the airport." She gave the tickets back.

"Now that we have the tickets with a concrete date of March eighteenth, we can go to Babushka's for our farewell."

"Well," Mariana raised both hands in the air like she was entering a stage, "while you were gone, I went to talk to our brother, and I asked him to drive us all to Babushka's in his car this weekend, and he said he would. Isn't it awesome?"

"We could have gone by bus," I said.

Mariana rolled her eyes. "Mom bought Vitalic's car to have it as family transportation. He's not the king of it, you know, though he acts like it sometimes."

"Is he going to be sober for the trip?"

"His wife really straightened him up. He looks like a different man. He even said he'll pay for gas. It's a long way, and it's not cheap."

"That's different. The old Vitalic wouldn't make the time to drive us anywhere, and, honestly, I wouldn't trust him driving us either."

Mariana crossed her arms, looking at me like she'd just won a bet.

The day before our trip to Babushka Veta's, it rained nonstop for twelve hours, as if the skies had broken open, unable to hold so much water in.

"Should we cancel the trip until next weekend?" I asked my brother the night before.

"If it keeps raining like that, we probably should. But I work next weekend, so you'll have to take the bus," he said.

Overnight, the rain stopped as suddenly as it started. One thing had to go smoothly before we made it to America. I opened the balcony door anxiously to check the weather outside. The morning skies were still gray and grumpy, but the sun was already peeking from behind the clouds, warming up the ground underneath, and though the asphalt was still wet, dry patches were popping up here and there.

My brother barged into our apartment. "Are you all ready?" he asked. "It'll take us two hours to get there and two hours to get back. We haven't got all day."

"We're coming. We're coming." I rushed into the other room to get the kids: "Go get your coats and put your boots on."

"Mom, can I put on my cute shoes since we're taking the car?" Lica asked.

"No. If it rained in the country like it rained here, you'll need those boots, trust me."

"Mariana, get in the front seat," Vitalic called for his favorite sister when we all finally got outside.

"Let Ira sit in the front," she answered. "She always gets car sick. We don't want to deal with her puking everywhere."

"Oh, yeah, I forgot about that," Vitalic recalled. "You used to puke every time on the bus when we were kids, but didn't you grow out of it?"

"You haven't ridden with me in a long time, so how would you know?" I had to say it. He bent over to get in his driver seat without saying much. "Don't worry. Now, it seldom gets me, mostly when I'm in the backseat and the road is bumpy."

"Is everyone in?" Vitalic looked in the back of his Mitsubishi at Mariana and the kids.

"Yes," all three of them answered at once.

"Hold on to your seats. We're launching our rocket," he joked.

"Don't drive it like a rocket man, though," I warned him.

"With our roads you'll be a dead cosmonaut in five minutes."

He took off slowly and got us on the road smoothly, avoiding the potholes and even letting other cars get around us.

"The road looks wetter and wetter as we move north," Vitalic noticed. "It rained longer and harder here," he concluded, and he was right. When we turned from the main highway to the gravel road to Babushka's village, the car had to work twice as hard to get us up the hill, skidding and spitting exhaust like a mad bull. I could feel the gastric juices bubbling close to the surface. *A few more jerks like these and I would definitely erupt a green volcano out of my mouth.*

"Look at that mud," Vitalic whistled when we reached the top.

We all looked downhill through the windows. For another kilometer from that spot to Babushka's house, there were no more rocks. The country road was covered with mushy, uneven swells of black soil, as if little bombs were dropped here and there before our arrival. You could see the marks from human and animal feet trying to make their way through this mixture of black clay and dirty water. There were two deep tracks from a car or a carriage going downhill, as if we were on the top of a ramp designed for mud ski jumping.

"We'll get stuck," Mariana said.

"Not if you're with an ace like me." Vitalic felt confident. He rolled his car downhill, like the slowest ski jumper in the world, staying on the tracks trailblazed by someone else before us. The Mitsubishi was cranking and swerving. We could feel the mud scratching the bottom of the car, then holding on to its wheels like a possessive mother grabbing onto her child.

"Hurray!" We all clapped when Vitalic managed to get the car off the main country road intact, but our joy was short-lived once he turned to the side roads.

Vitalic finally gave up. "We'll have to go on foot from here."

"But we are at least three blocks away," Mariana objected.

"Are you going to push the car in your fancy coat if we get stuck?" Vitalic asked.

"We can walk. It's not that far," I agreed with my brother. I opened the door of his car and got my feet onto the ground first. I heard a squishing *swish* as my boots were quickly swallowed by the mud up to my ankles.

"Oh, my God," Lica yelled from the back side. "A little more and the mud will get inside my boots."

"Get to the side of the road, where the grass is growing," I said, giving her a tip from my childhood. "The soil is harder there, so it's easier to walk."

"I'll go there too," Serghei said, then he yanked his foot but ended up shoeless with his right foot above his boot that was now solidly stuck in the mud. "Help," he yelled on his way down. His hands were stuck in the mud, his left foot was in the mud also, his right foot dangling in the air.

"You look like an ostrich." Mariana laughed. "Don't touch me with your dirty hands." She backed off when she saw Serghei reaching for her coat.

"Don't be so precious," I said. I went around her to rescue Serghei's boot and put it back on him. "We'll get even muddier before reaching Babushka's gate. This is how they roll in the country, up to their necks in mud to put food on the table." I pulled Serghei up. "Go wipe your hands on that grass. We'll wash you up when we get to Babushka's house."

"Surprise!" we yelled from the gate when we spotted Babushka Veta standing in the middle of her front yard, feeding her chickens who were making rounds around her like she was their mama hen.

"Walk slowly until my chickens get used to you," Babushka warned instead of greeting us. "You'll scare them off."

We slowed down our walk, almost tiptoeing. The chickens lifted their heads, examining us, but opted for the corn seeds on the cement porch instead of running away.

"Did you come on foot all this way in the mud?" Babushka looked at our shoes. "You even brought the kids? Must be a very important reason." Babushka choked up, as if only now realizing what our visit meant. "Are you here for your farewell before leaving for America?"

"We have two more weeks." I coughed, needing to clear my throat.

"So, you'll stay for a day or two?" It pained me to see the hope in her eyes.

"We're going back today, Babushka," Vitalic answered for all of us. "We got our car a few blocks away. If it rains again, it will be hard to get out."

"Smart. You don't want to get stuck here. You'll stay, at least, for lunch, right?" Babushka looked at us.

"Yes," we said almost unanimously, feeling hungry all of a sudden.

"Then you better get busy cooking. I didn't know you were coming, so I didn't cook a big meal today."

We looked at each other with a smile. Even in distress, Babushka Veta was still Babushka Veta, though she walked away into her summer kitchen hunched over more than usual.

"Pick a chicken you like. We'll make a stew from it."

"Do you mean one of those that you just fed?" Lica asked with horror.

"I don't know how it is in the city, but in the country, meat doesn't grow on trees," she used her old joke on her granddaughter like she did when we were kids.

"You pick, Babushka," I said. I didn't want to make a decision today, but I took my coat off to get ready.

"All right." Babushka grabbed a hand of corn seeds from her bucket that she used earlier to feed the chickens. "*Tzyp, tzyp, tzyp, tzyp,*" she called her chickens closer to her, then leaned forward and grabbed one of them by its leg. "Go cut off her head in the back." She gave it to me. "I'll warm up the water so we can pluck it."

Serghei's eyes opened wide. "Are you gonna kill it?"

"Do you want to eat or not?" I turned to him.

"Yes." He put his head down. "I'll go with you, if you want me to."

"No, it's not going to be a pretty sight." I left him behind and went for the hatchet.

I could hear Lica gasp when I put the chicken's head on the wooden trunk and dropped the hatchet on the chicken's neck like a swift guillotine. I let the bird out of my hands on the grass to bleed out, watching how the blood was gushing out of its neck in small squirts, spraying red, sticky liquid everywhere. Its body convulsed and flopped its wings so violently that it raised itself up. For a few seconds it looked like the chicken was sitting down, and even pushed itself on its feet once. *That's how they came up with the expression "running around like a chicken with its head cut off."* I turned my head away. Even for me, someone used to butchering pigs and chickens since my childhood, today felt a little too graphic.

I heard my aunt Dusya's voice. "Ira, I thought it was you. Are you leaving for America already?"

"We came to say our goodbyes," I confirmed. "Come join us for lunch before we leave."

"I see Babushka put your American ass to work."

"Not American yet." I smiled.

"That's all right. It might be the last time you have do that. I doubt you'll have to butcher your own chickens in America."

"Well, if I ever have to, I'll know how. As Babushka says: 'You don't have to do everything yourself, but you need to know how.'"

"Yeah, Babushka is all about cute sayings. Let me grab some sweets for you for the road. I baked last night." She went back inside her house.

"The water is ready," Babushka called for me. She took the chicken out of my hands and dipped it in the bucket of hot water until the water covered its whole body.

"Mariana, come help me," I called my sister. We both pulled the chicken out of the bucket by its legs and dropped it on the ground on a piece of oilcloth that Babushka had for these occasions.

I gave her the command: "You pluck that side. I'll do this side."

"My God, I forgot how creepy it is to pluck chickens," she said, pulling on the chicken's feathers and dropping the clumps of wet, red feathers on the oilcloth.

Lica caressed its oily, yellow skin, which was losing its feathers the more we plucked it. "Poor chicken."

"You'll forget how sorry you were about it when we cook it," I said.

"Mom, really?" Lica shushed me.

Dusya offered: "Here, try my sweet rolls." Dusya gave Lica the bag with her baked goods. "I haven't baked those in a while, but yesterday, out of the blue, I just had to bake them. I felt it, I felt that someone would be visiting us today." She coronated herself to a prophet so effortlessly.

"Thank you." Lica took the bag out of her hands and went to share them with her brother.

"I'll help you set the table outside," Dusya volunteered.

"Isn't it too cold to eat outside?" Serghei asked.

"It's not that cold. After all, it's already March," Babushka agreed with Dusya for once. "Besides, there's a lot of us. We wouldn't fit in my little kitchen." She lifted the square, wooden kitchen table that my grandpa put together half a century ago and brought it outside.

"You, youngsters," Babushka addressed Lica and Serghei, "get the chairs from the house, plates and forks, and cups, and put it all on the table while we're finishing up the cooking. We'll have you all here on Babushka's porch under the vine branches so you remember how we dined under the sky."

"Your food is always delicious, Babushka," Lica said, dipping a piece of *mămăligă* in the chicken stew covered in aromatic, white sour cream sauce.

"Enjoy while you can." Babushka patted her on the back. "You won't get food like that in America."

"The Americans probably don't eat outside in March either." Lica smiled.

"Is it raining?" Serghei jumped when a few droplets fell on his face unexpectedly.

"Everybody, finish up your food. Fast." Babushka grabbed her empty plate. She was always a fast eater.

Dusya said, "It's just a few droplets." She was gauging the rain probability by looking at the sky.

"We probably should get going," Vitalic got up, "before a serious rain starts."

"Let me pack some produce for you before you go," Babushka said, and then ran into the house to bring a carton with eggs, a bag with flour, potatoes, beets, and whatever else she could grab on her way out, like she always did when we visited her.

"Don't bring too much," Vitalic insisted. "We can't overload the car. We barely made it here as it is."

"Besides, we're leaving," I said. "We can't eat that much in two weeks,"

Babushka stopped, the realization hitting her once more. "That's right, you're leaving."

"Everybody ready?" my brother asked less cheerfully this time.

"All right, Babushka Veta, it's time to say our goodbyes," I said, my voice cracking as I hugged her. She held on to me until Angelica and Serghei hugged her from the other side and kissed her on her left check and then on her right.

"May God be with you all the way to America," Babushka said

as we repeated the same ritual with Dusya. "I'll go with you to your car." She wiped the tear from the corner of her eye.

"It's a long way," we warned her.

"I've been walking on these muddy roads all my life. I'll be fine," she insisted. "You start walking ahead with the bags. Angelica and I will be right behind you." She grabbed my daughter's hand, leaning on her while walking.

"When will I see you next?" I heard Babushka ask Angelica.

"I don't know," Lica said. "Mom," she called for my help with a breaking voice.

"Will I ever see you again?" Babushka stopped as if needing to catch her breath.

I went back to give her a hug. "I don't know, Babushka." Serghei and Mariana joined us too.

"Will I ever see any one of you again?" Babushka Veta burst into a loud, uncontrollable cry, rocking her body back and forth, holding on to our hands, unwilling to let us go, as if she was at our funeral and not at our farewell.

Chapter 43

Serghei's Birthday

"How can we plan a birthday party after such a farewell with Babushka?" I asked Mariana the day after our trip. Babushka Veta gave us a whole new perspective on our departure. What if we could never come back home? What if I would never see Mariana and my mother again? Or even if we could come home years later, Babushka was already in her eighties. How long could she last?

"Do you want to cancel it?" Mariana asked.

"No," Serghei jumped in. "This is my last birthday at home—ever! Please, please, please don't cancel it," he whined.

"All right, but you're cooking and cleaning." That seemed to be Mariana's default answer as far as parties were concerned. Though somehow, that never deterred any of my kids.

"It's not only Serghei's birthday," Lica reminded us. "It's also our goodbye dinner with our family." She had avoided the word "proshchalny" (the Russian word for "goodbye forever") since we came back from Babushka's because it sounded so permanent, like death.

I said, "That's right. We're going out with a big fanfare." I took a piece of paper and a pen to write down the dishes that we were going to prepare. After all, Babushka sent us off with a care package of produce. "We'll need wine," I concluded after looking up and down the list to see what was missing.

"We could go to uncle Vasya for that," Mariana suggested.

"It's too late for big trips. Besides, a bus ticket to the village will cost us the same as a bottle of wine in the city. I'll just stop at the wine store tomorrow." I put my pencil down.

The Cricova Cellars store didn't look much different since the last time I was there with David. Though it seemed a little brighter and the traditional Moldavian music in the background was a nice touch. Its neatly organized shelves showcased different bottles of the cellars' collection. The traditional dark-green bottles with red wine intermingled with the light-green and clear bottles of whites and rosés. Then there were the fancy collectables. One of them was placed in a cardboard box with a portrait of a Moldavian girl in a traditional costume, holding an old-fashioned ceramic jug on her shoulder, smiling like it weighed nothing. A bottle of red wine shaped in a form of a violin caught my attention. *That's new.* It jolted me, imagining how David would react to that, opening his mouth in awe and saying something totally American like: "That's so cool!"

"That's so cool," I heard a woman at the counter saying in perfect English while pointing at the violin bottle. That spooked me as a weird coincidence, but there was no mistake. The woman, undoubtedly, was American. She even opened her mouth wide in awe like David would. "What kind of wine is it? Is it sweet or tart?" she asked the saleswoman.

"Um, ah…" She shrugged, looking around for something, then gave the American woman a brochure.

"I don't need a brochure." The buyer pushed it back. "I just need to know what kind of wine it is."

"Not understand," the sales woman answered after a few more failed attempts, visibly annoyed that she was expected to speak English when she was not paid enough for these high expectations. I stepped in to translate:

"She's asking you what kind of wine it is."

"Ah." The cashier smiled, relieved. "Honestly, that's a crappy wine. The one in that ugly bottle in the corner is a better Cabernet."

"She suggests you buy that Cabernet in the corner," I said to the American woman, smoothing out the edges. "This one is not the best."

"But the bottle is so cool," she dismissed us both. "Let's wrap it up. I'm going back to the States next week. My friend would love a souvenir like that."

"I'm going to America next week too." I got a flash all of a sudden, feeling a strange connection to this woman, as if we were friends a long time ago and destiny had brought us back together.

"That's so neat." The woman smiled at me. "Bon voyage," she said, still smiling, while picking up the wrapped bottle of wine from the saleswoman. "Thank you very much for translating. Hope to meet you one day in America. Bye-bye." She waved and left the store.

How are we going to meet if we didn't exchange contact information? I wondered, but the woman was long gone. *I guess I'll make American friends when I get there. I'm just here to get wine.*

On the sixteenth of March, we got Mom's festive china out of the cupboard and started setting the tables, placing the silverware and the napkins folded into triangles next to each plate like Mom used to do.

In a chaotic but somehow orchestrated rhythm, we brought our classic Moldavian dishes from the kitchen, spreading the aroma all over our apartment, merely avoiding bumping into each other in the narrow corridor. There they were: the grape leaves stuffed with rice, meat and veggies and sour cream on the side; fried, round *plăcintăs* made out of dough stuffed with feta and dill, stacked on the plate like a tilted Pisa tower; steaming potato goulash with floating, bright-orange carrot pieces in red tomato broth; the beet salad with shredded boiled potatoes, carrots, and eggs in the middle, grabbing your attention with its bright Bordeaux color.

"We did well," I told Mariana, looking at the full table. "Our mama would be proud. The kids need something to drink, though.

Bring the *compot* from the pantry." I turned to Angelica. "The one with sour cherries from Babushka."

"Don't you want to take Babushka's sour cherries to the American Baptists?" Mariana laughed.

"You want me to go through customs with a three-liter jar of red liquid? You'll hear about us on the news."

Mariana giggled. "Poor American Baptists will have to wait."

"So how many kids are we having as our guests?" I turned to Serghei.

"Victor from the first floor, Pavel and his brother—from the fourth floor—Larisa's daughters..." Serghei was bending his fingers one by one.

"You invited kids when you don't even know their names?"

"Everyone wanted to come." Serghei bulged his eyes like that was so obvious that it didn't need an explanation, but ran away to open the door when he heard the doorbell ring.

"Come in," he said to his first guests: two girls in cute doll dresses with white bows tied in their hair.

Mariana clapped when she recognized Larisa's daughters. "Dorina and Sorina are here."

The taller, seven-year-old Dorina handed Serghei a wrapped box. "Happy birthday," she said.

He immediately ripped the wrapper to see what was inside, barely getting a "Thank you" out of his mouth.

"Serghei, don't act like a savage," Mariana scolded him, but then grabbed the red toy car out of his hands to examine it closer. "That's so nice," she said, pushing it on the floor.

Serghei grabbed the moving car and ran away giggling while she was trying to hit him on the shoulder, following him into the room.

"You have no sweets on the table?" the five-year-old Sorina probed curiously.

"We'll have the sweets later," I said. "After dinner."

Sorina looked at me with such disappointment that in one glance she won the case of why mixing an adult gathering with kids was not a brilliant idea.

"Here," Mariana said, pulling the bowl with candy and baked rolls out of the cupboard and dropping a few of each in Sorina's hands. "We'll have a cake later too." She winked at her, and Sorina's face lit up.

"Mom, Pavel is here," Serghei yelled from the hallway, playing the host when the next doorbell rang. "And what's your name?" he asked the younger boy. "And Pavel's brother Andrei is here with a present." He opened the bag that Andrei was holding in a hurry, getting out a T-shirt, but he immediately got distracted by another visitor who was coming up the stairs.

Serghei was excited. "Victor, come in."

The teenager put his hands in his pockets awkwardly and said, "Mom said that I shouldn't come because we don't have money for presents. I just wanted to say goodbye, that's all."

"Victor, get in here," both Mariana and I said in one voice. "Today is not about the presents. Let's get you all to the table. The food is getting cold."

"Do you have a computer to play video games?" Dorina asked.

"Unfortunately, we don't." But I found a better solution: "I'll turn on the TV for you. Look, an American movie just started. *Princess Bride*, or something."

"Mom, this one is with subtitles," Lica noticed.

"That's all right," Victor said, stopping me before I changed the channel. "I like movies with subtitles. It helps me learn English. I can hear the pronunciation of English words better than in the ones that are dubbed."

I liked the way Victor was thinking, but Mariana made a good point: "You can't expect the preschoolers to read subtitles. We'll need to find something else for them to do."

"Mom, that's fine." Serghei came up with a better idea: "We'll eat really quick and go out to play hide and seek." He bit a quarter out of a plăcintă from his plate, shoving the dangling part of it with his fingers.

I looked at the other kids at the table. You could tell by the way they were eating how well-off their families were. The brothers Pavel and Andrei filled up their plates with random stuff to eat without hesitation, keeping an eye out for the sweets. Victor was taking one dish at a time, eating it quietly, then going for seconds after he made sure that no one was looking. Larisa's daughters took their time, picking and choosing.

"When are we having cake?" Sorina asked.

"It's a little early, don't you think?" The "voice of reason" Lica asked.

Serghei jumped on the idea. "Cake, cake!"

The girls and boys looked at each other mischievously, their eyes sparkling with excitement. *We cooked all day, and all the damn kids want is a store-bought cake? On the flip side, the faster they get their sweets, the faster they'll be out of the house.*

"*Voila*," I said, and brought the cake from the kitchen. "We don't have ten candles, unfortunately, because we forgot to buy them. Just pretend this one burning candle is ten of them."

"Pffft," Serghei blew on his candle.

"Wait, we didn't even sing the birthday song yet." I quickly pulled the cake away from his mouth before he blew it out completely.

"*Mulţi ani trăiască, mulţi ani trăiască. La mulţi ani!*" The chorus of kids mumbled the traditional Romanian wish of many happy years, clapping their hands in unison. Serghei was tapping his foot impatiently as the song was about to end, and blew his candle as soon as the clapping stopped.

Mariana tiptoed behind Serghei and grabbed him by his ears. "One, two, three." She started pulling his ears up.

"Ah, not the ears," Serghei complained, trying to get her hands off him.

"No, no, that's the tradition. We have to pull your ears up ten times so you grow bigger this year," she said. "Four, five, six," she continued, and the rest of the little monsters joined, jumping and cheering. They had their ears pulled every birthday, so they knew the drill.

"Then I want to be lifted on the chair too." Serghei was bargaining for some reward for his "sufferings."

"All right," Mariana agreed. "Seven, eight, nine, te-e-e-n." She pulled on his ears the hardest on the last word while Serghei tried to offset the upward movement by pulling her hands back down. "Now, go sit down on your chair."

"Move the chair to the left so it's not right under the chandelier, or you'll bust his head with it," I yelled at the last minute while the restless hands of the participants were grabbing the chair seat from all sides.

"Sereoja, hold on to the seat so we don't drop you," Mariana warned him. "Ready?" she asked the rest of them. "One, two, three," she started the count again. Lifting the chair with Serghei up to the ceiling evenly was no easy task when every kid was a different height. Serghei's body was wobbling in the chair. He was giggling hysterically, trying to hold on, but slid to the side when the last "ten" was counted.

"Everyone, let's have cake now," I said, and breathed out, relieved that no glass or bones were broken so far. Sorina went directly for the pink frosting, leaving a smudge on her left cheek. Dorina was more subtle, poking with her fork more ceremoniously than her sister. Everyone got quiet, munching on their pieces of cake. I could now, finally, hear the TV.

Victor was listening intently. "Oh, I understood everything he said." Victor jumped in excitement when the actor on the TV screen, with his flopping long locks of black hair, charged forward to poke his enemy with his sword. He repeated the same phrase again, moving his mustache up and down, oddly resembling the mustache on the Moldavian cultural male dolls.

"What? What's he saying?" Serghei put his ear to Victor's mouth so he could whisper the translation to him, then he ran to his backpack to pull out his ruler. Holding his left hand above his head, like Mr. Mustache on TV, he poked Mariana on her thigh with his ruler, repeating the words in perfect English.

"My name is Inigo Montoya. You killed my father. Prepare to die."

"Stop!" Mariana pushed Serghei away. "Do you even know what you're saying?"

Lica pointed at TV. "Mom, does it mean that someone killed his father?"

Serghei poked Mariana with his ruler one more time. "Yes. You killed my father."

I laughed. "Serghei's first English phrase had to be about killing someone."

Mariana slapped him back. "Ira, tell him to stop. That's really annoying."

"Hey, what's going on in here?" I heard my childhood friend Valentina's voice over my shoulder.

"You came?" I gave her a kiss.

"By the way, your entrance door is wide open. Everybody, come right in," she joked.

"Sereoja, was it you who didn't close the door after your last guest?" I found the culprit.

"Nuh-uh," he deflected but, just in case, got out of the room quickly. Pavel and Andrei rushed after him. Dorina and Sorina, done with their cake, lost interest in hanging out with adults and followed the boys too.

"Am I the only adult guest?" Valentina asked, looking at Victor.

I gave her the run down. "Vitalic is working late. His wife doesn't want to come without him, so they both will come after eight p.m."

"Thank you for inviting me," Victor said, and got up suddenly. "I will leave you now so you can have time with your family. I'm sure you'll find a lot to talk about. You don't need a stranger to listen in." He moved away from the table.

"You're the only smart friend my son has," I said. "I still don't get what you two have in common. You're three years older than him."

"We played chess together."

"He just learned it last summer at his father's. He can't be that good."

"He's getting better. Just make sure he still plays it in America so he doesn't forget it." He looked at me with his mature eyes. "I wish you a safe trip and a happy life wherever you're going." He shook my hand and left the room.

"Who is this young man?" Valentina asked in awe.

"He's our neighbor's kid," Mariana answered. "His older sister was in my class in school. She's very smart. All three siblings are because their parents are teachers. They struggle financially, though."

"Of course, they do, on teacher's salary." Valentina grimaced. "I'm a teacher at an athletic school. In good times, that was a juicy job to have. Not anymore. But having parents as teachers doesn't automatically make the kids smart. There must be something else."

"Their father is a mathematician, so he's tutoring all three of them and checking their homework every day. Their mother is a literature teacher. Their house has almost no furniture, but it's full of books. They all read a lot. Victor can read a book a day, easily," Mariana explained.

"You see what's going on behind that wall?" Valentina pointed at the wall in front of us. "Smart kids with smart parents are going to waste. Where will a boy like Victor go after he graduates? What will his sisters do after they graduate?" She shook her head. "Pour me some wine." She pointed at the bottle of Cabernet. "Let's celebrate your departure to a land where your kids will have a better chance." She lifted the glass bottoms-up. "Now let's talk about pleasant stuff. Do you still have that album with our school photos?"

"You really want to go through them?" I laughed. "We both looked goofy at that age."

"That's why I want to go through them, so we can laugh a little." Valentina smiled, ready to embarrass me, I'm sure.

"I'll bring it, I'll bring it," Angelica offered enthusiastically. "I know where it is." She ran to the other room to bring the photo album. When she brought it, she didn't skip a beat. "Mom, look." Lica pointed at a photo of me from the first grade. "You look like a boy."

"I know," I admitted. "Your Babushka Katya hated long hair because she didn't want to deal with braids, so she was cutting my hair short for my entire childhood."

"You have longer hair in this one." Lica pointed at a photo of me in the school uniform: a dark-brown dress with a white apron. My hair reached my shoulders and my bangs were cut sideways. I had a full smile on my face.

"That's me in the sixth grade, when I made a decision to grow my hair long, and I haven't cut it short since."

"And Babushka Katya let you?" Lica was amazed.

"I was at the *internat*-school, away from your babushka's eyes all week. By the time she got around to dealing with my hair, it was so long, she finally gave up."

"What's internat-school?" Lica asked.

"That was a boarding school for orphans and kids who only had one parent. After my father died, Mom moved from the village to the city, but she discovered very quickly that living here was expensive, so she enrolled me and Vitalic into a school where the state was providing room and board for the students. It was like a military-style school, except for civilian kids. We were living in the school's dormitories and going to school on the premises. We could go home only on the weekend."

"I didn't know you lived away from home when you were a kid." Lica looked at me with sadness.

"It wasn't that bad," Valentina said.

"Not bad?" I scoffed. "I loved our school. We had a great curriculum with emphasis on mathematics and algebra. My literature teachers were amazing. In a way, I had a lot of freedom to do what I liked, like read books and play volleyball. Besides, I was away from my mother, who couldn't wait to cut my hair."

"I've had long hair all my life." Lica caressed her braid. "Except once, when Babushka Tamara cut my hair one summer because I got lice."

"That really pissed me off because she did it without my knowledge," I said. "My mom threatened to cut my hair when I got lice in seventh grade. I said, I'd let her wash my hair with the most stinky anti-lice solution, and have her comb my hair with the thickest comb to get the lice out, and let her pull my hair one by one to get all the lice's eggs out, but I refused to cut my hair."

"I remember that year." Valentina laughed. "Our entire dormitory got infested with lice. It was so bad that the school ran out of treatment. We were pulling lice from each other's hair by hand. Which was both hilarious and infuriating because those bloodsuckers are fast."

"Do you remember when someone brought a bottle of kerosene from the country so we could wash our hair to kill the lice?" Valentina and I started laughing at the same time, interrupting each other with details.

"My God, we stank up the entire dormitory with that thing," Valentina said, barely able to catch her breath.

"Hey, it worked." I pointed at her. "We didn't have lice after that for the entire year."

"The stories you two tell," Mariana said, joining our laughing therapy.

"Do they have lice in America?" Lica asked.

"I hope not," I said, though that thought had never crossed my mind before. "But if they do, we'll be prepared." I put my hand in Lica's hair and fluffed it with my fingers, as if I was trying to scare off the imaginary lice.

"Mom, stop it. It's creepy." She pushed my hand away.

Valentina touched my hand. "Come on, take your wine glass and let's go to the balcony to get some fresh air." That was code that she wanted to talk to me about something in private, so I followed her. She opened the balcony window in silence, sticking her head out, letting crisp air come in.

I looked at the kids playing outside. Serghei and his friends were running around, trying to catch each other, steam coming out of their mouths. My heart ached. *Do American kids even play together outside like that, or do they only play video games alone in their rooms?*

"How do you feel about leaving our motherland?" Valentina asked me, sipping from her glass.

"I've already made up my mind. I'm ready." I took a sip too.

"How do you feel about David? Is it really true love?"

"I don't know what true love is anymore. I thought I knew the answer when I was younger. Now, I just want stability and a normal life and a future for me and the kids. Right this moment, I feel that David is the right man for me. Is this true, lasting love? I don't know."

"You're leaving all your support systems behind. There isn't going to be another Mariana there to jump in and babysit the kids, and your Babushka Veta can't send you produce from Moldova, and your mother wouldn't be there to help you if something doesn't work out with David."

"I know." I gulped the rest of my wine. "I'll just have to do what I always do when I'm trapped in a corner: take care of shit by myself."

Valentina was quiet then, likely coming to terms with what I already had. There were people I would miss, and I was leaving the only home I'd ever known, but I knew I was making the right decision. If anything, I had to be sure of myself—for me and my kids.

"What are you gossiping about?" Mariana interrupted us.

"Not much. When are you leaving?" Valentina asked, as if nothing had happened.

"On the eighteenth of March," I said with finality.

"So, you have one more day. Come to the Hirbavat monastery with me tomorrow. There is a spring blessed by monks there. They say if you dip yourself in it, it's good for your body and for your soul."

"There is no way people jump in a spring in March, even if it's holy water. It's cold outside."

"People go there for the healing year round."

"It's not the holy water that heals them. It's the doctors. This holy-water legend is a way for churches to make money on believers."

"Let's at least visit the monastery," Valentina pushed. "It's a beautiful, spiritual place. It was recently restored after it was destroyed during Soviet times. You'll need the monk's prayer to loosen up that burden of yours that you're taking with you to America."

"Our flight is at six a.m. It will be nice to rest the last day before such a long trip," I said, rationalizing my refusal.

"It might be your last opportunity to go to an Orthodox church," she kept pressing on. "It's just an hour away. If we leave early, you'll be back home by tomorrow afternoon."

I finally gave in. "All right."

Chapter 44

Reflections in the Holy Water

"Get up, get up." I shook Valentina's shoulder when I saw the clock on the wall showing nine a.m. She opened her sleepy eyes for a few seconds, and closed them back up. "You know what? Let's just cancel the monastery."

"No, no. I'm getting up." Valentina pulled herself off the bed and slowly walked into the bathroom to brush her teeth. I put a pair of pants and a sweater on, getting ready for the trip. "Let's have breakfast," Valentina said, rolling out of the bathroom, grabbing a frying pan to fry some eggs. "What leftovers do you have from yesterday?" She opened the fridge.

"We have to leave," I reminded her.

"You don't want to go on such a long trip without eating."

"You said it's not far."

"If we're talking travel time, it's not that far. However, micro-buses to the monastery run only once an hour. We don't want to be stuck at the bus station hungry before even leaving the city." She was stirring the eggs in the pan like she had all day. "Then we'll spend at least two hours at the monastery. They don't have food there for purchase. It's in the middle of nowhere."

"Now you're telling me this?"

"You'll be fine. We have plenty of time." She put the eggs onto my plate, smiling. I should have known better. Valentina was great at pillow talk, but she had no concept of time. At school, she was late to almost everything we planned together. *Forget about it*, I almost said it, but the thought of the Orthodox monks praying for my safety gave me incentive to carry on with our mission.

It was ten a.m. when I looked at my watch the next time. *If we leave the city by noon, I should be back home by four, five p.m. tops.*

The interurban microbus was taking us northwest from the city, deep in the country, where the paved highway ended and a long dirt road began. *Oh, no.* I got queasy from anticipation of another muddy drive, but, luckily, the roads had already dried out from the recent rain. I was looking out the window at the picturesque view with open fields of black soil freshly plowed by a tractor, which was still making its rounds. A flock of black crows was walking on the juicy dirt behind it, digging out the earthworms with their sharp beaks. *Caw, caw*, the crows would cry and flop their wings, trying to scare off the competition. *Those birds are so clever.* I smiled.

Suddenly, the village opened up in front of us like an album of Monet paintings. The country houses built close to each other and separated by green, blue, and brown fences were peacefully standing on both sides of the hills. The cherry and apricot trees popping up here and there in people's yards were showing signs of blooming. *The late frost can kill the harvest if they bloom too soon.* My heart ached for those trees behaving like careless children, playing a dangerous catch-me-if-you-can game with the spring frost.

The trip to Babushka's was full of emotions, so I didn't have time to enjoy my country scenery one last time. Now I saw it for what it really was: gorgeous, heavenly but somehow inhospitable to its own people. A lump in my throat was making it hard to breathe. I turned my head away, taken aback by the feeling of guilt for leaving all this beauty behind. *But how can I stay?* I asked myself, like a wife hanging onto her cheating husband who was not willing to change. *Shit, Valentina was right. This place is freaking spiritual.*

"The monastery is right ahead of us," the driver said as he

stopped his microbus. "There is a mountain spring on that rocky range to the left." He pointed with his finger. "The water from that spring is believed to have healing qualities. You can fill up your bottles and take some water home."

I said, "You don't believe in this voodoo, do you?" I looked at Valentina.

She smiled. "What's the point in coming all the way here if not to go to the magic water?"

I tried to reason with her. "We don't even have bottles with us."

"You can drink the water from the spring directly. It still helps," a woman who overheard us talking said on her way out from the microbus.

"Come on." Valentina led the way. "It's not far."

I looked uphill at the dirty road, which was a mixture of black mud and brown rocks, to where the driver pointed.

"It's quite a distance from here," I said. "We don't even have proper hiking shoes." I pointed at my winter boots with heels, but Valentina was already gone.

I bolted uphill after her, bent forward like a pissed-off bear ready for a hunt, but stepped on my long winter coat. *God damn.* I almost fell down twice. *Forgive me, God,* I murmured quickly, afraid that being so close to the monastery was like cursing directly into God's ear. I pulled up the front of my coat angrily, but the wet dirt was still reaching its bottom. *Why, of all the days, did I put on a long coat today?* No doubt I looked like a classic city slicker lost in the countryside.

"Wait for me," I called to Valentina, wiping the sweat off my forehead. "I thought the driver was just supposed to drop us off at the monastery. You didn't tell me we had to climb a mountain."

"Come on, come on. It's downhill from here," she yelled back from the top of the hill.

"There is *more* walking?" I sighed when I reached her. I could hear the water from there, but I couldn't see it. We took the narrow path down to the bottom of a small lake, and I looked up to see where the noise was coming from.

"God Almighty," I whispered, forgetting instantly that I was mad at Valentina. I stopped to watch how several streams of water were running down from the top of the rock, cascading in a small waterfall. The sunlight was playing with the water, changing its colors from transparent with a tent of white to blue and light-green. "I've never seen anything like this before."

"You'll feel better after this," Valentina said, and she moved closer to the waterfall where a few women were already filling up their bottles. "Remember how we were drinking water from the outside faucet in front of our school?" She laughed, cupping her palms, trying to catch the evasive running water that seemed to have a mind of its own.

I did the same, but the stream was so strong that half of the water was overflowing from my palms, and another half was slipping through my fingers. It was splashing on my clothes and my shoes, leaving big, bulging drops on them. I put my palms to my mouth and fast, before it could run away, I drank it all in one gulp. The water was fresh and cool, going down so easily that my entire body demanded more.

"That's definitely nothing like the faucet water," I said with a smile and water dripping from my chin.

"I told you. It's holy," Valentina said.

"I doubt the monks can holy up the spring that doesn't even belong to the monastery."

"Don't worry, there is a spring at the monastery too. That water is definitely holy."

Almost an hour later, we finally reached the monastery Valentina had brought me here for in the first place. I caught my breath and looked around. The premises were in a state of half-finished construction. The dirt, dug out to make room for its foundation, was still lying there. The church building was unfinished from the outside, showing its neatly stacked white stone blocks. I opened the heavy, ornate oak door to get inside the church.

"So quiet," I whispered to Valentina, trying not to disturb the visitors who were making their rounds from one icon to another. I raised my head to look up at the high, round ceiling. It was painted in heavenly blue with white clouds on both sides. God, surrounded by angels with wings, was floating in between the clouds with his right hand up, looking straight at me with his judgmental eyes. The icon of St. Mary and baby Jesus in her arms was tall and intimidating. I made the sign of the cross and went back to the entrance door where two long-bearded monks wearing black robes and little black hats were selling wax candles and incense.

"Can you read a prayer for my parents and my grandparents?" I asked one of the monks.

"Did they pass away or are they living?" He handed me two pieces of paper and a price list for ten leis each. "This one is for reposed souls of those who are already in Heaven, and this one is for the health and wellbeing of those who are still with us on earth. Write their names in, we'll pray for them. You can also buy some candles—it's only a lei and a half. Light them up in their names right in that corner." The commercial side of the Orthodox church always rubbed me the wrong way, but today didn't seem like a good day to take a stand.

Ecaterina, Elizaveta, I wrote on the first list for the monks to pray for Mom's wellbeing in Italy, and for Babushka Veta's at home.

Mikhail, I wrote the name of my deceased father on the second list. *Wouldn't that be ironic, considering he was an atheist?* My dear, sweet, loving papa shocked his family when he became a communist. He was a man of few words, but when he spoke, he spoke with fire, especially when he defied his family once again by bringing home a Ukrainian girl as a bride. That was not the nice Moldavian girl from the village they arranged for him to marry, so they gathered a family council. Six uncles, two aunts, Grandpa Ivan, and Grandma Irina, for whom I was named after, tried to convince him to drop her or be disowned. Mom loved telling me this story and my father's exact words to his family:

"You might not want her, but I do. Katya's the woman I love. If you accept her, you'll have a son and a daughter. If you reject her, you'll have no son."

These words should be engraved somewhere, so after I'm gone my kids can tell that story to their kids. I felt a burning sensation in my chest. He was about my age when he died from stomach cancer. *Gone so young, so senseless.* I felt tears coming out of my eyes.

This one's for you, Papa. I lit a candle for him, breathing in the strong smell of the incense floating in the air all around me. Its familiar, distinctive smell was throwing me into a vortex of emotions, sucking me in so deep that I felt breathless.

"I'm getting dizzy," I told Valentina and ran outside to catch a breath of fresh air. Was this place really sacred? Or was it the thought about spending my last day at home tormenting me so violently? I couldn't tell.

I noticed the spring in the back yard. *Is that it?* I went closer to examine it. This waterfall was miniature in comparison to the one we saw in the mountains: much slower, much quieter. Its water was filling up a hole made of rocks on the bottom of it. An uneven pool was looking like a baby lake.

Two women, one in her sixties and one in her thirties (most likely, mother and daughter), were taking off their top clothes near the spring. *What the fuck?* I shivered, looking at the older woman in her old-style underwear (resembling a pair of shorts more than panties) standing barefoot at the edge of the pool. She fixed her grayish bra that was long passed its heyday, and slowly walked into the ungodly frigid water, rapidly changing colors from pink to Cabernet. *No way.* I clenched my teeth, looking at the younger woman following her mother, stripped to her underwear and her bra too. Two monks walked by, minding their own business, as if they'd seen icy pirouettes like that every day of their lives.

"Aha, here you are." Valentina spooked me with her sudden appearance.

"Look." I pointed at the women in front of us. "They're definitely crazy."

"I told you people dip themselves in holy water here."

"I thought you were being metaphoric, or maybe they washed their faces with it."

"Hold these." She put something in my hands. "I bought these towels from the monks so we can dry ourselves after."

"After what?" I was getting suspicious.

"After we jump in the holy water, just like they did."

"Are you crazy too? Steam is coming out of their mouths." I pointed to the women in the pool. The duo, unaware of my turmoil, was moving in the water slowly, like two majestic swans rippling the waves with their wings. They looked almost divine. *If they can do it, why can't I?* "These are very tiny kitchen towels," I threw in my last argument. "Good enough for one of my boobs."

"You are young and healthy. You are not going to die." Valentina took her coat off first.

I threw my coat on the ground too. "This water better be super freaking holy. If I get pneumonia right before my flight, I'll be very, very pissed." I pulled my boots off, then stepped on them to take my pants off, balancing on one foot at a time like a stork. The sweater and the undershirt went last.

Brrrr. I started shivering. I stepped in with my bare feet at the edge of the pool and hugged myself with both my hands, trying to keep warm while gathering the courage to do it. My padded bra hardened from the cold. *This padding will absorb a lot of water*, I realized. *Hell with it.* I unhooked the bra, threw it back onto my stack of clothes, covering my naked breasts with my right arm. "God help me!" I screamed and jumped into the water.

A million of little ice needles attacked my body from all sides. My lungs refused to breathe for about thirty seconds. "God have mercy on your soul," I heard the angels say, hovering over my head as my soul was about to jump out of my body. "You're blessed now," I heard them again when I finally caught my breath. My body was convulsing uncontrollably like I was holding a jackhammer in my hands.

"Chi-i-cken," I called to Valentina who was still on the shore dipping her toes in the pool.

"Ah-ah-ah." Valentina rolled into the water finally. "Do you fee-eel ble-e-sed now?" she mumbled with her purple lips.

"Like a cra-zy Rus-si-ian win-ter swim-mer who's bap-tized in an icy lake." My teeth were chattering wildly. *Is that how those swimmers feel?* I wondered, when my body started adjusting to the cold, or it was becoming so numb that it couldn't feel anymore. "Let's get out. That's enough… blessing… for me."

Stepping out of the pool, though, felt like getting rubbed with sandpaper. *Pop, pop, pop.* My skin covered in ostrich goosebumps in an instant. I wiped my face with one of the towels.

"It might as well be a napkin," I said, turning to Valentina who had picked up the second one. Quickly, before the water turned to ice, I grabbed my T-shirt and slid it up and down my body, wiping it intensely more to warm myself up than soak the water. I felt like a chimney with steam coming out my mouth and my pores. Two young monks pretending to observe the scenery behind me couldn't take their eyes off my jiggling breasts.

"Hoo-ook my bra." I turned my back to Valentina and to the monks before they had a heart attack. "Pants—on." I pulled my jeans up. My bottoms sucked the water from my underwear like a sponge. The rest of it was dripping down my thighs, tickling me unpleasantly. "Let's warm up in the church," I said, putting on the rest of my clothes, finishing it with the socks. It never felt so good to have my feet in my boots again, though they were still cold and stiff.

It was warm and heavenly inside the church, which was almost full of people (local and the city folks) who had come for the six o'clock ceremony. A small chorus of monks in the front row were singing their prayer recitals, asking Lord for mercy: "Gospodi, pomilui; Gospodi, pomilui; Gospodi, pomilui." Their layered voices, from smooth falsettos to raspy baritones, were rubbing honey on my roughed-up skin. My brain, however, was full of rambling thoughts.

Maybe I should have been a more devout Christian and gone to church more often. Maybe it was God's hand that was guiding me through, when I thought I was alone.

I felt at peace all of the sudden. "Now, can we go home?"

"Just a little longer," Valentina insisted.

"I have a plane at six a.m. tomorrow. We have to go."

Though she wanted to stay longer, Valentina indulged me; otherwise, we could have been there all day.

I was looking through the window of the microbus taking us away from the church with a smile and a sense of accomplishment. My eyes were absorbing the images of moving by pastures one last time. By my calculations, we would be in the city by eight p.m. Much later than I thought, but still—plenty of time to catch the city bus home before the route closed for the night.

"I'll be soooo tired tomorrow morning, but this trip was soooo worth it," I said, and touched Valentina's hand. The bus suddenly stumbled, making a funny gargling noise, and stopped.

"Did someone cut us off or something?" Valentina yelled from her seat.

The driver cursed and got out of the microbus to open the hood. Some passengers got out too. Valentina and I followed them to see what had happened. The driver pulled a tool bag with wrenches from under his seat. Whatever the reason, it didn't look good.

"Oh, no, no," I said, afraid to even think what would happened if we got stuck here.

"Are you going to call for a different microbus?" the older woman who swam with me in the pool earlier asked the driver.

"We're thirty minutes away from the city. By the time I get a hold of someone and they send a replacement, it will have been hours. Just give me thirty minutes," the driver said, intensely twisting a nut.

"Do you even have spare parts with you?" a male passenger asked. The driver didn't answer. "We'll be here all night." The man flopped his arms, sending a shock wave through the crowd.

"Oh, God, please, please, please," I sent a prayer. "Not today. Any day but today."

"Calm down," Valentina whispered, touching my shoulder.

"I can't calm down." I pushed her hand and walked away, pacing back and forth on the side of the road like a scorned tiger. "I don't even have a phone to call Mariana and the kids. I'm sure David will call tonight too. Oh, my freaking God!" I kept on making laps.

After two hours of pushing, shoving, and cursing, the driver finally started his microbus, and I jumped as if I'd seen the Messiah. I kept looking at my watch once the microbus took off from the troubled spot. *Nine p.m.; nine-fifteen; nine-thirty.* I was tapping my foot nervously.

"I have to run or I'll miss my last bus," I said, and bolted out as soon as the driver stopped in the city. No pleasantries, no proper goodbyes. *Sorry, Valentina.* The ten-minute walk from there to the city bus stop stretched my nerves like an elastic on a slingshot.

I was counting every minute for the entire half-hour ride to the other end of the city, where I had to transfer to the ten-thirty bus for the grand finale to my boonies. Nevertheless, the city lights, as scattered and weak as they were, were giving me comfort. At least I was in the city.

Several people were at the bus stop when I disembarked for my transfer. *Good. I will not be alone.* This bus stop gave me the jitters every time I had to stay there at night. The incident with the taxi driver who ambushed me and dragged me into his shed had happened a few blocks away. *Don't think about it right now.* I raised my eyes at the bright light that was shining from the top of the tall pole like a beaming umbrella to distract myself. A few steps away from the stop, there were no more poles with lights like that. Just pure, soulless darkness ahead.

"What's taking our bus so long?" a man said to his friend, prompting me to look at my watch. *A quarter to eleven? Indeed, the bus was supposed to be here fifteen minutes ago.*

"It's probably broken again," the other man said.

Maybe it's running late. Not like it's the first time. I dismissed the man's theory. I couldn't have been so unlucky to get two broken buses in a day.

"For fuck's sake," the first man cursed five minutes after eleven. "I've heard sometimes they don't send night buses on this route to save gas. They didn't run night buses yesterday either." I started hyperventilating. *If I'd only known that this morning.* "Let's walk," he said, and gestured to his friend. "It's only two kilometers to the village. We'll be home in an hour." The darkness swallowed them a minute after they took off.

I looked at my watch in desperation. *Eleven-fifteen.* Another couple, a husband and wife, took off, unwilling to wait. *Shall I go too? What's the point in staying here until midnight if no buses are coming?* I saw another man leaving. I counted to fifty, letting him get a head start, just in case. I didn't want to end up alone with an unknown man in the middle of the road with empty fields on both sides. At least, if I were alone-alone, all I had to worry about was a wild animal or a hungry stray dog jumping at me. *What if that dog mauls me to death?*

I dropped my foot down off the curb onto the cracked asphalt on the road. *You shouldn't stay away from the forest because you're afraid of the wolves.* My literature teacher taught me that. Rapidly, as if my boots were on fire, I marched away from the bus stop, looking over my shoulder one more time. I didn't want anyone walking after me either, just in case.

The road ahead was showered with moonlight. It was creepily quiet. *What's that?* My heart jumped when the wind swished through the tall, dry grass uncut from the fall. My eyes, still adjusting to the dark, were seeing silhouettes. The ghost-like shadow threw me back into my childhood.

"There are no ghosts or devils," I said it loud and clear like when I was six, forcing myself to walk in the dark to overcome my fear, lingering after my father's death. I sped up to get away from the brush, as if I were too close to it, that unknown creature might try to catch my feet or grab me by my shoulder.

What's that? I picked up something else. This time, it was the sound of a person talking. *Just keep on walking and look ahead. You are halfway there.* However, the sound intensified, and now I could hear that two men were talking. I turned around to get the peace of mind that nothing was there. Two men in flesh in blood were right behind me, and they were moving fast.

I sped up, almost to a running speed, trying to keep my distance, but my heavy coat was slowing me down. I braced myself to calm the phantom swarm of ants moving up and down my sleeves. *Thump, thump, thump.* I could hear the men's steps like a drum beat, closer and closer. *Really, after the serene day at the monastery with smell of incense, holy water, and monks with angelic voices, I might end up dumped here in this field? Lifeless.*

Is this my last day on earth, God? I looked up. *How foolish of me to put my family through this one day before our trip to America?*

The two men caught up with me right before the sign with our village's name. *So close.* They passed me without saying anything, still engulfed in their own conversation, completely unaware that I labeled them as serial killers. "Fear has big eyes," I heard Babushka Veta's voice. I crossed myself three times in disbelief. *Thank you, holy water.*

Serghei jumped at me the minute I opened the house door. "Why are you home so late?"

"It's midnight," Angelica said, and hurried to show me the clock.

"David called you three times already!" Mariana yelled. "I couldn't even explain to him that you were at the monastery. None of us knows how to say it in English. Only God knows what David's thinking. Why aren't you home before the most important flight of your life?"

Before I was even able to respond, the phone rang.

"Go, pick up!" Mariana yelled more forcefully this time. "I'm sure it's David again."

I ran to the receiver. "Hello," I said. "Yes, that's me. I was at the monastery today. I just got home. I'm sorry to get you all worried. I didn't know it was going to take so long. Yes, we are flying out of here tomorrow. I can't wait too." I put the phone down to catch my breath.

It will be all over tomorrow. I won't have to be scared like that anymore.

Chapter 45

America, America

Driiiin, driiiin, the alarm clock was buzzing. *So soon?* I opened one eye. *Three a.m. already?* I dropped my feet onto the floor to turn off the alarm. I felt woozy as I got up and wobbled like a sleepy penguin to the other room to wake up the kids. I wished I could sleep one more hour, and the kids could sleep one more hour, but there was no more time. The long-awaited day of March eighteenth, 2002 had arrived.

I touched my sister's shoulder. "Mariana."

She almost jumped off her bed. "What?"

I shook my daughter's shoulder. "Lica." She mumbled but didn't open her eyes. "Lica, get up." I shook her again.

"Okay," she groaned, and opened her eyes this time, then walked slowly to the bathroom, stumbling on one of our bags in the hallway.

I shook my son's shoulders. "Sereoja," I said, but he ignored my first two attempts, then rumbled, pushing my hands away.

"One more minute," he mumbled.

"Get up." I shook him harder. There was no time for touchy feelings. We were left with the last five dollars in my wallet. If we were to miss that flight, we would be in big trouble.

"Mmm," Serghei murmured, ready to cry. I dragged him to the bathroom to wash his face with cold water. *That will wake him up.*

"Is everybody ready?" my brother asked when he entered the house. He looked at the kids all in different stages of undress. Serghei had his shirt on but not his pants; Lica had her pants on but decided to change her sweater at the last minute. Mariana was standing in her T-shirt with her underwear sticking out.

"Am I going with you?" Mariana asked, holding a pair of pants in her hands, scratching her uncombed hair that was fluffed up like Madonna's in the eighties.

"I don't think so. Ira has seven duffle bags," Vitalic answered. "I can barely fit the three of them with their luggage. There is no room for you."

"Ah." Mariana threw her pants away, resembling Serghei with her childish pout.

"*Posidim na dorojku?*" Lica asked. "Papa always liked us to sit down before a long trip, so we can think about what's waiting for us ahead and whom are we leaving behind."

Vitalic showed me his watch and puffed like an annoyed horse.

"Just take the two bags downstairs," I told him. "We'll be down in a few minutes."

"What did you pack in these? Bricks?" He growled when he picked up the two biggest bags.

"Albums with our photos, and our books," I said, and sent him out of the crowded hallway, where we all had gathered to put our shoes on. "All right, let's sit down 'na dorojku,'" I eyed the bench. Lica and Serghei sat down on our bags, like they always did when we traveled. Mariana squeezed me to sit down next to me. I put my hand on her knee.

"Once we get to America, I'll call you," I told Mariana. "Don't give up on college. If you need money, call Mom and she will send you some. If you need other help, or you get yourself in trouble, like getting pregnant or something, call me first."

"I'm not stupid," Mariana said, and pushed my hand away.

"You're eighteen." I put her hand on my knee. "Nobody is that smart at your age, so you call in this exact order: me first, our mother second, and your father third. Your father doesn't know how to handle a teenage daughter. Neither does our mom, honestly, but she's our mother."

"What can you do from America, and Mom from Italy?" Mariana teared up.

"I'll prep you up mentally, so you can deal with your father. He'll probably yell at you and call you names, like he always does, so you'll need someone to talk to."

"I'll be fine." Mariana wiped her tears.

"Don't cry," Lica and Serghei said, and embraced her from both sides, barely holding their own tears.

"You're still sitting here?" Vitalic came back.

"We're coming, we're coming," I said, and gave the kids one bag to carry down together. Vitalic took the other two, and I grabbed the last two and looked at Mariana. She gave me a kiss on the cheek.

"Go," she said. "I'll be fine. Really." She looked so sure of herself, as if she'd matured ten years in that moment.

"I raised you right, so I know you'll be fine." I smiled. Or at least, that was what I wanted to believe.

* * *

The tiny Chişinău airport was semi empty at such an ungodly hour in the morning. Just a few drowsy couples were standing at the check-in counter, where we were heading. I handed the agent my passport and our tickets to check in.

"Oho, a visa to America. All the way to Seattle?" The agent looked at me surprised. "I don't see everyday passengers flying out so far. Put all your bags here." He pointed at the scale. "Seventy-five kilos," he whistled.

"Will we have to carry our bags from flight to flight?" I sighed, only now realizing that was the weight of an adult human. "We have two layovers: one in Paris and one in New York."

"No, the luggage is transferred automatically. Otherwise, I don't know what you were thinking."

"I guess that's it." I turned to my brother.

"Godspeed," Vitalic said, and hunched over me to give me a hug.

I watched him exit the airport and the double doors close behind him. As if the gates of purgatory with all my worries and anxieties slammed shut, leaving everything behind in that dense darkness outside that made the windows look like they were painted with resin.

"Mom, where do we go now?" Angelica asked.

"To… America, America," I tried to sing the two words that I remembered from the entire song.

"Mom, seriously," Lica interrupted me. "What gate are we going to?"

"The beauty of a small airport is that there is only one gate out." I fixed my purse on my shoulder and grabbed my kids by their hands.

We zipped through the security gate, then went through a door that brought us into a small, bright waiting area with high ceilings. The seats were mostly empty, so the kids ran to take the best ones—closer to the window. I looked around the room aimlessly, hoping to find a familiar face, as if I needed solidarity or someone to chat with to calm my nerves down.

No way. My heartrate accelerated when I found one: the American lady I had met in the Cricova Cellars store a week before.

"Hello," I said when I approached her. "What a coincidence to meet you here." She looked at me, confused, with caution, as if trying hard to recall who I was. She probably didn't recognize me. Why would she?

"Ah, that's you, from the wine store? The one who is going to America." She finally smiled back after a few seconds of awkward silence, when I was ready to walk away. It then occurred to me that we never formally introduced ourselves, so neither of us knew each other's name.

The kids came back to report on their misfortune. "Mom, it's too dark outside. We can't see anything."

"Oh, you are taking the kids with you too?" the American woman asked me. "Are you one of those Internet brides?"

"I guess I am," I said, not quite catching if that was a playful tone or sarcasm in her voice.

"How long have you known your groom?" she asked.

"For over a year," I said cautiously.

"Have you met him in person?" I felt interrogated, thinking about the woman at the consulate grilling me with similar questions, but I still nodded politely. "You be very careful out there. There are some American men who prey on Eastern European women, bringing them to the U.S., then abuse them. I'm not saying that your groom would do that, but if that ever happens to you, here is my card. I work for a non-profit organization that is helping those women."

"Thank you," I said, and took her card and read her name. "Jane, thank you for your offer." I backed away, trying to keep my smile on, assessing if Jane deserved my "thank you" or if I should have told her to mind her own business. But her words shook me to my core. *What if David is one of those abusers? What if something happens to me? Or to my kids? What was I going to do? What could I do, if I don't have any means to come back?*

"Passengers flying to Paris, come to the counter," a female agent announced in her speakerphone.

I took the kids by their hands and walked decisively to the boarding gate. It was too late to change my mind now, after what we went through. I'd have to assess the situation when I got there. I looked back to see if Jane was coming, but to my delight she was still in her seat, probably taking a different flight.

"*Kruto*," Serghei said when he jumped into his seat. "I've never flown on a plane."

"Actually, you both have, but Lica was two years old and you were three months old, so you don't remember," I explained.

"I remember how a lady on the plane gave me candy and played with my curls," Lica said with a smile. "How long is our flight?"

"About two and a half hours."

"Paris is so close to us?" Lica was amazed.

"If you don't consider that for seventy years there was an Iron Curtain between the Soviet Union and the civilized world, then, yeah, Paris was always close to us," I said, keeping it short.

The landing in Charles de Gaulle Airport was surprisingly smooth. I didn't know why I was expecting a hard landing. I looked through the widow at the tarmac with futuristic looking domes with glass roofs, which appeared to be individual terminals not connected to each other. A bus was waiting for us outside when we disembarked the plane and went down the stairs one by one. I raised my face up at the drizzling rain, breathing in the fresh air of Paris, feeling relieved like a prison escapee who had made it to safety.

"Where do we go now?" Angelica asked when we got inside the nearest dome.

"I don't know," I said, and looked around, disoriented by French signs with occasional English translations. I was shuffling through my memory for long-lost French words that I'd learned in high school. "Let's look for a departure board." I pulled the kids inside the building until we found ourselves at a crossroad.

"This looks like an anthill." I was pacing nervously from one corner to another for about five minutes, trying to figure out which way to go. The kids were following me like two scared puppies. "*Monsieur*," a surprising French word popped out of my mouth when I saw a man in a pilot uniform. "New York," I said, and pointed at our tickets in my hand. "New York *avion*." I smiled, proud that I still remembered how to say "airplane" in French. He looked at our tickets and answered something in French from which I roughly understood that we were in Terminal B but needed to get to Terminal A. "How do I get there?" I asked him in English.

"Come," he said with an accent. We followed him. "Elevator out." He used his fingers to imitate our walk up the elevator. "Bus to Terminal A, to right." He pointed through the window to the dome on the right. "No left," he cautioned me. "Left, Terminal C. *Comprenez vous?*"

"*Oui,*" I answered. It was easier to just say "yes" than to conjugate the verb "understand." I shook his hand in gratitude. "*Merci.*"

"*Mon plaisir.*" He smiled and went back to his duties, leaving us at the elevator.

"French language is so pretty," Angelica said as we took the elevator up. "I didn't know you could speak it."

"I haven't spoken it since high school." I smiled. "But, apparently, I can still fake it."

"Yeah? It sounded all right to me," Lica said.

After twenty minutes of escalating, busing, walking through Terminal A, and getting lost a few times, we finally arrived at the gate for our connecting flight to New York, just on time to hear them announce it was time to board.

So far, so good, I got to the end of the line with the kids. I was watching the people around me holding their passports in their hands and tried to guess by the color of their passports what country they were from. The customs officer, a lady in a navy-blue uniform with a very serious face, processed several passengers with the dark-blue U.S. passports within seconds, then a couple with a bright-red Spanish passport, and a group with green Saudi Arabian passports went through a few minutes later. *A Moldavian?* I noticed a young man handing a light-blue passport, like mine, to the lady officer. She ran his passport through the computer.

"Student visa," the Moldavian clarified when she asked him something with a frown, examining his visa very carefully. "For a year," he answered her other question. Yet, with every next answer, she had more questions to ask until five minutes later, she finally let him through. *Why was she drilling him like that? Wasn't the visa in his passport enough?* I started getting nervous jitters, feeling like a fugitive about to get caught.

"*Moldave?*" The customs officer was flipping through the pages of my light-blue passport with the same intensity as she did with the student. Then she raised her precious eyes at me and asked me for my tickets. I gave her our boarding passes.

"*Billet de retour?*" she asked me in French.

"I don't have return tickets," I answered her in English in a trembling voice, as if I just got a punch in my gut. "I'm going to America on a fiancé visa," I explained. "I'm getting married there and won't be coming back." *Perhaps Svetlana was right all along when she tried to sell me the return tickets.*

"*Où est le visa pour les enfants?*" The officer looked at the kids with a puzzled expression on her face, making me even more nervous.

I pointed at the three separate pages in my passport with visas for all three of us, including the kids. Assuming that I understood her just fine, she continued with additional questions, but my limited French vocabulary couldn't detect any more familiar words after "*père.*" The matter was getting too serious for me to continue with my guessing game, and I honestly told her, "Sorry, I don't understand you."

She looked at me disappointed, as if I was acting up just to piss her off. She put her upset lips together in a tight circle and told me in English with a thick French accent: "Where is the permission of father?"

"Whose father? What permission?" I asked her back.

"The children's father," she said impatiently.

"Are you asking about the father's permission for my children to leave the country?" I finally got what she meant.

"*Oui.*"

Why would French officials need additional documentation for my kids, when I had three valid American visas in my passport and my own country didn't even question my exit? I felt a hot flash so severe that I had to unbutton my coat. The veins on my temples were pumping my blood up and down so fast that I could hear it. I breathed out slowly and answered her calmly: "The father's permission with the English translation is in my immigration package, but this package is sealed, and I'm not allowed to open it until I reach New York."

The lady officer showed me to step aside to let the rest of the passengers board, and called somebody on the phone. Two other customs officers showed up. They were talking about something in French, looking through my passport, then at my tickets, then through my passport again, flipping through the pages back and forth and comparing the pictures of my kids with their faces. Sensing that something bad was about to happen, I cautiously intervened with my last resort suggestion:

"I have the original document, but it's in Ukrainian." I handed them the shiny certificate written on a colorful yellow-blue paper with gold edges, hoping that the huge stamp at the bottom would convince them that this was an undisputable official government document. One of the officers took the certificate, turned it over, but gave it back to me.

"We don't have a Ukrainian translator in the airport," he said.

"Then what am I supposed to do?" I asked, shaken.

They looked at each other. It didn't seem they knew what to do either. One of them checked the computer one more time, while the other person was processing the last two passengers boarding the plane. There was no one left but us. The three of them had a quick discussion in rapid French, as if throwing the coin on what to do with us. After which, the lady officer finally gave me back my passport and showed me with her finger that we could proceed to boarding. She didn't have to ask me twice. I grabbed the kids' hands and ran down the jetway to the airplane, still feeling the cold sweat dripping down my back.

"Oho! This is huge," Serghei summed up the Boeing jumbo jet cabin as we entered it.

It was definitely different from anything I had flown in before. The inside of the airplane was wide with two aisles of three seats on both sides, and a row with five seats in the middle that seemed endless. *That's a long way out if the airplane goes down,* I thought for some reason, when we finally found our three seats in the very back.

"We apologize, but there is a delay at the departure gate," the flight attendant announced on the speakerphone. "We are being asked to stand by." A heavy sigh rippled through the plane.

Serghei stood up to look around an hour later. "Mom, when are we taking off?"

"We apologize for any inconvenience, but there is another delay," the flight attendant announced. The passengers around me grumbled again.

"Go to sleep," I told the kids, hoping they wouldn't take us off the plane, at least. It felt safer to be on it than being questioned again by the French customs. A half an hour later, we were still on the ground. Cramped, hungry, thirsty, with no clear endgame. The more time was passing, the harder it was to stay calm, as if we were hostages on the plane waiting to be rescued.

What if they take us off the plane? I dreaded the possibility. I got up to stretch my legs and looked in the back for unspoken clues from the flight attendants. They didn't look nervous (which was a good sign), but they were definitely annoyed every time someone dared to ask: "How much longer?" I returned to my seat, almost losing the last of my hope, when I heard the cheerful voice of the flight attendant on the speakerphone:

"Please buckle your seatbelts. We are ready for take-off. We'll land in New York seven hours from now."

Thank God. I felt relieved when the plane was finally in the air. Now, I could let my guard down and rest, surrounded by the calming zoom of the engines. *We're on our way, America,* I murmured and closed my eyes. I felt weightless, as if my body flew out of the airplane and was floating in the air in between the clouds. Bright sunlight jumped from between the clouds, blinding me, so I dived into their soft, fluffy belly, pretending to swim. It was calm and silent inside. *Is this how paradise feels?*

"Go back," I heard a commanding woman's voice from above.

"Go where?" I opened my eyes, jumping in my seat.

"Back to your seat, sir." The bossy voice of a sturdy, forty-something flight attendant was coming from the aisle. A passenger was blocking the food cart that she was pushing. She was not a skinny, dolled-up youngster, which I was used to back home (when to be a stewardess meant to pass the "face and body control"), but rather an ordinary-looking lady, tired and grumpy, as anyone would be on such a long transatlantic flight. My brain, trained by years of perception of how a stewardess should look like, was trying desperately to process this discrepancy. *Why am I judging her?* After all, I wouldn't like to be judged like that either. It felt right and proper that an American airline wouldn't toss to the curb a stewardess when she was no longer young and pretty.

"Thank you," the flight attendant said in a sarcastic voice when the man returned to his seat, making it clear who was in charge of this plane.

What else would be different in America? I wondered, looking at her in fascination. *How long will it take me to adjust to all these differences? Will there be some things that I could never understand?*

"Careful, it's hot." She gave the food container to a drowsy passenger one row away from us. A pleasant aroma of warm food reached my nostrils.

I shook the kids. "Lica, Serghei, wake up."

"Are we there already?" Angelica opened her eyes immediately.

"No. They are bringing food," I said. Serghei, who was murmuring something incoherently a minute before, jumped.

"They give us food on the plane? I didn't know that," he pouted, as if upset that he missed out on such luxuries before.

I passed on the food containers to the kids once one of the flight attendants reached us. "Careful—it's hot."

"Wow," Serghei was saying every time, fascinated by absolutely everything: how the foil made noise when he opened the container, and how the steam was coming out of it. He pulled the fork out of the plastic bag and poked his food, biting on his bread roll enthusiastically. Then he opened the little silver package with a shiny white cube and put the entire piece into his mouth.

"How does it taste?" I asked, trying to restrain myself from laughing.

"This candy isn't sweet at all, and it's melting," he said, clearly surprised.

"No kidding." I had to laugh this time. "That's because it's butter."

"Really? They have very tiny butters on this airplane?" Serghei kept on chewing, undeterred that he'd been fooled.

I looked at Angelica, who took her first bite. "How does your food taste?"

"It tastes weird." She cringed and continued chewing, mulling over the new flavors.

"Mine too," I said, when I tried my mashed potatoes. "Not even close to the potatoes from our babushka's yard."

"'A hungry man can't be picky,'" as Babushka would say, "but does all American food taste like this?" Lica asked, going for the second bite.

"I don't know, but that's how preserved food tastes. I'm sure we'll try a lot of other new foods we never knew before."

"How long before we land?" Lica asked.

"Two hours." I looked at the flight map on the screen. I adjusted my watch to match the New York time. "Then we take another plane." I dove into my purse and pulled out our boarding tickets for the Seattle flight. "Wait a minute." I looked at the tickets that showed our flight was leaving from New York was at nine-fifteen p.m., but my watch was showing seven p.m. New York time. And we still had two hours of flight.

How is this possible? And then it hit me. *Shit!* I couldn't believe that it never occurred to me until now that the two hours delay in Paris could make us miss the connecting flight to Seattle. Why would it? Not like I was taking intercontinental flights with multiple connections all my life.

Maybe the airplane will land a quarter-hour earlier. I was tapping my foot nervously, watching the time on the flight map that was shrinking too fast. *Thirty minutes until the next flight is all we need.*

"Welcome to New York," the flight attendant announced when we landed. "Local time is eight-fifty-five p.m." *Twenty minutes until the next flight? We can do it.* I felt optimistic until I saw the long, multilayered customs line inside the JFK Airport. A punch in the gut would have been less painful than seeing the sea of people that was in between me and my next airplane.

I looked with sorrow at the U.S. Passport and Green-Card Holders lane that was moving fast. I wanted to be in there. Instead, I was stuck in the slow-moving Non-U.S. Citizens lane, which felt like walking slowly on broken glass.

I was on my last drop of patience when I finally reached the window with the middle-aged short and pale customs officer at five minutes after nine p.m. I handed him my passport and the yellow sealed package with my trembling hands.

"What is this?" he asked, as if it was the first time in his life when he saw someone with a package like this going through his window.

"That's my immigration package from the U.S. consulate in Bucharest," I explained, looking at my watch.

He opened my package and extracted the voluminous file out of it, surprised by its size. He read each paper slowly, as if trying to solve a puzzle, then asked me:

"It says that you are traveling with kids. Where are their passports?"

"They don't have one. Their photos are in my passport." I pointed with my finger to the page where the children's photos were. His bushy eyebrows sprung above his bleak eyes. It must have been the night of surprises for him.

"Where are your return tickets?"

"I don't have return tickets. I have a K-1 visa. I'm getting married in the U.S., so I'm not going back," I answered in a trembling voice. *Déjà fucking vu.*

"Is your fiancé meeting you here? We may need to call him in."

"He's meeting us in Seattle." I knocked impatiently with my fingers on the board outside his window, trying not to create a scene.

"What's wrong?" he asked suspiciously.

"My connecting flight is in five minutes."

"I wouldn't worry about that right now. You won't make it. But if I don't clear you for entry into the United States, the missed flight will be the least of your worries," he said in a casual voice of a man who had all the authority in the world over me.

Flight? What flight? The customs officer's words worked on me like a magical eraser. *Could I really be denied entry into the United States, after all we went through?* The officer pulled my file closer to himself and started reading it again one file at a time, spitting on his fingers to turn the page. A kink was going straight to my spine every time he took too long to move to the next one. When I least expected it, he swiftly pressed his stamp into a sponge with blue ink and smacked it in my passport.

"Welcome to the United States," he said, then handed me my passport. "You may proceed."

"Let's go," I said to the kids, walking away from the U.S. customs checkpoint like I had cotton legs. Relief-spiked-with-panic was the name of my cocktail that was making me lightheaded.

Chapter 46

Welcome Home?

Now what? My heart rate kept going up every time I tried to think of a solution. *Do I have to figure a way out of this mess by myself on my first day in America?* I looked for a payphone to call David, wondering how much a phone call from the airport would cost. *Not yet.* I brushed off the idea. I had to be very careful on how I spent the last of my money. Besides, I needed to find out how much we needed for the replacement tickets.

"Proceed to collect your luggage," a lady in uniform directed us to the conveyor belt.

"I thought they transferred our luggage to the next flight," I said, glancing at our lonely bags that were going in circles on the carousel.

"If New York is your first port of entry in the U.S., your luggage has to go through the customs security check here. The next gate will collect your bags for the transfer."

"What if we missed our flight?"

"Then proceed to the ticket agent to rebook your flight."

Rebook with what? I was about to scream.

"Mom, look—carts," Serghei said, running to pull one of them from the row at the wall, but the cart wasn't moving.

"You need to slide a quarter in to unlock it," the official yelled at us.

"I don't have American coins," I said, and raised my hands in frustration. "Do we have to carry them by hand?" I dropped my hands down in anger, but she just shrugged, moving on to the next passenger. "We'll have to carry them one at a time like we did when we were bringing food from Babushka's." I imagined Babushka Veta shaking her head right now. "Serghei, you stay here with these six bags. I'll be back. Lica, you'll help me carry this one as far as we can go. Ready?"

Angelica and I lifted the first "monster" with a sigh, and walked fast, almost ran without stopping for about a hundred meters until the handle fell out of Angelica's hand.

"I can't hold it anymore," she said, looking at me apologetically.

"Sit down on it, then," I told her, and I walked back to Serghei for the next bag. I brought the next one by myself, then the next, and the next one to where Angelia was stationed. The seventh one, Serghei and I brought together.

"Let's take a break, and we'll do it again," I said. I rubbed my burning shoulders and my sore palms. We repeated the same trick five different times. The process was slow and irritating, and both physically and mentally draining. I was rushing to the ticket counter, running against time. As if arriving there only fifteen minutes after our plane's departure would have been better than getting there thirty minutes after our plane took off.

"I ... lost ... my plane," I told the ticket agent in an exhausted voice with my brain in full-blown revolt, refusing to form even the simplest English sentences.

The ticket agent, an African American woman with multiple braids neatly arranged in a ponytail, looked at me puzzled. "You lost your purse?" she said with a distinct accent.

Was that how New York people talked, losing half of their words? I didn't know. What was obvious was that we had a communication problem. I covered my face with my hands, trying to pull myself together, took a deep breath, and tried it again.

"I lost my flight and I don't know what to do," I explained, and my hands started shaking. "I only have five dollars in my wallet." I felt hot, salty tears burst out of my eyes and run down my cheeks in rows, dripping on my coat. My entire body was shaking, as if my bottled anxieties were trying to get out all at once, fighting at the exit in the most violent way.

Serghei said, "Mom, don't cry." He stroked my hand and started crying too. Lica came to my aid from the other side. I wiped my tears immediately. Freaking out the kids was not a smart move.

"Do you have a credit card, ma'am?" the agent asked me.

"What's a credit card?" I asked her back. "Is that like a card from the bank?"

A man in his sixties with a full head of gray hair, standing in line behind me, intervened. "The card that you're referring to is called a debit card. The card that she's asking you about is issued by a credit company," he said in clear, clean, academic English, without rolls, which I could understand. "Since you don't know what that is, you probably don't have one."

I nodded in agreement. "I don't have one. What do I do now?" I looked at him with the eyes of a drowning person grabbing to a straw, like he was my savior who had all the answers.

"Let's first find out: Why did you miss your flight?"

"They hold our plane in Paris for two hours," I said, realizing as the words were coming out of my mouth that I butchered the conjugation of the verb "to hold." "Held, they held our plane in Paris," I corrected myself, embarrassed, like I had nothing else to worry about but my English grammar.

"Okay, so you had a two-hour delay that was not your fault," he said a little slower than the first time, making sure that I followed him.

"Yes." I nodded. "That was not our fault." I felt like he was getting somewhere with this, but I didn't know how he was going to help us. He raised his eyes at the ticket agent.

"Okay then," she said. "Give me your ticket information."

I handed her our tickets. She clicked on the keyboard loudly with her long, pink nails.

"I rebooked your flight for tomorrow," she said, handing me our new tickets.

"How much?" I looked at her, afraid. "I can't pay."

"They are at no charge."

"No charge?" I repeated, trying to figure out if I understood her correctly. I turned to the man behind me for help.

"That means free. No money," he said.

"Really? Thank you." I grabbed his hand, almost ready to kiss him as if he himself bought the tickets for us. I turned around to the ticket agent. "Can we sleep in the airport?"

"You could, but you don't have to. I'll give you a voucher to the Best Western hotel and a food voucher for dinner and breakfast."

"How much?" I asked, not understanding what "voucher" meant.

"It's free for you," the man explained. "When you miss a flight because of the airline, they have to replace your tickets and put you in the hotel for free."

It all finally made sense. *Why wouldn't she explain this to me earlier? Didn't she see how freaked out I was?* The thought that I had rights gave me courage to ask her one more question:

"How do I call from the airport?"

She pulled something from her draw and gave it me. "Here, a calling card." I looked at the card in my hands with a silver line across it, like on a scratch lottery ticket.

"Do you know how to use a calling card?" my helper asked me.

"Do I just put it in the phone like a debit card?" I asked, guessing that it could be some type of single-use telephone card.

"No," he said with a smile. He took the card out of my hands, got a coin out of his wallet, and scratched the silver line across the card with it.

Serghei, who was peeking over his elbow, yelled in excitement, "Numbers!"

"These numbers are called a pin code," the man told him, then turned to me. "I saw a phone booth down the corner. When you get there, dial this eight-hundred number. Then you enter this pin code, then you dial the telephone number and you can talk until the five-dollar credit on this card is finished. That should give you plenty of time for domestic calls."

I was repeating what the man told me step by step, trying to memorize it all and not forget before I got to the phone booth.

"Do I need money to call this number?" I asked him, still looking for something that I needed to pay for.

"No, the eight-hundred number is free."

"It's amazing how many things are free in America for passengers in our situation," I spat out quickly. My English—fully restored. He smiled and gave me one last piece of advice:

"Take the elevator to the ground level and find the stop where the hotel shuttles are picking up the passengers. Look for the one that says 'Best Western.' It will take you there."

"Is that a taxi?"

"No, it's a bus. I really don't know why they call them shuttles." He shrugged, probably for the first time in his life, questioning the use of this word.

"Is that one free too?" I asked, just to make sure.

"Yes." He smiled again.

"Thank you. You are so kind." I walked away, still in awe of this stranger who had so much patience, navigating through my broken, accented English, and being able to anticipate what I might need, when even I had no clue what I needed.

I found the phone booth around the corner and, following all the instructions that the man gave me, I dialed David's phone number to tell him the bad news.

"Are you going to be okay?" He was melting down, I could tell. "Do you want me to take the first flight to New York?"

"No," I said calmly. "Our plane is at ten a.m. tomorrow. By the time you got here, we'd be on our way to San Francisco. We change planes there."

"San Francisco? Why?" David interrupted me. "You won't be home until tomorrow night. There are direct flights from New York to Seattle. You need to ask them to change your tickets."

"I don't want to deal with it right now. It's almost ten p.m. here." I looked at the kids, barely standing on their feet. "We're tired."

"Okay. Go to the hotel. I'll call the airline when I get home."

I led the kids to the elevator down in silence but with relief. The balm that our gracious helper had put on my broken spirit was making me confident that we would be okay on our own for one night in New York.

"Where can we take the shuttle to Best Western?" I asked a young, blond, chatty attendant barely in her twenties. She looked at the clock on the wall: ten-thirty p.m.

"They don't run late at night unless we call them," she said. "Wait outside, I'll call them for you."

We dropped on the bench outside, breathing in the cold, dusty air of JFK Airport. There was not much to see there under the plastic roof, so I just observed how the passengers were picked up by nimble, yellow cabs. I was jealous of all these people who would be home soon, sleeping in their beds, while our shuttle was taking its time. Twenty minutes passed. I looked at my watch and went back inside to talk to the attendant.

"How long does it take for the shuttle to get here?" I asked.

"Oh, sorry. I forgot to call the hotel," she said nonchalantly and grabbed the phone.

"Do you have any idea what we've been through today?" I wanted so badly to pull her by her pretty blond hair and yell into her face, but my anger locked my vocal cords, and all I could produce was a heavy sigh. *At least she didn't lie to me.* For some reason, that gave me comfort. *But we could have been in bed by now.*

"Mom, how do you turn the light on in here?" Serghei asked when we finally dragged all our bags in our hotel room after dinner. He pressed on the switch—nothing. I pressed on it—nothing.

"There must be a way," I said, trying a few more times. "We can't walk around in the dark like this." I dropped my hand down in anger. My coat sleeve touched the switch, turning on a dim light. "Seriously? We need to twist it instead of pressing it?" I was amazed but glad that we now had the light.

"These beds are bigger than in the Bucharest hotel," Serghei said, and jumped on one of the neatly made queen beds with white covers.

"Hey, hey!" I yelled at him. "We all need to take a shower first."

Serghei ran to the bathroom. "This is so big," he echoed from inside it. "Mom, no water's coming out." Serghei was twisting the knob of the bath tub all the way to the right, then all the way to the left, but nothing was happening. "Maybe they turn off the water at night here."

"We are in America, son. They don't do that here." I picked up the phone and called the reception desk. "Do you have water in the hotel?" I asked, dragging my question, that, no doubt, sounded stupid to the person on the receiving end, especially when she took a long pause before answering it.

"Y-e-e-e-s. Are you having trouble in your room, ma'am?"

"We twisted the handle, but the water is not coming out."

"You need to pull it, ma'am."

"Pull it, like to myself?" I was confused. "Wouldn't it break?"

"No, it won't," she said as politely as she could. I imagined her putting the phone down and telling someone at the front desk: "Can you believe this shit?"

After hanging up, I went back and pulled the knob of the faucet in the bathroom sink to check her theory. The water gushed out, splashing all over the vanity. I twisted the handle to the left, then to the right several times, as I would have done at home, trying to turn the pressure down but nothing was working.

Serghei laughed. "It broke." I slammed the knob hard, mad that I'd have to call the receptionist again. The water miraculously stopped running.

"Aha!" I got excited like I'd just solved a mystery. "That's how the darn thing works: pull up to turn on." I pulled the nob out carefully. "Then push down to turn it off."

"It's hot!" Serghei, who was holding his fingers under the running water, screamed. I played the pull-and-push game with the faucet a few times, but the temperature wouldn't change. Disappointed, I turned to the bath tub and pulled the knob there. "It's cold!" Serghei backed off.

I called the receptionist one more time and said, "Sorry to bother you again," and after a few minutes of hesitation, "Do you have hot water in the shower? The water is cold."

"Just give it a few minutes, it will warm up," the receptionist said, sounding more bored than irritated.

We let it run for a few more minutes, as she said, but the water was getting colder instead of warmer.

"Why is the water in the sink hot but in the bath tub cold, when we pulled both knobs the same way? We're doing something wrong, but I'm not calling the receptionist again. Brush your teeth and go to bed. It's already midnight," I instructed, finally giving up.

"Who makes faucets like these?" Lica shook her head. "Does America have to be so different in everything?" she said on her way out of the bathroom.

"We got our first taste of America today," I said, lying in bed, trying to put my rumbling thoughts to rest. This country was different and sometimes confusing but resourceful, and people could be simultaneously rude and polite. *Mind-boggling.* I looked at the kids, who had already fallen asleep, while I was still trying to.

Drrrin, drrrin, I heard the phone ringing, and jumped to pick it up, confused why the receptionist would call us so late.

"Hello, honey," I heard David's voice on the phone. "I called the airline." *I totally forgot about that.* "I raised hell that my fiancé on her first trip to America is stuck in New York with two children due to their fault. They changed your tickets for a direct flight to Seattle. You'll have a five-hour flight tomorrow instead of an entire day."

"Thank you," I said. *Yeah, America is definitely different. The airline agents at home would just hang up on you if you yelled at them like that.*

"You're flying out at six a.m. tomorrow."

"Six a.m.? We just went to bed, and you want us to get up in four hours?" I was about to curse. "We're so tired. I can't even describe it."

"I just can't wait to see you and hold you in my arms. It's been such a long time." David sniffled.

"A few more hours wouldn't kill you," I snapped. "I really have to sleep now. Good night." I dropped the receiver. The jetlag and the craziness of the day was about to put some words in my mouth that I might regret later. I closed my eyes. It was time to sleep, indeed.

* * *

Our airplane made a semicircle and was gliding down through the clouds over the rippling, shiny, silver water that was washing a rough mountainous coast covered in green pine and fir trees. The scenery under the wing looked like a giant bowl that broke on one side, spilling the water into the ocean. Compared to my home city, Seattle looked big and structured. Its land was separated into neat quarters sprinkled with houses, as if someone dropped a bucket of gray cubes of butter from the sky.

"It's so pretty," both Lica and Serghei said simultaneously as the airplane dropped suddenly, preparing for landing.

"Ah!" I grabbed my ears, consumed by such an intense pain as if someone was drilling my eardrums. I dropped my forehead on the front seat, trying to breath in and out calmly. *Not now.* I could feel how I turned pale, or green, like the puke that was about to come out of my mouth.

"Welcome to Seattle," the flight attendant announced in her speakerphone to my relief.

"Ready?" I asked the kids, straightening my back, preparing to bolt for the exit the minute they opened the door. My body felt weak and my legs were shaking, but my mind was already outside, celebrating the finale of our two-day-long transatlantic ordeal.

I saw David from afar, showered in the bright light of the SeaTac airport. His large, tall figure was standing out, towering over the crowd, even here, on his home turf. He was wearing shorts *(in March?)* that were exposing his black orthopedic boot. His large, white T-shirt had a bright-orange stain on the right side. *So typical.* He was holding a handwritten sign in his hands with uneven, crooked letters: "Welcome home!" The word "home" short-circuited in my brain. I was trying to reevaluate what "home" would mean from now on for me and the kids.

"David!" The kids finally noticed him and ran ahead to give him a hug.

"Why are you crying?" David asked, and gave me a smooch, tearing up himself, while still holding on to the kids on both sides. I leaned on him, shivering.

"I do-don't kno-ow," I stuttered, bursting like a broken dam.

"Maybe I'm tired as fuck." I wiped my face. "Or maybe I'm emotional because it's like the entire America is welcoming us home. Finally." I wiped my snot.

"Well, I don't know about entire America, but my older brother Delbert brought my mom to the airport so she can meet you all."

"You brought your mother to the airport for our first meeting ever? What were you thinking? I have dark circles under my eyes. I stink. I don't even know where my hair brush is." I combed my unruly hair with my fingers nervously.

"You look gorgeous. They'll all love you," David said, smiling.

"Aha," I said, using Babushka Veta's tone.

David loaded our seven bags from the conveyor belt onto the cart with the same question as my brother:

"What did you load in them? Bricks? I told you not to bring much stuff. We'll buy you all new clothes here." He pushed the cart to the exit effortlessly, like it was a toy car. *Where was this giant when I needed him?* "This way." He led us outside of the airport, beaming like a newlywed.

I looked up, searching for the afternoon sun, but the patch of sky peeking through the concrete structure of a multilevel garage was as gray as the garage itself.

"It's about to rain, isn't it?" I asked David, disappointed.

"Don't worry," he said with a serious face of a joker that was trying hard not to crack. "It only rains twice a year in Seattle: August through April and May through July."

"So always?" I punched him for his stupid riddle. He giggled, covering his mouth like a child, hiding his fallen teeth.

It dawned on me: *What if I hate it here? No, no, everything is going to be all right. It has to be. To be continued... Isn't that what they say when a story isn't finished yet?*

Babushka Veta's grapevine hanging over her porch.

Babushka Veta's house hidden behind the prune trees.

Babushka Veta's well, the only source of water in her village.

Babushka Veta's room in her country house, with a rug woven by her hanging on the wall. In the background, the iron stove, the only source of heat in the winter. The clay bed behind it heats from below when the iron stove is in use.

My mother, Ecaterina (Katya), circa 1985.

Babushka Veta, 2005.

Left, my ex-husband, Igor (in the middle), my sister, Mariana, and my kids, Serghei and Angelica. This photo was taken in the day care where I worked at the end of the Christmas matinee, circa 1998. Serghei is still in his haitori costume. Right, me in the pink dress at the College Graduation Ball, 2000.

Studio photos for the dating agency, November 2000. *Left:* Me in my black pants and the black sweater that I took off my sister, Mariana, for the photo shoot. *Right:* Me with the purple flower.

David's arrival in Bucharest. Our first photo together, May 2001.

Photo taken by Mariana during a family day out for our immigration package. Me, David, and the kids, May 2001.

Our first photo together of David, me, and the kids
after our arrival to the U.S. in April of 2002.